# Yangtze! Yangtze!

## Debate Over the Three Gorges Project

# RELATED BOOKS BY EARTHSCAN

*Damming the Three Gorges: What Dam Builders Don't Want You to Know* (Edited by Margaret Barber and Gráinne Ryder)

*In the Name of Progress: The Underside of Foreign Aid* (by Patricia Adams and Lawrence Solomon)

*Odious Debts: Loose Lending, Corruption, and the Third World's Environmental Legacy* (by Patricia Adams)

# Yangtze! Yangtze!
## Dai Qing

Translated by Nancy Liu, Wu Mei, Sun Yougeng
and Zhang Xiaogang
Edited by Patricia Adams and John Thibodeau

Probe International

EARTHSCAN
London · Toronto

# LIST OF FIGURES AND TABLES

# EDITORS' NOTE

*Yangtze! Yangtze!* is a collection of Chinese documents debating the Three Gorges project. This English translation is organized in a manner similar to its Chinese predecessor, with interviews, essays and letters to Chinese officials forming distinct sections. But this edition, which is being published after the project has been given the official go-ahead, also reflects the continuing struggle against the dam: 10 new chapters are included here, which both update and expand the material contained in the original Chinese edition.

Part One of the book presents new material about the struggle to publish *Yangtze! Yangtze!* in China, its subsequent banning, and the vote to pass the Three Gorges project at the 1992 National People's Congress. Each of the subsequent parts also benefits from new and updated material.

Because each chapter is distinct and capable of standing on its own, some repetition between chapters was unavoidable: To remove such repetition would have compromised the integrity of the arguments which the authors have gone to such pains to convey. Also, because in some cases four years have elapsed between the writing of the newest and oldest chapters, the authors' data (for example, project budget estimates) has sometimes changed. We present the data in its original form, to reflect the arguments being made at the time.

Except where marked, all footnotes have been written by the editors.

Numerous friends and colleagues have made the publication of this book possible. We would like to thank the World Wildlife Fund for an early translation of *Yangtze! Yangtze!* which became the basis for this expanded edition. We would also like to thank Lawrence Sullivan, Nancy Liu, and Wu Mei for their tireless translation and extensive editorial assistance on the original manuscript and the new material. Thanks also to Zhang Xiaogang and Sun Yougeng for their translation.

Special thanks to Margaret Barber, who so generously volunteered her time for editing and fact-checking. Her unflagging support and good humor is greatly appreciated. Special thanks also to Lawrence Solomon for his patience and guidance throughout the project.

We would also like to thank those who volunteered their time to help complete the project, especially Peter Gorrie and Norman Houghton for their editorial contributions, Philip Williams for his technical review, and Paul Brooks, for helping with graphic design

For their timely assistance and encouragement in the many and diverse tasks of book production, we are grateful to Jeffrey Ashizawa, Nancy Hearst, Tanyss Horsley, Robert Paarlberg, Marcia Ryan, and Joan Stabile.

For making the translation and publication of this book possible we would like to thank the Environment and Development Support Program of the Canadian Environmental Network, the Canadian International Development Agency, the Margaret Laurence Fund for the Promotion of Peace and the Environment, and Probe International supporters who donated generously so that the efforts of the Chinese government to keep this book from dam-building professionals and the public would be foiled.

We would also like to acknowledge Jiang Hong and Qian Jiaju for their invaluable contributions, and to honor the memory of Hou Xueyu and Zhou Peiyuan.

Above all we would like to honor Dai Qing and the 40 journalists, scientists, artists, and economists who prepared this book with courage, expertise, and dedication.

# PREFACE

## THE THREE GORGES DAM AND THE CHINESE POLITY
by
Lawrence R. Sullivan[1]

The materials in this book condemn the Chinese government's plan to build the world's largest dam in the scenic Three Gorges area of the Yangtze River. These documents are also an indictment of the political system that produced this decision. The contributors to this volume are generally *not* liberal, Westernized dissidents. Many are long-time loyal communists; others are veteran members of China's normally compliant satellite parties. These are not the young idealists who filled Beijing's streets in the democracy movement of 1989, but largely elderly officials with scientific and technical backgrounds who have opposed the dam out of a genuine concern for China's economic health and political stability.

The criticisms that fill the following pages focus on a closed decision-making process that grossly distorts technical data and analyses to meet the political needs of a self-sustaining elite. Despite high-level rhetoric since the inauguration of China's reforms in 1978 about creating more "open" (*kaifang*) and "democratic and scientific" policy-making, this book portrays a Party-state apparatus that remains profoundly authoritarian in structure and function.[2] Outspoken opponents of the project have

---

[1] Lawrence R. Sullivan is Associate Professor of Political Science, Adelphi University, Garden City, New York and Research Associate, East Asian Institute, Columbia University, New York.

[2] See Deng Xiaoping's major August, 1980, proposal for political reform, "On the Reform of the System of Party and State Leadership," in *Selected Works of Deng Xiaoping: 1975-1982* (Beijing: Foreign
(continued...)

been silenced, especially since June, 1989, as key decision-making arenas deliberating on the Three Gorges dam have been packed with obedient and technically illiterate supporters. Opposition views are not treated as mere differences of opinion, but evidence of disloyalty and "counter-revolutionary" intent. The political atmosphere surrounding the controversy over the dam is no different from the late 1950s when early critics, such as Chairman Mao Zedong's ex-secretary Li Rui, were branded as "anti-Party." *Yangtze! Yangtze!* itself has been a victim of the intense politicizing of this issue and the book was banned in 1989. Crushing students in Tiananmen Square not only allowed the communist leadership to remain securely in power, but also provided convenient cover to purge the Party and state apparatus of dam opponents.

The following documents, in short, portray a bare-knuckles political battle in which opposition to construction of the dam involves enormous risks. Western observers who portray policy-making in China as a process of "consensus-building" and "bargaining" must confront the realities described in the following pages.[3] The fundamental lack of checks and balances in the Chinese political system is made explicit through the proliferation of committees that are used to confound and confuse rather than to enlighten. Newspapers carry only "positive reporting" on the dam; microphones at the National People's Congress (NPC) meeting considering the issue are shut off; and prominent opponents, such as the eminent scientist Qian Jiaju, are left with no choice but exile. Nor does the long arm of Chinese government control end at the country's borders. Chinese engineers recently traveling in the United States to raise funds for the project were

---

[2](...continued)
Language Press, 1984). In August, 1986, a leading 'liberal' in the Communist Party leadership, Wan Li, called for more "scientific and democratic" decision making. In 1992, while chairing the National People's Congress meeting that approved the project, he ruled that "no debate is permitted."

[3] See David Lampton, "A Plum for a Peach: Bargaining, Interest, and Bureaucratic Politics in China," in *Bureaucracy, Politics, and Decision Making in Post-Mao China*, eds. David Lampton and Kenneth Lieberthal (Berkeley: University of California Press, 1992), pp. 33-57.

sheltered by their American host (Merrill Lynch) from an inquiring Voice of America journalist who had hoped to broadcast interviews on the controversy surrounding the dam back into China.[4]

"Consensus" is achieved. Case closed.

More than hard-line dictatorship, however, explains the ability of dam supporters to secure approval for the Three Gorges project. While clearly demonstrating the reliance of the Chinese Communist Party on standard totalitarian tools to deter political pluralism, this book also reveals more subtle and well-honed methods of countering potential opposition. On full display here are stock measures of "divide and rule" used by the pro-dam leaders to prevent a critical mass of opponents from coalescing among the scientific and intellectual elite. This is a masterful illustration of isolating critics and keeping such bodies as the NPC fragmented and incapable of challenging central Party decisions. Thus at the March, 1992, NPC session (that formally approved the dam) NPC delegate and dam critic Huang Shunxing attempted to distribute opposition literature among delegates only to discover that members of different delegations were prohibited from direct contact or exchange of materials.[5] With no meaningful sharing of information, there was no debate, and no viable opposition. Procedural guidelines of the nominal legislature were blithely ignored as once again the Communist Party relied on ad hoc measures that totally defied any pretense of institutional process.[6]

Dam opponents also confronted the familiar features of the "mobilization of bias" in favor of the project that makes opposition to such megaprojects difficult to achieve in any bureaucratic environment—totalitarian or otherwise. The

---

[4] The Chinese engineers were to be interviewed along with Dai Qing on the pros and cons of the dam.

[5] For more on this event, see Chapter 10.

[6] The role of ad hoc decision making in authoritarian political systems has been analyzed most notably in Stalinist Russia and Nazi Germany, but generally ignored in China. See Michael Burleigh and Wolfgang Wippermann, *The Racial State: Germany 1933-1945* (Cambridge: Cambridge University Press, 1992), p. 59, and Abdurkhman Avtorkhanov, *Stalin and the Soviet Communist Party: A Study in the Technology of Power* (New York: Praeger, 1959).

enormous momentum and pressure created by the large-scale bureaucracies composed of the Ministry of Water Resources and the powerful Yangtze Valley Planning Office have effectively stifled any "rational" policy process. All the ingredients familiar to bureaucratic machinations are here: promises of administrative position and influence, buying off of potential grass-roots opponents, unrealistic budgetary figures that seriously underestimate true costs, "smoke and mirrors" methods of financing, glossing over and even ignoring potential dangers while exaggerating the benefits, falsifying data and fixing crucial technical experiments, and bureaucratic manipulations to insure that viable alternatives never come up for discussion, let alone a decision. Readers of *Cadillac Desert*, Marc Reisner's exposé on dam building and federal water projects in the American West, will feel right at home with *Yangtze! Yangtze!*[7]

Crammed in the volume's highly detailed chapters, the facts seem to favor the dam's opponents. Also represented here, unlike the government's handling of the controversy, is an "opposing view" in the form of a long statement by a strong supporter of the project, Li Boning. Yet the ongoing effort in China and abroad to block construction of the Three Gorges project, even after its official launch in 1992, confronts many obstacles.

Chief among them is that for many in the Party leadership the dam is much more than just another large-scale project. In the rich tradition of "engineering giganticism" that China's leaders have found so perennially attractive, the dam is one of the last refuges of the old-style planned economy with secure and everlasting financing, personnel, and political power. Insulated from the economic reforms now sweeping the country, the massive project is a political, ideological, and economic sinecure—derisively referred to by dam critics as a "long-and-dragged-out project." The Three Gorges project is proof of the Chinese government's determination to inspire people to collective action for national goals. In the face of advancing individual consumerism, "poisonous bourgeois liberalism," and growing economic power in the country's regions, it demonstrates that the center can still be

---

[7] Marc Reisner, *Cadillac Desert: The American West and Its Disappearing Water*, rev. ed. (New York: Penguin Books, 1993).

the boss. If, as a common Chinese saying goes, "only China can save socialism," then the Three Gorges dam may be intended, in part, as political CPR.

Another major obstacle confronting dam opponents is the identification of the project with Chinese nationalism and ethno-centrism. This is to be the world's largest dam and, like many aspiring great powers, China wants to be "number one": in walls, cities, grain production, and now dams. Small is *not* beautiful in a country with 1.1 billion people. Opponents calling for a series of smaller and less costly dams on the tributaries of the Yangtze River constantly run up against the powerful force of Chinese nationalism, now in a communist guise that prefers grandiose monuments over efficiency. On top of this there is the deeply psychological notion that international standards, and indeed even universal physical laws, don't apply in China, the "center of the world." In a political and cultural milieu that values socialism, democracy and just about everything else with "Chinese characteristics," dam opponents are fighting an uphill battle in citing "international standards" to back their opposition to this massive project. Proponents of the dam are identified with the power and glory of the Chinese state; opponents with the views and professional judgments of the easily maligned "foreigner."[8]

The battle to halt construction of the Three Gorges dam is, however, still far from over. The Chinese political system is

---

[8] Since the mid-1980s, the communist leadership has tried to mobilize 'nativist' opposition to so-called foreign conspiracies that they argue are trying to infiltrate the Chinese culture with Western values. The Chinese have derisively labeled this supposed infiltration "peaceful evolution." The perceived threat of conspiracies has probably not helped dam opponents who often cite international standards and foreign specialists in questioning project design and physical specifications. Ironically, Chinese dam proponents invited these international comparisons when, in preparation for securing foreign financing for the dam in the 1980s, they asked the Canadian government and the World Bank to prepare a feasibility study that would "firmly establish, on bases acceptable to international financial institutions, the technical and economic feasibility of the Three Gorges Project." See CIPM Yangtze Joint Venture (CYJV), *Three Gorges Water Control Project Feasibility Study*, Vol. 1 (1988), Appendix A.

changing, though ever so slowly. *Yangtze! Yangtze!* is still banned, but its courageous editor, Dai Qing, works at home and abroad to quietly mobilize opposition by the project's so-far apparently silent detractors among the communist leadership. News conferences by opponents have been recently held in China as the word in a genuinely more "open" society is gradually getting out. More importantly, the financial constraints of China's reforms and continuing inflation (running in 1993 at over 14 percent) also make this costly endeavor increasingly unattractive. Avoiding ruinous inflation and a financial black hole may for the foreseeable future be the most important consideration of China's new generation of leaders.

Nevertheless, in a system where "rule by the voice of one" is the norm, support for the dam by China's paramount leader Deng Xiaoping propels the project forward. In fact, construction is to be speeded up so that damming the river will coincide with another great national event: the reincorporation in 1997 of Hong Kong into China. One can only hope that with Deng's health evidently fading, the opponents whose voices fill this volume may have time and money on their side.

# PREFACE TO THE CHINESE EDITION

## WORKSONG ON THE YANGTZE RIVER
by
Wu Guoguang[1]

In China, nothing is free of politics. Although it should be a scientific issue, the Three Gorges project has, unfortunately, been dragged into the political arena. The tragedy of the "Li Rui anti-Party Gang"[2] is just one example of the extent to which "pervasive politicization" affects a society where political power is so highly concentrated that it overwhelms all considerations of consciousness and scientific standards.[3]

Such despotic and almighty political power can ruthlessly destroy the most upright personality. This is what has happened to the Three Gorges project over the past decades. An invisible political hand has twisted facts and smothered voices of scientific

---

[1] Wu Guoguang is a former staff member at the *People's Daily*, the official newspaper of the Central Committee of the Chinese Communist Party.

[2] Li Rui is a former secretary to Communist Party Chairman Mao Zedong and a long-time opponent of the Three Gorges project who was purged in 1959. For more on Li see Chapters 6 and 11. Also, see his own book, *Lun sanxia gongcheng* (On the Three Gorges Project), (Hunan: Hunan Scientific and Technological Publishing House, 1985).

[3] "Politics" (*zhengzhi*) in this context means an emphasis on ideological orthodoxy, arbitrary administrative control and the exercise of absolutist authority rather than the dialogue, give and take, and efforts at compromise characteristic of democratic political systems. For an excellent analysis of the intrusion of politics into scientific matters in China, see "Lysenkoism in China: Proceedings of the 1956 Qingdao Genetics Symposium," in *Chinese Law and Government*, ed. Lawrence Schneider (Armonk, N.Y.: M. E. Sharpe Inc., Summer 1986).

debate: it has turned a topic of popular concern into a fearful taboo. Now, we begin to hear a work song along the Yangtze River, that, unlike ordinary work songs, challenges absolute political power. It is coming from Chinese intellectuals, who have broken long years of silence, calling the attention of all Chinese people to this issue which touches their lives.

I believe that science will reveal its objectivity and justice only when it is free of the yoke of political power. Of course, those scientists who favor the Three Gorges project have their reasons; however, the disagreements among scientists should always be solved within the discourse of science itself. When science is forced to serve political interests, it becomes hypocritical, weak and uncertain. I am not saying that science and politics should always be at odds, but that they can only form an alliance for the benefit of mankind when science is in control. In the past decades and even centuries, the tragedy for the Chinese lies in the fact that political issues have always been in control. Politics has not only dominated science, but all aspects of social life, including the human mind and conscience. This is what results from totalitarian dictatorship.

As for the Three Gorges project, the question is not whether the idea of such a project is a poetic fantasy, but why the project should be presented as a mandate from heaven. We have discovered that this craving for the grandiose is a common weakness for all wielders of absolute power. Science is definitely unwelcome when the holder of unrestricted power enjoys manipulating everything. Thus, we should not be surprised to hear of so many "great projects" such as, "Let West Water Flow East," "Build a Dozen More Oil Fields like Daqing"[4] and now "Let the Three Gorges Project Begin Now."

The fact that scientists are breaking the political shackles by expressing their different opinions is important. In China, the major official newspapers never carry a second opinion. But, today, many journalists have initiated their own dialogues with scientists, expressing their own personal perspectives. Confronting the changing face of China, they have courageously called for

---

[4] Daqing was an oil field idealized in the Cultural Revolution as a model of the nation's self reliance.

a scientific approach to various plans for the Yangtze river, the main artery of their motherland. With their comrades in the field of science, they are trying to bring about, however feebly, the separation of politics from other aspects of social life. This is an important historical act on the part of Chinese intellectuals, who in singing their "Work Song" raise a question that all Chinese must face: "Do you have the wisdom, the courage, and the ability to be responsible for your own nation?"

# INTRODUCTION

## OPPOSITION TO AN UNVIABLE DAM
by
Patricia Adams and Philip Williams[1]

On February 28, 1989, an extraordinary alliance of Chinese journalists, scientists, engineers, scholars, and army generals organized a press conference in Beijing to release their independently produced book criticizing the proposed Three Gorges dam on the Yangtze River. "For the first time ordinary Chinese people have decided not to keep silent on a weighty economic policy decision," these journalists and scholars stated at the press conference. "They don't want to see an endless repetition of foolish policies."

Their book, *Yangtze! Yangtze!*, marked what the *Far Eastern Economic Review* called "a watershed event in post-1949 Chinese politics as it represented the first use of large-scale public lobbying by intellectuals and public figures to influence the governmental decision-making process."

*Yangtze! Yangtze!* was a feat of breathtaking determination. Produced in under four months—to influence delegates attending

---

[1] Patricia Adams is the executive director of Probe International, a Canadian public interest research organization which forced public disclosure of the Canadian-World Bank feasibility study for the Three Gorges project in 1989. Probe International subsequently published an independent critique of that study titled *Damming the Three Gorges: What Dam Builders Don't Want You to Know*, 2nd ed., eds. Margaret Barber and Gráinne Ryder (Toronto: Earthscan Canada, 1993). Philip Williams is a consulting hydraulics engineer who has reviewed much of the engineering analysis for the Three Gorges project. Dr. Williams is president of the International Rivers Network, which is the world's leading citizen's organization dedicated to protecting rivers and watersheds.

the Chinese People's Political Consultative Conference and the National People's Congress (NPC) meetings in March-April, 1989, at which a final decision to build the dam was expected—*Yangtze! Yangtze!* is credited with the State Council's decision to postpone the dam for five years.

But the daring act of launching China's first public campaign against a project supported by the highest levels of government —China's largest capital works project since the Great Wall—came at a cost. Dai Qing, the book's chief editor, and the country's best-known woman journalist, was arrested soon after the Tiananmen Square massacre and jailed without trial in a maximum security prison for ten months, during which she was told she would be executed. *Yangtze! Yangtze!* was banned on the ground that it "abetted the turmoil." To this day, criticism of the Three Gorges dam is strictly forbidden.

With the critics silenced, Premier Li Peng, a Soviet-trained hydraulic engineer and one of the project's prominent champions, revived the Three Gorges dam, aiming for its approval at the National People's Congress of 1992. There, despite another extraordinary display of opposition to the dam—one-third of NPC delegates registered their opposition to the dam by voting no or abstaining—the Three Gorges dam was finally approved.

Though banned, some 25,000 copies of *Yangtze! Yangtze!* that evaded seizure remain in circulation, an annoying reminder to the government and the world's dam building industry of the disdain held by independent experts for their rosy arguments in favor of the Three Gorges dam.

*Yangtze! Yangtze!* exposes, before it is too late, the extravagance of the proponents' assertions and the poverty of their analysis justifying the dam: for operational, geographical, and structural reasons, the dam will fail to control flood damages; navigation will be impeded rather than enhanced; and promised electricity supplies will not materialize. Meanwhile, *Yangtze! Yangtze!* explains how the same services—flood protection, navigation, and electricity—can be provided more safely, more quickly, and at less cost.

*Yangtze! Yangtze!*'s contributors reject the proponents' assertion that 1.3 million people can be successfully relocated to make way for the dam's reservoir. And they dismiss the argument that the evacuees welcome the dam as a stimulus to their depressed economy, arguing that the citizenry cannot exercise its rights, and that the region remains poor because for decades no one invested there under threat of inundation.

*Yangtze! Yangtze!* describes the plan to build the world's largest dam as "a day-dreamer's delight, and a pragmatist's nightmare." It predicts the Three Gorges dam will be plagued by the same problems afflicting megaprojects around the world: their large scale, technical and organizational complexity, and experimental nature handicap them. Because megaprojects take so long to build, politicians must protect them by insulating them from changing economic conditions (by applying various subsidies) and technical innovation (by granting various forms of monopoly control) that soon make them redundant and even more uneconomic. Consumers and taxpayers are ill-served in the process.

Like commentators in other countries, the contributors to *Yangtze! Yangtze!* exhibit a common-sense disbelief in centralized, long-term planning, opting instead for incremental, decentralized investments that allow new information to be incorporated, and adaptations to changing circumstances to occur.

The irrepressible and universal desire for the freedom to debate important development decisions courses through *Yangtze! Yangtze!*'s pages. Why, if the dam is such a good idea, such an engineering marvel, do the proponents refuse to defend it? Why are the public and scientists prohibited from debating the pros and cons of the dam?

The only way to separate the real development projects from the charlatans is to stop what *Yangtze! Yangtze!* describes as the Chinese pattern of reservoir construction, where "those who have suffered are not the beneficiaries while those who have benefited are not the sufferers."

That requires an end to the secretive and unaccountable conditions that surround the Three Gorges project. As long as China's decision makers need not account in the legislature, the courtroom, or along the river bank, to the people they displace from their homes, farms, factories and temples, there is no limit to the number of people that can be displaced. As long as decision makers spend the state's funds rather than their own, in an environment free of scrutiny and challenge, economic efficiency can be compromised. As long as scientists and engineers are exempted from or coerced into abandoning their professional responsibilities, imprudent projects can be endorsed.

The people in China who have dared to challenge the Three Gorges dam are not alone. From the Canadian Arctic to the Amazonian rainforest to the vast flood plains of Asia, millions of people are challenging the dam-builders' creed with massive demonstrations, scientific critiques, and legal challenges.

*Yangtze! Yangtze!* enriches the debate and fuels the resistance. By contributing to the growing body of independent critiques of proposed dams, *Yangtze! Yangtze!* helps document how a large dam like the Three Gorges can only be justified with unsubstantiated engineering and compromised economics, by denigrating the cultural values of the people affected, by discounting current economic activity in the ecosystems to be destroyed, by treating the environment as dispensable, by making unscientific and uneconomic choices, and by carelessly assigning risks to others who would not assume those risks themselves.

*Yangtze! Yangtze!*'s prediction of failure parallels worldwide experience. In a 1992 exposé of the legacy of large dams, *The Economist* revealed that "the draw-backs of dam-building have become more apparent, and many of the purported benefits have turned out to be exaggerated.... No solid retrospective studies exist of the costs and benefits of large dams in developing countries."[2]

"Taxpayers who eventually foot the bill, should look on dam-building with suspicion," *The Economist* warned, adding "as always, things look better when some costs are left out." The taxpayers include both those in the industrialized countries whose governments and institutions such as the World Bank (the largest single financing agency for large dams) may be asked to bankroll the building of the Three Gorges dam, and those in China. According to Dai Qing, that suspicion has already begun, with Chinese taxpayers demanding a voice in public expenditures.[3]

The Chinese government may come to regret its reprisals against *Yangtze! Yangtze!* and those who dare to debate the wisdom of the Three Gorges dam. By denying the good informa-

---

[2] "The beautiful and the dammed," *The Economist*, 28 March 1992.
[3] Jin Jun, "Dam Project Ignites China's Intellectuals," *Asian Wall Street Journal Weekly*, 20 March 1989.

tion and good judgment of the Chinese people, whether professor or peasant, the Chinese government dooms the entire country to pay the price. By denying the public the right to debate the wisdom of the dam, they doom themselves. Dai Qing, in accepting the prestigious Goldman Environmental Award in 1993 for her determination to ensure such a debate, quoted an ancient Chinese philosopher who warned: "It is more dangerous to silence the people than to dam a river." China's authorities are doing both.

# Part One

## Banned in China

# CHAPTER ONE

## THE STRUGGLE TO PUBLISH
*YANGTZE! YANGTZE!* IN CHINA[1]
by
Dai Qing[2]

*It has been almost 70 years since the Three Gorges project was first proposed by one of the founders of the People's Republic, Dr. Sun Yat-sen. Since then, hundreds of government agencies, bureaucracies, and academic bodies, both Chinese and foreign, have participated in detailed studies of all aspects of the megaproject. While pressure from the Chinese Communist Party (CCP) for an immediate start to the project has fluctuated over*

---

[1] This chapter, written after the 1989 publishing and subsequent banning of *Yangtze! Yangtze!* in China, was not part of the original book.

[2] Dai Qing, a newspaper columnist for the *Enlightenment Daily* from 1982 until 1989, was the first Chinese journalist to publicize the views of dissidents such as astrophysicist Fang Lizhi. The daughter of a revolutionary martyr executed by the Japanese, Dai was adopted by her father's comrade-in-arms, Marshal Ye Jianying, who by 1980 had become one of the five most powerful men in China. Trained as a missile engineer, Dai worked in military intelligence, which led to a growing disenchantment with the draconian policies of the Chinese government and exposure to a community of writers. While at the *Enlightenment Daily*, Dai began questioning the proposed Three Gorges dam, leading to the publication of *Yangtze! Yangtze!* in 1989. Jailed, banned, and then fired from her job at the *Enlightenment Daily*, Dai Qing has not relented in her struggle for government accountability, press freedom, and public debate on important matters to the Chinese people. In recognition of her contribution, she was awarded Harvard University's prestigious Nieman Fellowship for journalists in 1991, and the Goldman Environmental Award in 1993. Today, Dai works as a freelance journalist, writing on a variety of subjects, including a series of books on the history of dam building in China. *Yangtze! Yangzte!* is the first of that series.

2

*the years due to ideological struggle, the chaos of the Cultural Revolution, economic troubles, and prolonged governmental debate, pressure for a rapid start to the project was once again mounting in the late 1980s.[3]*

*Despite roughly 70 years of debate within the Chinese government, the voices of opposition to the dam—whether those of National Peoples Congress (NPC)[4] members, Chinese People's Political Consultative Conference (CPPCC)[5] members, academics, journalists, or ordinary Chinese citizens—have been repeatedly suppressed by the Chinese government. (EDITORS)*

Since the mid-1980s there have been only three occasions when the Chinese people have openly voiced opposition to the Three Gorges project. The first occasion occurred in 1986, when the Economic Construction Group of the CPPCC submitted a report titled "The Three Gorges Project Should Not Go Ahead in the Short Term" to the State Council and the Central Committee of the Communist Party. Opposition surfaced a second time when the People's Publishing House of Hunan published two books on the Three Gorges project by Tian Fang and Lin Fatang, *On a Long-Range Strategy For the Three Gorges Project* (1987), and *A Second Look at a Long-Range Strategy For the Three Gorges Project* (1989).[6] The third instance was when I and several colleagues first published this book, *Yangtze! Yangtze!*, in China. *Yangtze! Yangtze!* was a joint effort by more than a dozen journalists from Beijing and was titled by 92-year-old Sun Yueqi,

---

[3] For a chronology of events covering the history of the dam, see Appendix A.

[4] The National People's Congress is China's parliament and, in theory, its highest organ of state power. In practice, it is controlled by the Communist Party and serves as its rubber-stamp organization.

[5] An advisory body to the Communist Party whose annual assembly generally meets in conjunction with the NPC's annual meeting. It is composed of mainly non-communist figures from academic, bureaucratic, and intellectual backgrounds, who, especially in the mid-1980s, strongly opposed the Three Gorges project.

[6] A third book on the subject was also published: Tian Fang and Lin Fatang, *A Third Look at a Long-Range Strategy for the Three Gorges Project* (Hunan: People's Publishing House of Hunan, 1992).

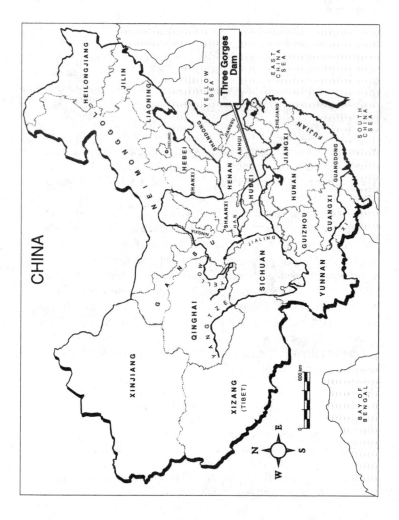

a CPPCC member, and former chairman of the National Resources Committee of the Nationalist Government.

In China, the media is regarded as a propaganda tool of the
Communist Party. This is in keeping with Mao Zedong's cardinal
doctrine: "Revolution depends on two barrels, the barrel of a gun
and the barrel of a pen." Though Chinese citizens hold valuable
opinions, they do not have access to the media. The media provides only jingoistic propaganda, such as "we only want to encourage bright communism and to discard decadent capitalism";
and "the Communist Party and its leadership has been great,
glorious and errorless." The propaganda is full of obvious paradoxes. For example, a country that was referred to as a "comrade-in-arms" yesterday, can be referred to as an "arch enemy"
today, or an "intimate trading partner" tomorrow. But the Chinese
know never to question such paradoxes.

Ordinary people do not understand why the officials who
control the propaganda machine will not allow an open academic
debate on an engineering project such as the Three Gorges dam,
especially since it does not involve bothersome issues such as
humanitarianism, egalitarianism and freedom. Many people are
concerned that, if it is not handled properly, the project may spell
the end for the Communist Party and the People's Republic in a
similar way as construction of the Great Wall more than 2,000
years ago brought down the First Empire of Qin (BC 221-207). It
is unacceptable for the officials to forbid debate in the media on
such an important project.

On every occasion where limited opposition to the Three
Gorges project arose it was suppressed by various kinds of political movements.[7] At the height of the reform and "open policy,"[8]
Sun Yueqi and the Economic Construction Group of the CPPCC
voiced their opposition to the project. The group, composed of
senior scientists, had, in 1986, conducted a 38-day field trip along
the project site. The scientists came back to Beijing with many

---

[7] Here, political movements refer to communist political mass
movements such as the Anti-Rightist Campaign in 1957 and the Cultural
Revolution (1966-1969).
[8] Open policy refers to efforts by the Chinese government to open the
country for trade and investment to the outside world.

opinions and a lot of advice, only to discover that no widely circulated, non-specialized newspapers had objectively reported the findings of their study.[9]

As it happened, Lin Hua, the deputy leader of the group, was a friend of my mother, whom I used to call "uncle." Since government officials controlled the media tightly and were not allowing objective reporting, he asked my mother to invite me to conduct an interview with them.

My mother rarely asked me for favors. However, when she phoned this time, I knew she was as determined on this issue as she had been with her communist beliefs, even though she had repeatedly suffered for those beliefs.[10]

I went to the CPPCC auditorium where the construction group was to officially release its fact-finding report. At first, I thought that I was in the wrong place because there were no more than 100 people in the large auditorium. I took a seat at the side. Uncle Lin Hua, who presided over the meeting, spotted me and made reference to me in his opening speech. "A journalist from the *Enlightenment Daily* is present today!" he said. To my great surprise, the audience immediately began to applaud. All journalists know that reporting on meetings is a difficult task. Usually, journalists are fortunate to find a way to sneak into them without being driven away. Journalists were not usually given such warm

---

[9] During their trip, the CPPCC members visited eight cities that would be affected by the dam and convened more than 40 open forums to hear from all concerned ministries and bureaus, from experts and scholars, and from local and national CPPCC members. At the end of their trip, they submitted their findings to the Central Committee of the Communist Party and the State Council, with the recommendation that the project should not go ahead in the short term. This report and its effects on the debate over the Three Gorges project are more fully examined in Chapter 3. For the complete report see Economic Construction Group of the Chinese People's Political Consultative Conference, "The Three Gorges Project Should Not Go Ahead in the Short Term," in *Megaproject: A Case Study of the Three Gorges*, eds. Shiu-hung Luk and Joseph Whitney (Armonk, N.Y.: M. E. Sharpe Inc., 1993), pp. 110-120.

[10] Dai Qing is implying here that, although a committed communist, her mother suffered at the hands of the Party for pursuing issues such as the Three Gorges dam that challenged the Chinese Communist Party.

receptions! As I found out later, the applause was because there was a government-imposed news blackout on the event.

At the time of the meeting, I had no knowledge of the Three Gorges project. However, as a student of science and technology I felt that what these professionals were saying made sense. Nevertheless, as a newspaper journalist, I did not have the authority to make decisions on the content of the newspaper. Nor did I have the authority to dispatch reporters. My only hope for getting the story out was to consult the director of the Chief Editor's office of my paper. When I spoke to him, I asked why the paper did not send reporters to cover such an important event. He replied that there was a "spirit"[11] or unwritten rule from the higher authorities that allowed only "positive" reporting; that is, reporting that supported the views of the Party. Anyone who understood the politics of communist China would know that the "spirit" was something that only those people in the center of power could control. I told him of my own opinion and hoped that he would not take the rules on "positive" reporting too seriously. He was clear-minded and did what he thought was proper. Nevertheless, our effort seemed to be very limited in comparison to the powerful and resonant "positive" reporting campaign on the project.

After attending the meeting, I returned to my daily routine and did not concern myself with the Three Gorges again until the autumn of 1988.

That autumn, a group of writers, journalists and professors in Hong Kong (known as the "cultural celebrities") hosted a conference for writers from both China and Taiwan, and I was invited to attend. I was shocked to see that the Hong Kong media was full of stories on the Three Gorges project which had attracted almost no attention from ordinary people in China. I felt very ashamed that I, a Beijinger, paid so little attention to such an important issue. But, I was still not sure how I could help those opposing the Three Gorges project. Fortunately, those I made contact with in

---

[11] For a description of the origins and history of this "spirit" in the Communist Party, and its destructive consequences for opinionated intellectuals, see Dai Qing, *Wang Shiwei and "Wild Lilies": Rectification and Purges in the CCP, 1942-1944* (Armonk, N.Y.: M. E. Sharpe Inc., 1994).

Hong Kong sent me many clippings concerning the project. Without their help I could not have taken up the Three Gorges cause. The news reports that they sent made me both anxious and restless.

While I became personally committed to the cause, I was at a loss as to how my fellow journalists working in the science or news sections of their newspapers could do something to help, as the newspapers were under the tight control of Communist Party officials.

Then the big news came. The Hong Kong press had reported that the construction of the Three Gorges project would be started in 1989! Now, it was impossible for any Chinese journalist with a conscience to accept the old excuses for remaining uninvolved with the project—being "too busy" or "lacking a position of responsibility in a media organization" would no longer wash. It was then that I made up my mind to start minding the business of others.

Today, many Chinese and foreign newspapers and magazines have labeled me an "environmentalist." I am quite flattered by the title. Although I have a great deal of respect for the environmental movement, neither I nor my colleagues considered ourselves environmentalists when we were compiling and publishing *Yangtze! Yangtze!* Our goal was to push China a little bit further towards freedom of speech on the issue of government decision making.

Deng Xiaoping once said:

> Only when we realize democracy in our nation's political life with a readiness to welcome and accept different views from the public, can we avoid serious mistakes and correct the minor ones in a timely fashion.

In a similar vein Zhao Ziyang[12] said: "Make known the important matters to the people and let the people discuss them." Even under very strict authoritarian rule, we can still find some

---

[12] Former General Secretary of the Communist Party, Zhao Ziyang was purged after the Tiananmen Square massacre of June, 1989, and was replaced with the current general secretary, Jiang Zemin.

8

leaders' quotations to justify our work and serve as our arrow-shaped token of authority.[13]

Our first task in publishing *Yangtze! Yangtze!* was to interview the contributors and translate the academic language of these specialists into the popular language of the media so that ordinary people could make sense of it. The second task was to find a place to publish it.

The first task was relatively easy. Though I was unable to interview all of the leading scientists and scholars who opposed the project, there were many excellent journalists who, thanks to 10 years of reform, were no longer willing to act as mouthpieces for the Communist Party. We knew if we co-operated and worked together,[14] we could turn out 10 interviews in one week. But where could these interviews be published?

We knew there was little hope of having the Party-controlled newspapers publish our work. At that time, the Shanghai-based *World Economic Herald* had not yet been banned[15] and we thought it might be able to turn out a special issue. I carefully planned and discussed the issue with Zhang Weiguo, the director of the *Herald*'s Beijing office. Unfortunately, because of differences of opinion between myself and the paper's editors, the plan was rejected by the main office in Shanghai. There was no government interference.

Having no luck with newspapers, magazines were the next logical step. It was impossible with *Outlook* magazine because it was run by the Xinhua News Agency.[16] The *New Observer* was considered liberal enough to publish the material but they already had enough articles for their next few issues (a common excuse). We then asked to have our material included in the *New Observer*

---

[13] "Arrow-shaped token of authority" is a Chinese cultural term. In ancient times, emperors gave special arrows to their officials. To possess one of these arrows was to carry the emperor's authority and approval.

[14] This was no mean accomplishment since such actions by journalists outside direct Party authority could expose Dai Qing and her colleagues to political persecution.

[15] It was banned in 1989.

[16] The Xinhua News Agency is China's official news agency, and is at the top of the hierarchy of the Chinese mass media system. Its director is nominated by the premier and approved by the NPC.

as a supplement, but this was not possible because all supplements had to be approved by the authorities. We did not have time to seek such approval, nor did we think it would be granted. The *Journal of Natural Dialectics* was under the control of the Chinese Academy of Sciences, but the new leader of the academy was said to be a very nice man who did not want to cause any trouble. The *Voice of the Masses*, the *Chinese World* and other magazines were all contacted, but I was politely rejected by all of them. The Communist Party's control was so pervasive that it leaked nothing; not even a drop of water.

With my anger mounting, I recalled that there was a newly founded magazine called the *Science and Technology Entrepreneur* in Shandong province, which had been begging me for stories. I contacted them right away. They were so excited they sent an editor to participate in our interviews in Beijing. We agreed that they would send someone again three days later to Beijing to get the manuscripts. Incredibly, they did not want to charge us for the publishing; instead they offered to pay us in order to cover our expenses in Beijing. I was overjoyed by this unexpected good news! However, as I walked the editor out of the building after the interviews with the economists, he stopped and I sensed that something was wrong. My heart almost stopped beating. He then conceded that in order to publish our interviews and articles he would need our help in obtaining approval from the National Association of Sciences and Technology (NAST), which oversaw the magazine's affairs. Bravely, I said that this would be no problem. I knew that Zhou Peiyuan (a leading scientist and dam opponent) was the ex-chairman of the association, and hoped he would support us by allowing a scientific magazine to publish a special issue on the Three Gorges project. The topics were in the interests of the nation and the people and followed the guidance of the current leaders' directives.[17]

I did not expect that the plan would fall apart at the last moment. However, the Beijing correspondent of the magazine felt that permission from the ex-chairman alone would not be sufficient. The current chairman was Qian Xuesen, a renowned scien-

---

[17] This is a reference to the quotes by Deng Xiaoping and Zhao Ziyang mentioned earlier in the chapter.

tist and patriotic statesman, who was considered fresh blood in the Communist Party. When asked for his permission, Qian responded: "Who is this Dai Qing? We should pay no attention to things in which she pokes her nose."

I understood very well that Qian did not want to deal with anything that involved me. However, he was being disingenuous when he implied that he did not know me. Two or three years earlier, when I was a subordinate of his,[18] we met and I made the comment that every time I met a great man and listened to his brilliant speeches, his wife was always playing the piano in the background. Accustomed to musing on issues of science and politics accompanied by his wife's music, Qian asked me which of Beethoven's symphonies I preferred. "Number Five," I replied. Qian smiled and replied, "No, it should be Number Nine. This symphony represents his highest achievement—reconciliation, harmony and love between human beings." I felt enlightened by his comments. Unfortunately, by the time we sought his permission to publish our interviews, I understood that for some, reconciliation, harmony and love existed only in the music of Beethoven. At this point it was clear that the only option left for us was to publish our articles in a book.

Several publishers in Beijing were contacted. They all rejected me politely and I fell into complete despair. Suddenly, I received a phone call from Xu Yinong of the People's Publishing House of Guizhou province. Xu had joined the communist movement in the 1940s and was one of the most insightful and courageous senior editors in China. She did not mind making personal sacrifices to support good books and their authors. The most important thing for us was that as executive editor of the publishing house, she had the authority to give us a book number (ISBN). Finally, the "tightly controlled" system had developed a tiny loophole! Printing began immediately.

On February 28, 1989, we held a news conference in Beijing to announce the release of *Yangtze! Yangtze!* With the help of

---

[18] Dai Qing worked as an engineer in the Seventh Ministry of Machine Building when Qian was the vice-minister. During the Cultural Revolution she was one of the key activists in the faction in which he was involved.

fund-raising activities held by the cultural and press circles (including the participation of many foreign news correspondents) and voluntary help from scholars, writers, artists and friends in the publishing business,[19] *Yangtze! Yangtze!* was released as planned, to coincide with the annual assemblies of the NPC and the CPPCC, at which the Three Gorges project was to be approved.[20] During the meetings, the books were available in the stores of the hotels where delegates stayed.[21]

On June 4, 1989, immediately after the release of the Chinese edition, the Sanlian Publishing House released the Hong Kong edition with the revised title, *Debate over the Three Gorges Project*. In 1991, as a new wave of pro-dam campaigning picked up in China, the Xindi Press in Taipei released the Taiwan edition, under the original title.

Our efforts may look weak and limited in comparison with the government's strong and thunderous media campaign. Whether history proves the project to be a success or a failure, the fact remains that we were simply a group of journalists who took our profession very seriously. We tried to do what we felt was right at a time when we were needed.

---

[19] Xiao Rong reports that Liang Congjie, a scholar, topped the list of donors. Other supporters included writers from Taiwan such as Chen Yingzhen, Wang Tuo and Guo Feng and a number of cultural magazines in Beijing.

[20] For more on the NPC and CPPCC's opposition to the dam at this meeting and 1992 meetings, see Chapters 3 and 10.

[21] In fact, many CPPCC delegates were said to have sneaked out of their assembly meetings to attend Dai Qing's news conference.

# CHAPTER TWO

## THE BANNING OF *YANGTZE! YANGTZE!*[1]
by
Xiao Rong[2]


Due to the concerted efforts of scholars, reporters, editors and publishers, *Yangtze! Yangtze!* was published as intended just prior to the National People's Congress (NPC) annual assembly in 1989.

More than a dozen newspapers and periodicals carried stories or commentaries on *Yangtze! Yangtze!*'s release. The newspapers included the *People's Daily, Enlightenment Daily, Literary Gazette, Workers' Daily, Liberation Daily, Science and Technology Entrepreneur, Literature & Arts, China Daily, Beijing Youth News,* and *Newspaper Digest;* the magazines which carried the story included *Chinese Human Resources* and *Chinese Science.*

Because the press enjoyed increased freedom in the months prior to the Tiananmen Square demonstrations, most of the media reported on *Yangtze! Yangtze!*'s release in a favorable way, focusing primarily on the following three themes: First, the public's concern about the Three Gorges project should be seen not only as a patriotic or emotional reaction, but also as a logical response by taxpayers concerned with protecting their own interests.[3] Second, public debate on major government decisions was an

---

[1] This chapter, written after the 1989 publishing and subsequent banning of *Yangtze! Yangtze!* in China, was not part of the original book.
[2] Xiao Rong, formerly a journalist with *Wen Yi Bao* is now the director of a private company in China.
[3] In fact, Dai Qing has appealed for a Chinese version of a "tax revolt" over the Three Gorges, especially among the new, wealthier elements of Chinese society who must now pay income tax. Indeed, there have been calls by wealthy individuals for the government to recognize the "rights" of taxpayers.

important component in the democratization of Chinese national political life. And, third, it was unusual for intellectuals to make donations to fund the publication of an academically controversial book. In fact, in the June, 1989, issue of *October*, an important literary magazine, a non-fiction piece titled "The Three Gorges" by Ma Licheng and Qian Gang was published. Through favorable media reports such as this one, more and more ordinary people became concerned with the Three Gorges project. Finally, in March, 1989, a large number of delegates of the NPC signed a petition demanding that the Three Gorges project be stopped or postponed.[4]

After the March petition signing, the media voiced both pro- and anti-dam opinions. Although the public had more access to the relevant information—the *Voice of the Masses* magazine ran five consecutive articles contesting the feasibility of the project— the pro-project side succeeded in holding the dominant position in the media. On April 13, 1989, the *Asian-Pacific Economic Times* carried a long story with detailed figures and facts in an attempt to illustrate how the Three Gorges project was a choice that China had to make in order to survive as a nation. In late May, the *Books Herald* published an article critical of the way that *Yangtze! Yangtze!* was published.

Meanwhile, the first printing of 5,000 copies of *Yangtze! Yangtze!* was widely circulated throughout China thanks to NPC deputies who took copies of the book back to their various home towns. Showing unusual interest in the project, many people began contacting media organizations asking for copies of the book.

In this way, the media debate on the book and the project attracted interest from scholars and economists, as well as from ordinary taxpayers who wanted to participate. But this debate caused concern among some government agencies, who began to

---

[4] The petition, which recommended that the Three Gorges project be postponed until the 21st century and that the upper reaches and tributaries be developed first, was signed by 272 National People's Congress delegates, one-tenth of the entire body. For more information on this event see Chapter 3.

argue that their work had been "interfered with." Consequently they became alert to the possible evidence of a "class struggle."[5]

A number of private book sellers in Chengdu, Sichuan province, sensed that the book would be profitable and wasted no time in signing a contract with the People's Publishing House of Guizhou to have another 50,000 copies printed. These copies were distributed through private distribution and retail networks throughout the Yangtze Valley. Then came the political disturbance of June, 1989.

Although the book was banned after the June pro-democracy movement was crushed, the attack on *Yangtze! Yangtze!* had started well before the June crackdown. On May 11, the Yangtze Valley Planning Office (YVPO) of the Ministry of Water Resources and Electric Power[6] wrote to the Party Central Committee and the Guizhou provincial government. In the letters, the YVPO claimed that the book contained a number of factual errors and

---

[5] An ideological judgment characteristic of the Maoist era that would have justified political persecution of the authors.

[6] These two bureaucratic units are strong supporters of the Three Gorges project. The Yangtze Valley Planning Office, established in 1956 and headquartered in Wuhan, has more than 12,000 personnel. It has been subordinate to the Ministry of Water Resources since the 1970s. The YVPO has been responsible both for the overall plan for developing the Yangtze River and for the Three Gorges Feasibility Report completed in 1989 (discussed more fully in Chapter 3).

The Ministry of Water Resources was from 1958 to 1979, and again from 1982 to April, 1988, part of a hybrid ministry—the Ministry of Water Resources and Electric Power, which was headed for many years by Qian Zhengying. The electric power side of the hybrid ministry was most concerned with bringing new and cheap sources of electric power on line as quickly as possible and thus generally opposed the Three Gorges dam. In contrast, the water resources side was most concerned with flood control and strongly supported the dam. In the reorganization of April, 1988, the Ministry of Water Resources and Electric Power was once again divided. The Ministry of Water Resources was reformed while the electric power departments were merged with the Ministry of Power. See Kenneth Lieberthal and Michel Oksenberg, *Policy Making in China: Leaders, Structures, and Processes* (Princeton: Princeton University Press, 1988), pp. 94-102, 283-287, and Lampton, *Bureaucracy*, pp. 52-53.

personal attacks. It did not, however, question the political intentions or goals of the book. A Guizhou provincial Party official, who was in charge of propaganda and the media, started investigating the case. In response, the Party group of the publishing company submitted a report to the provincial Party Committee defending its decision to publish the book. In the report, the book's executive editor, Xu Yinong said that the decision to publish the book was based on two considerations:

> First, as a publisher, we are committed to providing an opportunity for public debate on important issues, such as the Three Gorges project, which affect both the national economy and people's livelihoods. Our decision was based on the guidelines charted at the Communist Party's Thirteenth Congress [September-October, 1987], which said that major issues should be known by the people, and be discussed by them. We should provide space for different opinions on the project to be published (whether they are for or against the project), so long as they are based on reason and fact. In the future, if there are pro-dam materials to be published, we would publish them with the same willingness. Second, we hope that the publication of the book will contribute to an improved study of the project. Thus, more scientific and technically correct information would be provided for the central government to make its decision.

On May 22, the publishing house wrote a letter to the YVPO (with a copy to the Party Central Committee), which stated that the authors were responsible for any factual errors contained in the book. The letter argued that publishers who decided to publish books that presented academically different views on a controversial issue should not be considered to have passed judgment on the material or taken sides on the debated issue. The publishing house had no right to take part in a debate, but was committed to the Party's cultural policy of "letting a hundred flowers blossom and a hundred schools of thought contend." The letter continued by saying that the publishing house hoped a unanimous conclusion would be reached on the Three Gorges project, which would be based on a fully justified study.

In the letter, the publisher noted that a majority of articles in the book raised questions about the construction of the project, and that these questions dealt primarily with issues of engineering, flood control, electricity generation, navigation, population relocation, environment, sedimentation, technology, and finance. After reviewing all of the articles, the publisher concluded that most of the questions raised were based on knowledge or information that was collected from the individual interviewees' or authors' personal research or work experience. "They spoke with good reason," the letter continued, "and they had sufficient grounds for their viewpoints." These materials were argued to be in line with the general principles of the company for publishing books on controversial issues.

Finally, the letter did note that some articles used inappropriate wording or were exaggerated in expression and that these cases were contrary to the principle of "convincing by reasoning." The publishing company apologized to YVPO for the inappropriate wording and hoped that the matter could be "settled satisfactorily."

After the June 4 crackdown in Tiananmen Square, Dai Qing was publicly denounced by the official media, and in July she was arrested. Now, the issue of *Yangtze! Yangtze!*'s publication became focused on the authors' political intentions. The Party Committee of Guizhou province began to receive phone calls and telegrams from the YVPO claiming that the publishing of the book was driven by the "ulterior motives of the disturbance activists." Also, in July, the YVPO delivered a report to the office of the Media and Publication Administration[7] requesting that *Yangtze! Yangtze!* be censored.

In September, 1989, two members of the Leading Group for the Assessment of the Three Gorges Project, which had been convened in 1985 to oversee and coordinate an assessment report

---

[7] The Media and Publication Administration falls under the State Council. Its functions include approving all publication licences, supervising the sale and distribution of newsprint, and studying press law. Originally conceived as a liberalizing force in the media, the administration has, since 1987, been controlled by conservative forces in the State Council.

on the project,[8] submitted a letter to the Party branch of the State Planning Commission.[9] The letter argued:

> [*Yangtze! Yangtze!*] advocates bourgeois liberalization. It is a book opposing the Four Cardinal Principles,[10] and a book that has provided opinions for the chaos (*dongluan*) and riot (*baoluan*). Comrades Lin Hua and Tian Fang of your unit were involved in this action. your unit and for the investigation of cadres.

The interviewers and authors of the book, along with the journalists who reported on it, were all subject to examination and punishment. The voices of opposition were viciously suppressed.[11]

---

[8] In China, leading groups are powerful bureaucratic organs led by a member of the Chinese Communist Party Politburo, the Party's highest decision-making body. Established in 1985 under the Ministry of Water Resources and Electric Power, and headed by Li Peng, the Leading Group for the Assessment of the Three Gorges Project oversaw and coordinated the 14 studies that composed the assessment report, which preceded a full decision by the NPC. See Carol Lee Hamrin, "The Party Leadership System," in *Bureaucracy, Politics, and Decision Making in Post-Mao China*, eds. David Lampton and Kenneth Lieberthal (Berkeley: University of California Press, 1992), p. 96. The studies covered various topics including: hydrology, flood control, sedimentation, navigation, power systems, and resettlement, among others. The leading group examined previous studies and conducted supplemental research. A directory of the sessions of the leading group and their functions is found in Appendix B. A partial list of experts from the various subject groups who held opposition opinions is found in Appendix C.

[9] Established in 1952, the State Planning Commission manages China's centrally planned economy. A supra-ministerial body, the commission develops five-year plans and guides the construction of significant projects such as the Three Gorges dam, which key bureaus of the Commission supported in the early 1980s. See Lieberthal and Oksenburg, *Policy Making*, pp. 64-65, 284-285.

[10] Uphold the Socialist Road, Uphold the Dictatorship of the Proletariat, Uphold the Leadership of the Communist Party, and Uphold Marxism-Leninism and Mao Zedong Thought.

[11] According to Shi He and Ji Si, authors of Chapter 3.

18

# Organizations and Their Relations Concerned with the Assessment of the Three Gorges Project

(14 Expert Groups [412 experts])

| Organization | |
|---|---|
| CCP | |
| NPC — State Council | Ministry of Finance |
| | Ministry of Geology and Mineral Resources |
| | Ministry of Agriculture |
| | Ministry of Construction |
| | Ministry of Communication |
| | Ministry of Water Resources and Electric Power |
| | State Planning Commission |
| | State Science and Technology Commission |
| | Chinese Academy of Sciences |
| | Chinese Academy of Social Sciences |
| | State Environmental Protection Commission |
| CPPCC | Economic Committee |

Yangtze Valley Planning Office

Specially Invited Advisors

Leading Group for the Assessment of the Three Gorges Project

Enlarged Session for the Assessment of the Three Gorges Project

Economic Construction Group of the Three Gorges Project

Experts' Group on Geology and Seismology

Experts' Group on Dam and Appurtenant Structures

Experts' Group on Hydrology

Experts' Group on Flood Control

Experts' Group on Sedimentation

Experts' Group on Navigation

Experts' Group on Electric Power System

Experts' Group on Mechanical and Electrical Equipment

Experts' Group on Population Relocation

Experts' Group on Ecology and Environment

Experts' Group on Multipurpose Planning and Reservoir Operation Levels

Experts' Group on Construction

Experts' Group on Cost Estimation

Experts' Group on Comprehensive Economic Evaluation

Then, in October, 1989, four months after the disturbance, the Media and Publication Administration and the Publishing Bureau of Guizhou province officially denounced and banned *Yangtze! Yangtze!* The Party Committee of Guizhou issued a resolution in October, 1989, which was announced at the staff meeting of the publishing company.[12] The resolution accused the book of launching a political attack under the guise of scholarly debate. The Party argued that the book's authors had disguised their true intentions, and were guilty of "engaging in preparing opinions for the chaos (i.e., the period of the pro-democracy movement prior to the military crackdown on June 4), and riot (i.e., the days of the crackdown itself)." The resolution ordered the publishing company to recall the remaining 30,000 copies of the book and destroy them immediately. This caused the publishing company to eventually lose 60,000 *yuan*[13] on the publication of *Yangtze! Yangtze!* (All documents between Beijing and Guizhou authorities concerning this incident have been sealed and the author was not able to access them for this article.)

As a further punitive measure, the executive editor of the book and the heads of the publishing company had to make self-criticisms[14] during the reregistration of Party membership after the June 4 crackdown. Nevertheless, Xu Yinong continued to speak openly (even after her self-criticism) in favor of *Yangtze! Yangtze!* She argued that the charges against the book were groundless. The editors and publisher had started planning the project at the end of January, 1989, and at that time no one had the faintest idea of the student demonstrations and political distur-

---

[12] According to some anti-dam activists, the director and chief engineer of YVPO submitted a proposal during the March, 1990, NPC assembly demanding that *Yangtze! Yangtze!* be handled sternly. (The existence of this proposal cannot be confirmed due to difficulties in accessing NPC motions.) The proposal apparently provided the keynote for the resolution that was read to the staff of the publishing company in October, 1989.

[13] In late 1988, the official exchange rate was US$1-Y3.7. By 1993, it reached US$1=Y5.7.

[14] Self-criticisms are a popular means of control in the communist system. Those seen to be acting out of line with Party policy must criticize their own behavior, either publicly or in written form.

bances that would ensue. In Xu's view, it was necessary to recognize first that *Yangtze! Yangtze!*'s authors demonstrated good will in trying to make the government's decision-making process more democratic and scientifically sound. Some inaccuracies were a result of inappropriate wording and should not be made a political issue. "I believe that history will decide whether the book is wrong or not. If there are any consequence that I have to face for keeping my own opinion, I am willing to face them," said Xu.

Xu later commented with good humor that *Yangtze! Yangtze!* seemed to have a fate similar to *China on the Edge*,[15] (another book she has edited), "they were both killed but still live." Although *Yangtze! Yangtze!* is, to this day, unavailable on the official market, the 25,000 copies that were sold before the ban have spread across the nation like wildfire. As of 1991, the publishing company was still receiving letters requesting the book. Fortunately, with the publication of the Hong Kong and Taiwan editions, and now with the publication of the English edition, *Yangtze! Yangtze!* survives abroad.[16]

---

[15] He Bochuan, *China on the Edge: The Crisis of Ecology and Development*, ed. Xu Yinong, trans. (San Francisco: China Books and Periodicals Inc., 1991), was originally published in China by the People's Publishing House of Guizhou, and was subsequently banned—evidently because of its devastating critique of economic mismanagement and environmental problems. Reportedly, it is still widely read by top Party and government leaders.

[16] It is worth noting that, despite being banned, as of March, 1990, some copies of *Yangtze! Yangtze!* were still on sale in Beijing. They were apparently displayed openly on the shelves of bookstores at the entrance to the auditorium of the Chinese People's Political Consultative Conference during its annual meeting.

# CHAPTER THREE

## THE COMEBACK OF THE THREE
## GORGES DAM (1989–1993)[1]
by
Shi He and Ji Si

*As Yangtze! Yangtze! was being prepared in early 1989, dam proponents and opponents were marshaling forces to sway delegates at the March-April meetings of the National People's Congress (NPC) and Chinese People's Political Consultative Conference (CPPCC). Opposition had gained attention in 1986 following the report of the Economic Committee of the CPPCC on its 38-day field trip to the dam site, which concluded that the dam should not go ahead in the short term because its cost would be three times the official estimate, it would not solve flooding problems, it would not effectively flush sediment out of the reservoir, and it was similarly flawed in the areas of navigation, power generation and safety.*

*The NPC had responded in 1986 by calling for further deliberations on the project and excluding it from the Seventh Five-Year plan (1986-1990).*

*Despite this setback, between 1986 and 1989 project preparations continued. The Leading Group For the Assessment of the Three Gorges Project, established under the Ministry of Water Resources and Electric Power, continued the preparation of its 14 studies, which the YVPO then used to compile a favorable feasibility report that it submitted to the State Council for approval in early 1989. Just prior to the YVPO's submission, a Canadian engineering consortium—commissioned by the World Bank, the Canadian Government and the Ministry of Water Resources and*

---

[1] This chapter, written after the 1989 publishing and subsequent banning of *Yangtze! Yangtze!* in China, was not part of the original book.

*Electric Power—completed and submitted its own favorable feasibility report. Despite this continuing preparatory work by dam proponents, opposition in both the NPC and CPPCC was gaining momentum. (EDITORS)*

On January 23, 1989, at the fourth session of the Seventh Standing Committee of the CPPCC, Yao Yilin, vice-premier and director of the State Council Examination Committee of the Three Gorges project,[2] issued the following statement on behalf of the State Council:

> It is impossible to begin the project within the next five years; therefore, it is not necessary to devote a lot of energy to debating it now. The debate over and the assessment of the Three Gorges project has been going on for quite some time. Those in favor possess ample reasons for their views, while those opposed also have their reasons. Again, since it is impossible to launch the project at the present time, our interests would be best served by not engaging in too much debate. When, in the future, a decision has to be rendered, ample debate will of course occur and proposals will be made to the NPC.

Despite its being published in the Hong Kong press, very few people on mainland China heard about this speech. Given only within the small circle of the Standing Committee of the Chinese People's Political Consultative Conference, this pronouncement did not stop dam proponents or dam opponents from pressing forward. Only two months later, at the tenth (enlarged) meeting of the Leading Group for the Assessment of the Three Gorges Project (February 27 to March 7, 1989), it approved in principle

---

[2] The examination committee, led by Yao, was set up to examine the leading group and YVPO reports. In 1990, a second examination committee, with Vice-Premier Zou Jiahua as its director, was set up to once again review the YVPO report. Both committees were staffed with dam supporters whose primary function was to legitimize the project.

the "Feasibility Report on the Three Gorges Project," conducted by the YVPO.[3]

Meanwhile, on February 28, the People's Publishing House of Guizhou held a press conference announcing the publication of *Yangtze! Yangtze!* The book had been churned out as quickly as possible in order to ensure that delegates to the NPC and CPPCC conferences (who were to vote on the dam project) would be fully informed about the opposition opinions on the project.[4]

When the NPC met in March, its opposition to the Three Gorges project was quite pronounced. Some 272 delegates, led by Xu Caidong, delivered a joint petition to the NPC titled "[We suggest that] the Three Gorges Project be Postponed Until the 21st Century and that the Upper Reaches and Tributaries Be Developed First." But this proposal, though presented by one-tenth of the delegates, was not even included in the meeting's formal "Collection of Proposals."

Meanwhile, at the CPPCC, opposition was also mounting. Three hundred CPPCC members presented eighteen different proposals demanding further assessment of the project. Also in March, Tian Fang and Lin Fatang's second collection of opposition opinions, *A Second Look at a Long-Range Strategy For the Three Gorges Project*, was published by the Hunan Science and Technology Publishing House. Since Tian and Lin's book was not accepted by the secretariat of the conference, the two editors bought a few hundred copies with their own money and personally delivered them to the hotel rooms of delegates.

On April 3, 1989, at a press conference held by the State Council, Yao Yilin reiterated that:

A debate has been held over the Three Gorges project. Those in favor have adequate supporting evidence, and

---

[3] At this meeting, members of the CPPCC, including Tan Xiudian, Wu Jing, Kang Daisha, Chen Shaoming, Lin Hua, Xu Guangyi, Yang Hanzhao, Lu Qinkan, Yu Siying, Luo Xibei, Zhao Weigang, Qiao Peixin, and Sun Yueqi, made speeches voicing opinions in opposition to the report, while Wang Xingrang delivered a written statement of opposition.
[4] Many believe that the publication of *Yangtze! Yangtze!* helped stop the project in 1989.

those opposed have a reasonable basis for their doubts. Therefore, this matter needs further and more detailed assessment. I personally think that there is no way the project can be launched in the next five years. No large-scale projects related to the Three Gorges will be submitted in either the present period of planned administrative reform nor in the upcoming Eighth Five Year Plan [1991-1995]. Thus, there is no point in putting a lot of effort into debating it. If, however, the Three Gorges project is to be launched in the future, it has to be approved by the NPC. So, once again, I suggest that we drop the topic for now.[5]

The next day, Yao's speech was reported in the *People's Daily*. At almost the same time (mid-April to the end of May), organizations including the Sichuan provincial government, the Chinese Society of Territorial Economic Studies, the Chinese Society of Hydro-electric Power Engineering, the Society of Energy Resources Studies, and the Society of Hydro-power Economic Studies became dissatisfied with their lack of influence in the decision-making process for the Three Gorges project and began to oppose it and other disastrous projects on the mainstream of the Yangtze. As a result, they began to promote the development of hydro-electric power stations on the upper reaches and the tributaries. These views were put forth in a report titled, "A Comprehensive Investigation of Hydro-electric Power Development of the Three Rivers (the Jinsha, Yalong, and Dadu rivers) in Sichuan" and in the book titled *Discussion of the Development of the Upper Reaches of the Yangtze River.*

Despite the State Council's public position (as elaborated by Yao) that "there is no way the project can be launched in the next five years...and there is no point in putting a lot of effort into debating it," the work of the leading group did not subside. In October, 1989, five months after the Tiananmen Square demonstrations, *Yangtze! Yangtze!* was officially banned and two

---

[5] This speech, unlike the one made by Yao on January 23, was reported by the Party-controlled media on the mainland, and thus can be argued to represent the consensus of the top leadership.

members of the leading group sent a letter to the Party Branch of the State Planning Commission accusing the book and its authors of advocating "bourgeois liberalization."[6]

Then, in July, 1990, a State Council meeting was held at which Qian Zhengying and Pan Jiazheng reported on the assessments of the Three Gorges project conducted by the leading group and the YVPO. Despite Yao Yilin's speech of April, 1989, the view favoring rapid implementation of the project was still prominent in government circles.[7]

While those with opposition views did have a chance to express themselves at the meeting, they were allocated only one-third of the time to speak. Also, it was at this meeting that the second Examination Committee, this one headed by Zou Jiahua, was set up. The committee was created to reexamine the YVPO's Feasibility Report for the project.

At the end of the meeting Yao gave a speech that was decidedly different in tone from the one in April, 1989. He said:

> The decision as to when the project will be launched should be made after examining the assessment report and based on results of a systematic analysis of the overall economy jointly conducted by various departments and on the country's actual economic capacities.

Yao especially emphasized that "we should continue at the present time with construction of the various engineering and non-engineering projects for flood control on the plains as decided in 1980."

Li Peng's attitude was summarized as follows: "In my opinion, whether and when the project will be launched involves both technological and economic issues, namely, whether it is beyond the nation's (economic) capacity."

At this point (mid-1990), the domestic political atmosphere was no longer as stringent as it had been a year earlier and thus

---

[6] See Chapter 2 for a more detailed explanation of this event.
[7] In fact, it appears that this meeting was convened by Premier Li Peng specifically to officially revive the discussions on the Three Gorges project.

journals published by the democratic parties such as *Voice of the Masses* started to once again publish articles by dam opponents Sun Yueqi, Hou Xueyu, Yang Jike, Lu Qinkan, Lin Hua, and Qian Weichang.[8]

Yet this somewhat mild atmosphere containing scanty elements of debate irritated two "old leaders": the 83-year-old native of Hunan, Vice-President Wang Zhen, and the 75-year-old native of Hubei and vice-chairman of the CPPCC, Wang Renzhong. Their irritation resulted in the now famous "Spring Festival Forum Promoting the Early and Rapid Launching of the Three Gorges Project," in 1991. Ten experts participated in this Guangdong meeting, which was convened by the two Wangs. The "Summary" of the meeting was published in the *Bulletin of Internal Trends* by the Xinhua News Agency. Although the two men were not personally in charge of the Three Gorges project, the summary stated in a rather authoritative tone: "The Three Gorges project should be started in the second half of 1992 and should come on line at the end of this century or the beginning of the next. By 2010, the entire project will be completed."

Dam supporters were greatly encouraged. In response to a question about the project during a press conference held during the April, 1991, CPPCC meeting, Qian Zhengying noted: "It's better for the Three Gorges project to be started rather than delayed, and the earlier, the better!" That reply conveyed a much more positive attitude than was generally held by the State Council. Nevertheless, Qian was likely able to make this statement, which by all means exceeded her authority, because of support from the "old leader"—Wang Zhen, who, while visiting Guangdong, had criticized those opposing the dam. He noted: "Li Rui opposes the Three Gorges project but he is by all means a black sheep among us Hunanese. And he is a contemporary counter-revolutionary!" This comment was not included in the meeting's summary, but it was communicated through the grapevine back to Beijing. In the face of such criticism, Li remained calm, replying: "I a counter-revolutionary? Then arrest me."

---

[8] For more on the types of articles published at this time, see Barber and Ryder, eds., *Damming*, pp. 17-18.

Despite the efforts by dam opponents,[9] it seemed that the decision to "launch the project as early and rapidly as possible" was assumed to be the final decision.

Zou Jiahua's Examination Committee reinforced this view when, in August, 1991, after concluding their examination of the YVPO's Feasibility Report, the committee approved the project. It stated that if funds could be acquired in time, it was feasible for the preparation work on the project to begin in 1993 and the entire project to be launched in 1996. The committee also decided to recommend to the State Council an early start to the project.

For supporters of the project, the next hurdle was to gain swift approval from the NPC. In pursuing this goal, they closely abided by one of Mao Zedong's instructions: "Never engage in unsure battles, and never be unprepared to fight." To insure that they gained the support of critical VIPs, dam-supporters spent several hundred thousand *yuan* from October, 1991, to March, 1992, organizing inspection tours to the Three Gorges for NPC members and others.[10]

Over a period of six months, more than 20 delegations comprising about 3,500 members participated in these inspection tours. Words of praise for the Three Gorges project gushed from their lips. Chen Muhua's report to the seventh NPC is illustrative:

Members of the inspection group held a unanimous view on the significance of the project for carrying out the four modernizations. We also came to the conclusion

---

[9] At this time, these included Zhou Peiyuan and Lin Hua in Beijing as well as Zhang Guangqin, Yang Shangming, Deng Mingcong and Xu Shangzhi and others in Sichuan who had submitted a letter to the top leadership describing the defects of the project in a very mild way (merely mentioning the possible suspension of the project).

[10] These tours included: The National CPPCC delegation headed by Wang Guangying, 27 members, 12-day tour; The Standing Committee of NPC Three Gorges Delegation, 25 members, 12-day tour; The All China Provincial Governors Delegation, 47 members; The Inspection Group of Officials from Education, Science and Technology, and Sports, headed by Li Tieying, more than 140 members; and, The All-China Journalist Delegation, organized by the Central Propaganda Department, over 100 members, from 50 media organizations.

that the project is feasible from a technological point of view and reasonable from an economic perspective. We agree that it's better to carry it out than to delay it: the earlier, the better. Thus, we would like to suggest that the State Council submit the project to the NPC for approval as soon as possible.

In adherence to the strict qualifying rules for membership in the inspection groups, anyone described as having "bourgeois liberal tendencies" could not join in. "Discipline requirements" imposed on the members also meant that only a few tidbits of information were made available to them.

These discipline requirements were used to keep Taiwanese NPC Standing Committee member Huang Shunxing from joining in the inspection group. When Huang asked why he was not included he was told: "We thought that given your health problems, you would not agree to participate."

Discipline requirements were also used to influence some members of the inspection groups. For example, the members of the education delegation were instructed, upon their return, to "spread the greatness of the Three Gorges project to the entire body of their respective schools in accordance with the unified position outlined by the Education Committee."

Similarly, when a member of the education delegation asked Li Tieying (State Education Minister) "Since the project has been approved by the State Council, the advantages must outweigh the disadvantages. However, since every issue has two sides, why not allow people to point out the defects in order to prevent future problems." After a moment of silence, Li finally replied: "Only the June Fourth [1989] elites in exile oppose the project!"[11]

In late 1991, following a government order, every newspaper in China, including the *Enlightenment Daily*,[12] began "guiding public opinion" by filling entire pages with reprints of "Questions and Answers On the Three Gorges Project," which had been

---

[11] Li was warning the delegate that anyone who expressed opposition to the project would be considered a counter-revolutionary on par with the pro-Democracy leaders.

[12] Where Dai Qing worked before the June 4, 1989, crackdown.

compiled by the Preparation Group of the Three Gorges Project Development Corporation.[13] In the next two months, the *People's Daily* ran numerous front page articles on the project by various VIPs, including one by Liu Guoguang that was a complete reversal of his previous view that the national economy could not support the project.[14] The scale of the propaganda effort was unprecedented, even for such an important Party-controlled newspaper. It was even greater than the propaganda campaigns during the Resistance War (1937-1945), the anti-Rightist campaign (1957), and the Great Leap Forward (1958-1960).

The real target of this strategy to mold opinion was three upcoming meetings: the January 17-18, 1992, "Working Conference of the Standing Committee of Vice-Premiers of the State Council "; the February 20-21 "Enlarged Meeting of the Standing Committee of the Politburo"; and the March 20 to April 3 examination by the NPC. At the NPC examination, the Three Gorges Project Feasibility Report, which had been in preparation for the past decade, was to be examined and the "Resolution on the Construction of the Three Gorges Project on the Yangtze River" was to come up for a vote. This was where the real decisions would be made.

The January vice-premiers' meeting agreed to construct the Three Gorges project, but it also proposed that:

> [the Three Gorges project] be carried out under a unified plan together with other hydrology projects including management of the Huaihe River, Tai Lake, the Xiaolangdi on the Yellow River and in coordination with the project to channel water from the south to the north.[15]

---

[13] While it is unclear exactly when the development corporation itself came into being (see reference later in this chapter), the Preparation Group apparently preceded the corporation by a number of years.

[14] Authors of other articles included: Shen Hong, Huang Yicheng, Zhang Guangdou, Tao Ziliang, Tao Shuzeng, Chen Bangzhu, Guo Shuyan, Yan Kai, Shen Gencai, and Mo Wenxiang.

[15] A plan to divert water from the Yangtze River northward, through a channel under the Yellow River, to provide water to the dry northeastern area of China.

Zhu Rongji especially emphasized "the issue of achieving a balance between the national economy and the various hydrology projects," and Yao Yilin held the view that "the state should consider this from an overall perspective."

Unfortunately, the Ministry of Water Resources did not share Zhu's opinion. The ministry remained both supportive of the Three Gorges project and lukewarm towards the other projects. Moreover, without specific instructions from the leaders to abort the project, the remarks were all in vain. In June, 1992, the erroneous policies and failure to implement flood-control measures resulted in catastrophic floods along the Huaihe River and Tai Lake. Instead of engaging in a self-criticism over its failure to follow the warnings given at the vice-premiers' meeting, the ministry used the floods as an opportunity to advocate the Three Gorges project.

At the enlarged meeting of the Politburo Standing Committee in February, 1992, Qian Zhengying and Yang Zhenhuai presented reports on the project. Noting the country's energy shortages, Qian placed great emphasis on the importance of electricity generation. However, the high-level cadres listening to her report were different from Mao Zedong, in that they were able to ask very intelligent questions about the project. For example, Li Ruihuan (Standing Committee member of the Politburo in Charge of Media and Culture) was able to pose questions about flood control, population relocation, and sedimentation, while emphasizing that "propaganda work should not be one-sided."

It was at this Politburo meeting that Yao Yilin fully discarded his view of 1989—that the project could not be started for at least five years—by agreeing to the go-ahead of the project. Yet, he also warned that the Three Gorges project "must be part of the general plan, and flexibility must be retained."

Qiao Shi also mentioned the issue of "one-sided propaganda" and emphasized that "opposition views should be voiced." His biggest concern was that people in the water resources and electricity area would be hot-headed and "oversimplify the issue of resettlement."

Bo Yibo also agreed to the construction of the project, but he stated that in the interim "a great deal of work must be done" and

31

that adequate explanations must be made to four people: Li Rui, Zhou Peiyuan, Sun Yueqi, and Qian Jiaju.[16]

Yang Zhenhuai reported on the issue of investment by stating that "revenues from the Gezhouba dam would be sufficient to pay for the Three Gorges project, along with additional revenues from such sources as an increase in the price of electricity and the issuing of state bonds, etc." Li Peng made it clear to Yang that revenues from the Gezhouba dam "belonged to the state," and not to the Ministry of Water Resources and Electric Power, nor to the Three Gorges project. Li Peng reiterated that this was not a "slush fund" for the ministry.

Yang Shangkun took a conservative view. In his opinion, further study was needed on when the big project would be launched. He also pointed to the problems in propaganda work. As a soldier, he was more concerned with national defense, and noted that the Academy of Military Sciences had expressed opposition to launching the project on the basis of the current state of preparation.

Wan Li merely agreed with an "early launch." Song Ping, given his work experience in industry, immediately focused on the key issue of technology. He stated that "the sedimentation model is only qualitatively sound, but not yet quantitatively acceptable." As for the question of when to launch the project, Song emphasized that it "must be part of an overall plan." In the opinion of Ding Guang'en, such a grand project "must be guided by more powerful leadership." However, he refused to comment on the character of the present leadership.

Finally, in his summary of the Politburo meeting, Li Peng discussed China's "Ten-Year National Economic and Social Development Program (1991-2000)," and noted that "the Three Gorges and the Pudong [development zone in Shanghai] were primary." The Party general secretary, Jiang Zemin, urged everyone "to end the debate." He also stated that he "had received many opposition views from abroad" and that "the issue posed financial difficulties—it could be launched only if there was adequate funding" and that "the biggest concern at the recent provincial

---

[16] Likely because they were the most influential and powerful of the dam opponents.

governors' meeting was that the Three Gorges project would squeeze out other provincial-level projects." Jiang Zemin also warned against "putting political labels on those holding opposition views."

On March 20, 1992, the seventh NPC and the seventh CPPCC were begun simultaneously. During these meetings, in addition to the positive news reports on the Three Gorges project in the major newspapers, there was also a large-scale exhibition on the project at the Military Museum in East Beijing, where experts, now in their later years, acted as guides.

Before the vote to approve the "Resolution on the Construction of the Three Gorges Project on the Yangtze River," the Water Resources and Electric Power Publishing House provided each delegate to the two conferences with a finely printed volume titled *A Small Series on the Three Gorges Project*. (It is worth noting that the text was printed on glossy paper, something not even used for the selected works of Mao Zedong or Deng Xiaoping). Since all the delegates were required to vote and since 90 percent of them knew nothing about hydrology, they asked that they be provided with opposition views. But this request was conveniently overlooked.[17] In the words of the delegates themselves: "The fate of the Three Gorges project was in the hands of people who knew nothing about it."

At the CPPCC meeting, 20 members gave speeches while 267 people presented 30 separate proposals, all on the subject of the Three Gorges project.[18]

While the NPC provided little in the way of opposition opinions for the delegates to its meeting, documentation challenging the feasibility of the project did make its way into the meetings. A delegate from Hong Kong brought 200 copies of articles (by Zhou Peiyuan, Xue Baoding, Li Rui, and Duan Nianci) that

---

[17] In contrast to the wealth of pro-dam material, each delegation was given only one set of opposition opinions for all of their members to share. Also, at the time of the debate, there was an information blackout on the project. This prevented the media from carrying opposition opinions that would have been useful for the debate.

[18] Some of the speakers included: Feng Zhenwu, Miao Yongmiao, Liu Kunshui, Cheng Yuqi, Ma Yuhui, Lu Qinkan, and Liu Bangrui.

had recently been published in the magazine *Contemporary Monthly*. Another delegate brought along 500 copies of the first, second, and third 1992 issues of *Science and Technology Herald* (these issues contained articles with opposition views) that had been published jointly in China and the United States. Huang Shunxing was also able to photocopy and distribute a few copies of *Yangtze! Yangtze!* at the meeting.

The common practice at NPC meetings is for the general secretary of the Communist Party to give a speech calling on all Party members to unify their thought, which Jiang Zemin did. However, in his speech on the project, he did not require Communist Party members to vote their approval of the project, as is usually the case. Instead, Wan Li, chairman of the Standing Committee of the NPC, despite having previously said that "opposition views could be expressed," commented three days prior to the casting of votes that:

> This project is of a tremendous scale and involves numerous fields. This is why the State Council has been so cautious in organizing the assessment by experts over the past 40 years. The result of the assessment is that the advantages far outweigh the defects and thus [we] should not continue to debate and postpone it.

Then, on March 21, Zou Jiahua gave a speech on the examination of the project that his committee had undertaken. Nowhere in that speech, however, did he compare the benefits of the immediate launch of the project with the possibility of postponing it. He also failed to address the key issue of whether it is more feasible to build a dam on the mainstream of a river or on its tributaries, and he offered no comparisons between high and low dams. His speech focused on only one issue: the superiority of the 175-meter plan.[19]

---

[19] Over the years many different dam heights have been considered. There is confusion and debate concerning the hydrological, environmental, social, and economic issues surrounding the various dam height proposals. For more on different dam heights see Chapters 16, and 23.

Later on in the NPC meeting, Huang Shunxing attempted to address the meeting and present a petition opposing the dam that had been signed by Chinese students studying overseas. Although he was registered to speak, the chairman refused. Huang stormed out of the meeting, held up his pass and said: "This is the last time."[20]

Huang later complained, and many other delegates agreed, that the resolution on the Three Gorges project had virtually taken him by surprise.

> Vice-Premier Yao Yilin announced two years ago, apparently on behalf of the central authorities, that debate on damming the Three Gorges was to be shelved for at least five years. Why, without advance notice, did the program suddenly appear on the NPC agenda?

Wang Ao, a delegate from Sichuan, said:

> Vice-Premier Zou Jiahua reports that the designers of the Three Gorges project collected opinions from all sources. In reality they did not. In the past year, there have been no discussions on the project by either Sichuan's provincial level authorities, or the NPC. It was not until this session was about to meet that I received certain relevant materials. A very tight schedule was arranged for the NPC inspection tour around the Three Gorges. It covered many places, but sometimes they could only afford to listen to one 20 minute report for an entire county. There was no time to hear opinions other than those of the officials.

In the view of Yang Xinren, a delegate from Jilin province: "The majority of the delegates are not fully informed of the technical aspects of the project. So no matter how we vote, we vote in blindness. How can we vote at all?"

---

[20] In fact, the chairman had the sound system in the auditorium turned off to prevent Huang's address. For more on Huang's opposition at the NPC meeting see Chapter 10.

Delegates from Zhejiang province concurred that it was "too difficult" to pass judgment on an issue of such complexity and consequence. Wu Wenqian said: "There have always been opinions against the project, however, neither the resolution nor the explanatory report that accompanied it mentions those opinions. How can my colleagues and I, with such a lack of information, determine how we shall vote?" Wei Runshi and two other delegates demanded in clear-cut terms: "Let the opposition come here to talk to us!"

Some delegates suggested that by having the resolution passed by the NPC in such haste, those who were in charge of the project had successfully shifted responsibility for it to the national legislature. Zhou Lang, a delegate from the city of Tianjin, commented:

I do not understand why the issue is being presented to the NPC. If it is because this is a major project, then why has the NPC not been allowed to examine other major projects, such as the Shenzhen Special Economic Zone, the Shanghai Pudong Development Zone, and the Daya Bay Nuclear Power Station?

Zhou then proposed that a plenary session be convened to hear opinions from well-informed opposition representatives. "Otherwise," he said, "the delegates would be intellectually handicapped from deciding whether to vote for or against the resolution."

Delegate Qian Guoying, from Qinghai province, opposed the one-sided nature of the debate on the project. He said: "Asked to vote while poorly informed, I have no choice but to abstain."

In the end, many delegates chose, despite their doubts, to consider the interests of the state and vote for the passage of the resolution. As Liu Yuanzhang, from Anhui province, said: "The material on such an important project should have been presented to delegates much earlier. It appears to be perfunctory to have us pass judgment on the issue with so little time for consideration." Nevertheless, he finally conceded: "From a long-range view, I agree that China should embark on the proposed Three Gorges project."

Some delegates from Guangdong province, having thumbed through the Three Gorges assessment report, claimed they had complete confidence in its "scientific and practical quality, "simply because it was the result of "many years of research, testing and investigation."

On April 3, the vote was finally taken. According to the Taiwanese media, when the NPC delegates faced the electronic voting machine to cast their votes, nearly all of them looked "cold and indifferent." Cold and indifferent not because of the "opposition" by Huang, but because a vote was being taken at all.

In the end, 1,767 NPC delegates voted in favor, 177 opposed the resolution, 644 abstained, and 25 did not cast their votes. The resolution was therefore passed. Based on suggestions from the Chongqing (Sichuan) delegation, the resolution was modified with the addition of a line that reads: "Research shall continue towards the proper solution of the potential problems that have been identified."[21]

But analysts said the conflicting statements made during the debate reflected the confusion in the delegates' reasoning and indicated the fragility of the consensus actually achieved. No matter how the delegates voted, most could only have made their decision, as a Chinese saying goes, as if in "clouds and mist."

Criticism of the plan to dam the Three Gorges did not end with the favorable vote. The voices of opposition have been suppressed, but not vanquished.

In elaborating on the resolution, Vice-Premier Zou Jiahua emphasized that:

In future work, ample estimation and attention must be given to possible difficulties and problems. Caution and earnestness must be adhered to, and views from all fields must also be heard in order to ensure more stability and reliability.

---

[21] A portion of the resolution, as reported by the Xinhua News Agency, is found in Appendix D.

# Site of the Three Gorges Dam

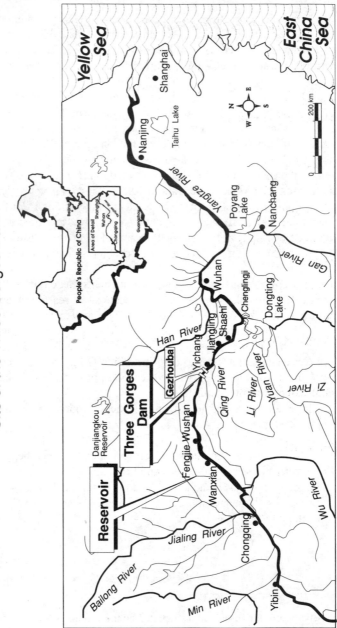

# Three Gorges Dam Specifications

| | |
|---|---|
| Crest | 185 m |
| Construction period | 18 years |

**Reservoir Functions**

| | |
|---|---|
| Normal pool level | 175 m |
| Flood control level | 145 m |
| Total storage capacity | $39.3 \times 10^9$ m$^3$ |
| Flood control storage | $22.15 \times 10^9$ m$^3$ |

**Power Generation**

| | |
|---|---|
| Installed capacity | 17,680 MW |
| Unit capacity | 26 units, 680 MW/unit |

**Navigation**

| | |
|---|---|
| Permanent lock | Twin 5-stage shiplocks |
| Improved channel | 570-650 km |

**Static Investment**

| | |
|---|---|
| Total | Y57 billion |

**Inundation**

| | |
|---|---|
| Population | 1,131,800 |
| Agricultural land | 98,753 ha |

Those remarks were subsequently used by opponents of the project to demand that the government not violate the resolution the NPC had passed.

Without further investigation or research, and without specific answers to the questions and concerns raised by NPC delegates during the meeting, the Three Gorges project was launched with unprecedented speed.

A major step towards the launch of the project was taken by the State Council on January 2, 1993, when it established the Three Gorges Project Development Corporation. Despite the State Council's claim that "this autonomously managed economic organization would serve as the proprietor of the Three Gorges project and would be in charge of the overall construction and management of it," no explanations of the terms "proprietor" and "autonomously managed" have been forthcoming. Up to now, the source of funding for this "corporation" has come mainly from "state investment."[22]

Two organizations exist under the corporation: "The Three Gorges Project Construction Committee" and the "Population Relocation Bureau." As a high-level decision-making organ of the project, the construction committee is directed by Li Peng himself. In addition to State Council Vice-Premier Zou Jiahua and member Chen Junsheng, former Hubei province governor Guo Shuyan (vice-chairman of the State Planning Commission), Li Boning (Ministry of Water Resources), and Xiao Yang, governor of Sichuan province, were also appointed vice-directors of the committee.

The general manager of the corporation is Lu Youmei, a hydro-electric engineer and former vice-minister of the Ministry of Water Resources and of the Ministry of Energy. Lu is a daring man who, prior to the formal approval of the corporation, encouraged his subordinates to "not be afraid and just do it [i.e., build the dam]. If they make some mistakes, I will take full responsibility." Following the old practice of viewing technical projects from a political perspective, he came up with slogans for

---

[22] Dai Qing argues that the organization is simply the Yangtze Valley Planning Office in sheep's clothing, set up as a business rather than a state agency.

speeding up the dam, such as: "Complete the work of blocking the river a year in advance and make it coincide with the year of Hong Kong's return to the motherland so as to turn 1997 into a year of double celebration!"

Following the establishment of the Three Gorges development corporation, Guo Shuyan announced, in April, 1993, that the State Council would invest Y2.02 billion for preparation work for construction of the project, including money for the first phase of rechanneling the water with a cofferdam, and the provision of water, electricity, and transportation supplies to the construction site. Construction on these projects was scheduled to begin at the end of 1994.

Then, on May 26, 1993, the document "Some Issues Regarding the Preliminary Design of the Three Gorges Project" was approved by the Examination Committee, including Zhang Guangdou.[23] The report concluded that both static and dynamic[24] investment estimates of the cost of the project were inadequate. Estimated static investment rose from Y36 billion in 1986, to a new figure of Y75.1 billion in 1993. Based on this newest figure, and including inflation and interest rates, estimated dynamic investment rose to Y224 billion.[25]

---

[23] The original Chinese text does not specify whether this is the committee headed by Zou Jiahua or whether it is a new committee set up to examine the assessment and feasibility studies once again. This document is found in Appendix E.

[24] Static investment excludes interest and price increases during construction. In 1992 the official estimate for total static investment was Y57 billion—Y29.8 billion for construction, Y18.5 billion for resettlement, and Y8.7 billion for power transmission projects. Dynamic investment includes interest charges during construction, until power production begins, as well as state-stipulated discount rates and shadow prices. See *Three Gorges Project: Key to Development of the Yangtze River*, compiled by the *Beijing Review* (Beijing: New Star Publishers, 1992), pp. 34-36.

[25] Having gained NPC approval for the project, the government likely used this committee to provide more realistic budget estimates. The tactic of using artificially low budgets to approve projects is one that many of the authors of the chapters written in 1989 feared would be used.

On June 1, Li Boning, director of the corporation's Population Relocation Bureau, formally announced that an eight-year experiment in population relocation had been completed and that further relocation work had begun. He also gave as a target the relocation of 20,000 residents and assets worth Y500 million for 1993. He noted that the resettlement plan emphasized local relocation and labeled as "sheer rumor" reports in the overseas press about relocation to far-away places. These reports had suggested that the plan had become a United States-China joint venture to relocate local residents to Weihai city in Shandong province.

As the resettlement continues, opposition views towards the project are becoming even more scarce. Some of the dam opponents have passed away, some have withdrawn from social life completely due to age, and some have been removed from their former positions with the Central Advisory Committee or the CPPCC. Others have become dam supporters by arguing that "decisions already made by the Party must not be debated further and [we] should maintain our integrity in our late years." Finally, many of the younger generation who had contributed a great deal to the dam opposition have decided to stop "fighting the project to the death" and give up their positions as opponents of the project.

Neither the eighth NPC nor the eighth CPPCC (held in March-April 1993) discussed the Three Gorges project. It was left to Liu Caipin—a delegate from Taiwan who, with Huang Shunxing, had objected so vocally when the resolution was passed—to deliver a written statement to the newly elected chairman of the NPC demanding that it "uphold the dignity of the law and earnestly study the issue of the Three Gorges project in accordance with the resolution decided at the previous NPC meeting." At that time (March, 1993), Li Rui submitted another written statement to Party General Secretary Jiang Zemin requesting that opposition views be heard.[26] Others including Huang Wanli, Lu Qinkan, Tian Fang, Lin Fatang, and Dai Qing also delivered written letters and telegrams challenging the assessment report.

---

[26] This statement is found in Chapter 6.

The final decision on whether the project is built as planned will be based not on its merits but on the ability to raise the necessary funds. It is therefore necessary to investigate the possible sources of funding.

According to a statement by Yang Yi, chief secretary of the Examination Committee of the Three Gorges project, as of June, 1993, nine possible sources of funds exist.

1. *Gezhouba Dam Electricity Fee:* It was decided at the end of 1992 that all profits generated at the Gezhouba dam hydro-electric plant should be turned over to the state. That amounts to Y200 million per year, which in 20 years' time is expected to rise to Y4 billion per year. The plant will be turned into a shareholding enterprise and issue shares on the United States financial markets.

2. *The Revenue from the Attached Electricity Generation Project of the Three Gorges Project:*[27] This has yet to be acted on.

3. *Special Project Fund Financed by the State:* This has yet to be announced.

4. *Capital Construction Investment Funds From Within the [State] Budget:* According to a rough estimate, since the leading group's assessment in 1986, the state has invested nearly Y1 billion, and in 1993 it will invest Y2.02 billion.

5. *Bank Loans:* These have yet to be announced.

6. *Foreign Investment:* According to the Three Gorges Project Construction Committee, foreign investment will involve bids and will be used in: 1) partial construction projects; 2) partial construction of accessory equipment; 3) purchasing equipment including the 680,000 kW turbine power generators and 500,000 volt high-pressure direct power switching equipment; 4) advisory and consultation services; and, 5) supplementary investigation of environmental issues. So far, the following have expressed interest in the project: the United States, Canada, Japan, Switzerland, France, Singapore, Taiwan, and Hong Kong.

7. *Advanced Sale of Electricity Use Rights (equivalent to the sale of shares):* This has not yet been put into operation.

---

[27] This is revenue that will be garnered by low-powered generation of electricity before the completion of the dam.

*8. Issuing Construction Bonds:* The Three Gorges Bond Company was established and approved by the China People's Bank with registered assets of between Y150 and Y300 million. This company is in charge of selling bonds and shares of enterprises located in the Three Gorges area, and issuing project bonds, exchanges, and transactions. The estimated shares for the first phase that will be sold to financial institutions and to large- and medium-sized enterprises in Hubei province are valued at Y50 million.

*9. Fund for Hydro-electric Construction:* This has not yet been announced.[28]

In addition, the group favoring an early and rapid launch of the project put considerable effort into urging the State Council to issue "policies" favorable to the local residents in order to make fund raising convenient. These "policies" include:

- A suggestion for turning Yichang, Wanxian, and Peiling cities into open cities;[29]
- Various kinds of favorable policies enjoyed by Special Economic Zones along the coast should be implemented in counties and cities where relocation will take place.
- Outside enterprises that establish businesses within the Three Gorges area should enjoy the same treatment as do foreign companies or joint ventures.

As of 1993, foreign enterprises that have publicly announced direct involvement with the Three Gorges project include:

---

[28] In the midst of fund-raising efforts for the Three Gorges dam, it was announced in June, 1993, that the Great Wall Investment Company, licensed by Li Peng, had been engaged in fraudulent activities. The governor of the China People's Bank, Li Guixian, who was involved in the scandal, was removed from his position, and a nation-wide investigation of the field of finance was launched. The Party subsequently issued documents substantially reducing the number of unnecessary projects sponsored by the state.

[29] These are economic zones that enjoy privileges regarding foreign investment and taxes.

- The Zhengda Group of Thailand—Owner of the Yichang Fodder Plant for Pigs and Chickens (Y1.7 billion in investment committed), and of the Yichang real estate company.
- Nippon Heavy Machinery Corporation;
- Construction Enterprise Association (president Huang Taiping), Taiwan;
- Yongshan Group, Hong Kong;
- Sanhuan Enterprises, South Korea;
- Merrill Lynch, USA

Despite such preparations, opposition continues. In July 1993, opponents gathered together to analyze the project and decided to once again publicize their opposition views.

"The Three Gorges project is not yet built, unlike wood already made into a boat," commented one analyst. "The NPC session is unlikely to be the end of the Three Gorges controversy, because it is unlikely to have an end at all. Once a new wave of reform rises it will further expose all the contradictions of the project, and arouse further debates."

# Part Two

## The Letters

# CHAPTER FOUR

## QUESTIONS AND SUGGESTIONS CONCERNING THE THREE GORGES PROJECT
### A Letter to the Central Committee of the Chinese Communist Party[1]
from
Zhou Peiyuan[2]

In September, 1988, I was appointed by the Chinese People's Political Consultative Conference (CPPCC) to head a Three Gorges project investigative group for Hubei and Sichuan provinces. We visited cities, counties and districts along the Yangtze River, from Wuhan, Hubei province to Chongqing, Sichuan province (two of several cities singled out for development) and investigated industry, commerce, science and technology, education, medical services and public health, as well as cultural activities. The investigative group was composed of 180 members of the CPPCC from Beijing, and, while on its field trip, listened to numerous reports by local government departments.

Among the group were many well-known scientists, including a few who had made important contributions to our national defense. Since the report of the trip has already been written, I would like to express only my personal opinions and suggestions on the issue of the Three Gorges project.

Since so many people in Hubei and Sichuan provinces, as well as members of our group, showed concern about this project, we took field trips to the Gezhouba dam, the Three Gorges work site at Sandouping, and the site of the planned reservoir. We read

---

[1] This letter, written on November 9, 1988, was included in the Chinese edition of *Yangtze! Yangtze!*

[2] Zhou Peiyuan, now deceased, was a scientist, past president of Beida University, and was vice-chairman of the Chinese People's Political Consultative Conference.

pertinent documents, listened to reports and held two forums with officials from the Yangtze Valley Planning Office (YVPO). The majority of our group showed concern and anxiety over this large construction project. That concern can be broken down into two basic questions:

    1.   In developing the Yangtze River, should the tributaries or the mainstream of the river be dealt with first?

    2.   Should the Three Gorges project be started immediately, or put off until a later date?

The first question asks whether the harnessing of the Yangtze should be carried out on a regional basis or as part of an overall development plan. Of course, the development of the mainstream and the tributaries at once would be best, but given our present national economic situation, it is impossible to do so. People from Sichuan emphasized that the project should not bring benefits solely to the area of the lower reaches of the Yangtze at the expense of others, as has happened before. They reiterated over and over that development projects for the areas of the upper reaches should be carried out, irrespective of whether or not the Three Gorges project is started. They also suggested an early start for projects to develop the hydro-electric resources on the upper reaches of the Jinsha, Dadu, and Minjiang rivers. This view, to my understanding, does not support an immediate start of the Three Gorges project.

Of course, the people in Hubei province have quite different views on this subject. But I am not going to describe them in detail here since there is a much more urgent problem, namely the energy shortages in Sichuan province.[3]

---

[3] Zhou Peiyuan is suggesting here that since Hubei as a downstream province would be a beneficiary of the electricity generated by Three Gorges, its provincial-level officials take a more positive stand on the project. Other downstream areas that stand to gain from the dam include the provinces of Hunan, Jiangxi, Anhui, Jiangsu, and the city of Shanghai, while upstream provinces such as Sichuan will receive few benefits in terms of electricity, and they may see flooding worsened by the project. See Lieberthal and Oksenberg, *Policy Making*, pp. 278-279.

Sichuan is a very large province, with one-tenth of the Chinese population (roughly 108 million people), that produces 6.7 percent of the nation's gross national product (GNP). The success of its economy will have a direct bearing on the realization of our national economic goal, which is to quadruple the GNP by the year 2000. However, Sichuan now suffers a yearly shortage of electricity of six billion kilowatt hours (kWh) or more, which means about 40 percent of the demand cannot be met. Many enterprises and factories have to shut down three to five days a week because of lack of electricity, thereby greatly reducing productivity. This problem demands an immediate resolution.

Sichuan is a province with abundant natural resources, especially at the upper reaches of the Yangtze, which possess a hydro-electric potential estimated at 150 million kWh. There are very favorable conditions for tapping these resources and it is estimated that 92 million kWh of this potential is exploitable. With the efforts of Sichuan's people and help from the government, smaller hydro-electric projects on the upper reaches of the Yangtze have the advantage of quicker completion, smaller investment, and immediate profits.

Similarly, Guizhou province could construct smaller projects on the Wujiang River, Hubei province on the Qingjiang and Hanjiang rivers, and Hunan province on the Xiangjiang, Zishui, Yuanshui, and Lishui rivers. Together these local projects could deal more efficiently with the common problems of flooding, hydro-electric power generation, transportation, and irrigation.

Despite all of the unresolved technical problems, the Three Gorges project, even if it is started right away, will not help achieve our national economic goal. The project will require dozens of years of resource inputs before producing outputs. It will require a longer time to complete, a large investment, and will begin to show profits only slowly. In other words, the Three Gorges project may retard realizing the desired economic objectives, by consuming so much capital funding that smaller projects, which could show quicker results, will have to be canceled.

Let me now comment on the second question regarding the best time and the proper conditions under which to begin the project. Quite a few members of the delegation agreed that "preparation had not been completed" and that technical problems such as how to flush sedimentation had yet to be resolved. According to the present proposal, it is easier to solve problems that will occur near the reservoir area. But regarding the sedimentation problem near the end of the reservoir (backwater reach), no effective remedy has yet been developed.

Navigation is another problem, and we debated whether the project would help or hinder it. The Gezhouba dam has only one sluice gate and a single ship passage requires 45 minutes. Since the dam is opened only when there are several boats lined up for passage, several hours are often required for any one ship to pass through. Unlike the Gezhouba dam, the Three Gorges dam will have five sluice gates, which means that a much longer time will be needed for boats to pass through. If any of the five sluice gates breaks down, this important channel will be totally blocked. Many members expressed serious concern about this problem.

The expense of population relocation poses another problem. The Y11 billion already proposed for the project is far from adequate. Thirteen cities and many factories have to be relocated around the future site of the Three Gorges reservoir in the hilly areas where the land still has to be leveled. The installation of auxiliary facilities (sewer and water) for the cities will also be very costly.

For such an important project, there should be more than one alternative so that comparisons can be made and the best choice selected by the decision-makers. Numerous options, including proposals favoring developing the tributaries first versus proposals favoring developing them later, should be compared. Only in this way can we help the leading organizations make the best decision possible. So far, many people in our group remain dissatisfied; I personally support the request for several options. I believe that the failure to work out a long-term plan now will create many problems in the future, so every effort should be made at this stage.

The last question I would like to examine is the budget for the project. So far, the amount projected is Y30 billion, not including interest charges. If the interest is included, Y50-60 billion (calculated at 1988 values) will be required. Y100-120 billion will be needed when potential price increases are taken into account. The total investment is sure to be even higher after all the probable expenditures are considered.[4]

During one of our discussion forums a former official who had worked on the project said the actual workload of the project is twice or two-and-a-half times greater than that of the Gezhouba dam project. And the machinery and power generating equipment will be six times as extensive as that required for the Gezhouba dam, with five times as many sluice gates, and a much larger population to be resettled. Upon hearing this, the group found it hard to comprehend the official calculations of time and workload, and many were worried.

As far as I am concerned, the major consideration of whether the project should be started or suspended should be based, apart from various technical issues that need further study, on considerations concerning our national financial strength. Especially at this critical moment of price and wage reforms,[5] the project would only worsen inflation and cause economic turbulence, hinder the implementation of the strategic policies decided upon at the Third Plenum of the Thirteenth Party Congress,[6] put psychological pressure on the population, and undermine political stability as well as the overall reform program. Therefore, I think the project should be postponed until such time as the national economic goal of quadrupling the gross national product is realized. By then, with a stronger economic base and higher standards in science and technology, this project can be successfully carried out.

During our trip, we heard frequent complaints from local people. Because officials have hesitated over the project for so long, many local development projects have become difficult to plan or have been delayed. Consequently, individual and local

---

[4] For a more thorough and up-to-date discussion of budget estimates, see Appendix E.

[5] This refers to the general economic and budgetary retrenchment that was begun in 1988, and the continuing debate over wage and price liberalization among the top leadership of economic reformers and conservative opponents of economic and political reform.

[6] This meeting, held in September, 1988, called for a slowdown in proposed price reforms because of inflationary pressure and "an end to confusion existing in economic activities, especially in the field of [monetary] circulation." See *Beijing Review*, 10-16 October 1988.

economic well-being have been badly affected which, I am afraid, is in itself a very serious problem. I therefore would like to suggest that the Communist Party Central Committee make a decision at the earliest possible time to delay the project in order to reassure the local people so that they can have more confidence in carrying out their own plans and programs assisted by central, provincial and local governments. This will also allow them to carry out rapid economic development, which has already been delayed for more than 30 years.

These are my personal views and suggestions, which may not be proper. I hereby present them only as reference for those who are concerned in the Communist Party Central Committee and the CPPCC.

# CHAPTER FIVE

## VIEWS AND SUGGESTIONS ON THE ASSESSMENT REPORT OF THE THREE GORGES PROJECT
### Written Statement Submitted to the Central Committee of the Chinese Communist Party by Ten Members of the Chinese People's Political Consultative Conference[1]
by
Sun Yueqi, Lin Hua, Wang Xingrang, Xu Guangyi, Qiao Peixin, Chen Mingshao, Luo Xibei, Yan Xinghua, Zhao Weigang, Lu Qinkan

The Leading Group for the Assessment of the Three Gorges project, led by the former Ministry of Water Resources and Electric Power, convened its ninth expanded meeting in late November, 1988. The discussion concentrated on reports concerning the two following subjects: "Overall Planning and the Water Level" and "A Comprehensive Economic Evaluation." After consultations between the Economic Construction Group of the Three Gorges project under the Chinese People's Political Consultative Conference (CPPCC), and the Leading Group For the Assessment of the Three Gorges Project, nine of us who are members of the CPPCC were invited to the meeting. Sun Yueqi was represented by Lu Qinkan. After listening to the reports and reading all the relevant documents, we put forward our comments and suggestions as summarized in the following:

## I. It Is More Advisable to Delay Construction of the Project

*1.   Considering the national economy and the principles and present tasks of the Party, it would be inappropriate to launch the*

---

[1] This statement, submitted in December, 1988, was included in the original Chinese edition of *Yangtze! Yangtze!*

*Three Gorges project soon.* The third session of the Thirteenth Party Congress (September-October, 1987) recently made an overall analysis of our current economic situation and set forth principles to bring our economic situation under control so as to further economic reform. In order to curb inflation and growing demands for investment funds, capital construction must be drastically reduced.[2] Faced with such a situation and task, we believe that an early launching of this extremely large-scale project is by no means appropriate, for it involves many complicated problems, will take a long period to complete, and will be very slow to produce results.

According to the strategy of national and economic planning laid down by Thirteenth Party Congress, it is of paramount importance at the present stage to effectively quadruple the gross national product and raise the living standard of the people to that of a well-off society by the end of this century. As far as this grand project is concerned, even if everything goes as planned, it will be another 12 years before electricity is generated, and another 20 before the project is complete. The early launching of this project will result in tremendous inputs but no outputs in this century. Moreover, it will not help realize strategic objectives, but will divert necessary resources and materials—which are perpetually in acute shortage—from other smaller-scale projects that would produce quicker economic results. It would be more appropriate for us to postpone the Three Gorges project until we have built a much stronger economic base and acquired more advanced technology.

   *2.   The funds required for investing in the project far exceed the capacity of our national economy.* The static investment of

---

[2] Investment in capital construction in China under the state-run economy has involved an enormous waste of resources over the years. These projects have consumed larger and larger shares of the state budget while providing thousands of state cadres with substantial sources of political and economic power. In some years, since the economic reforms were inaugurated in 1978, capital construction spending jumped by up to 30 percent over previous years, even as the central government proclaimed its commitment to substantial reductions. See He, *China on the Edge*, pp. 51, 140.

Y36.1 billion proposed by the assessment report is woefully inadequate. The estimated investment was based on 1986 prices, but 1987 and 1988 showed considerable price increases. Also, the overall investment failed to include the following: 1) the Y0.003 which will be retained from each kWh (amounting to Y250 million)[3] to form the "Construction Fund for the Reservoir Area"; 2) expenses for further relocation of the residents as a result of rising water levels caused by the accumulation of sediment in the reservoir; and 3) expenses to dredge the navigation route around the end of the reservoir. In view of all these facts, the actual static investment needed is far larger than Y36.1 billion.

According to the financial assessment conducted by the leading group, profits from the electricity generated by the Gezhouba dam and the future Three Gorges hydro-electric power station account for about 50 to 65 percent of the total investment forecast for the project, not including interest charges. But the Ministry of Finance indicated that the State Council approved the financing of the project with the profits generated by the Gezhouba dam, but not with the future profits from the Three Gorges project. The above-mentioned assessment was conducted in such a way that it could hardly convince anyone of the project's financial feasibility.[4]

Although some attention has been given to the possible increase in prices and interest charges, the Y93.45 billion proposed in the assessment report as a dynamic investment still seems insufficient. Based on calculations by the Construction Bank, the amount required for dynamic investment should be somewhere between Y200 billion and Y500 billion.

Is it really possible for our national economy to finance such a huge investment? The leading group's assessment report compared estimated GNP and national income figures with the estimated investment for the Three Gorges project over the next

---

[3] Retained from the revenue from power produced at the Gezhouba dam.
[4] Planning on the Three Gorges project was marked by a "paucity of pertinent economic analysis. Domestic economic reforms had not, by the mid-1980s, introduced economic analysis into decision making on the Three Gorges dam in a serious fashion." See Lieberthal and Oksenberg, *Policy Making*, p. 337.

20 years. Because the project represented only an infinitesimally small portion of the GNP and national income, the assessment report concluded that construction was feasible. But this is not an appropriate method of calculation. It is even less advisable to try to convince people of the capacity of our national economy to sustain such a project by comparing the investments in the Itaipu hydro-electric power station[5] with national incomes of Brazil and Paraguay in the corresponding years.

According to a report in the June 1, 1988, *Internal Bulletin on International Affairs*:[6]

> In order to maintain a 10 percent rate of economic growth, Brazil's military government launched quite a number of large-scale public projects, with the investment for the Itaipu hydro-electric power station alone absorbing US$18 billion. Faced with a serious shortage of funds and resources, the country has had to take out foreign loans and credits to complete these large-scale projects, which drove Brazil to the edge of an abyss of hyper-inflation. The inflation rate in 1980 reached three digits at 110.2 percent. The rate in 1984 was 223.8 percent and reached 365.95 percent in 1987.

The major task in the coming two to five years is to bring under control and consolidate our national economy, a process which in itself will involve numerous difficulties. If we rush into the construction of the Three Gorges project, which is 40 percent larger than that of the Itaipu hydro-electric power station, it is very likely that it will induce additional rounds of overheated investments. For this reason, one has to be very cautious.

*3.    Some intractable problems concerning the Three Gorges project.*

---

[5] Finally completed in 1991 at a cost of US$18.3 billion, the Itaipu hydro-electric power station is jointly owned by Brazil and Paraguay and has a capacity of 12,600 MW.

[6] An internal reference document for Chinese leaders.

*a. Sedimentation:* The Yangtze River is the fourth-largest river in the world and carries substantial volumes of sediment. As it stores flood waters, the Three Gorges reservoir would block the moving sediment and cause it to pile up on the river bed. Ever-growing heaps of sediment around the end of the reservoir might affect the navigability of the waterways, raise the water level and increase flooding at Chongqing, and worsen flood disasters in Sichuan province.

*b. Population Relocation:* The plan for a 175-meter high water level for normal storage conditions would involve relocating 1.13 million people by the year 2008. If the problem of sedimentation is also considered, the relocated population would increase by 300,000 after the reservoir had been on line for 20 years and would further increase by 500,000 in 50 years' time. By then, the aggregate number of people resettled would reach 1.4 to 1.6 million or more, most of whom would be resettled in Sichuan province. Then, the area around the reservoir would face serious food shortages because of overpopulation. With the construction of the reservoir, 430,000 *mu*[7] of arable land would be submerged, with thirteen cities and 657 factories relocated to nearby hills where reclamation must be carried out for resettlement. All this would far exceed the tolerance of the environment. Moreover, the relocation of several million people could provoke serious social problems. As Comrade Qian Zhengying said in 1985: "Population relocation is a key problem of both economic and political importance."

*c. Technical Issues:* The structures for ship passage at the Three Gorges dam would employ five consecutive levels of shiplocks, with the first of the five having to adapt to the tremendous changes of water levels in the reservoir. Both the size of the passage gate (34 meters in width, 38 to 42 meters in height) and the water input valve (50 meters in diameter) would exceed all present international standards. Besides, if any one of the five shiplocks were to become inoperable, all navigation would be disrupted, a problem of great concern to the Department of Shipping. The shiplift for lifting 11,500 tonnes up 113 meters would

---

[7] One hectare is equivalent to 15 *mu*. Conversely, one *mu* equals 0.067 hectares.

also break the world's record. Compared with the largest one in the world (in Belgium) the shiplift at the Three Gorges would have to be 30 percent more powerful in terms of lifting tonnage, and 55 percent higher in lifting height. In China the largest installed shiplift in the mouth of the Danjiang River (*Danjiangkou*) has a vertical carrying capacity of 450 tonnes and is 50 meters in height, far below the requirements of the Three Gorges project. Are we, with our present technology, able to build such a large-scale shiplift? It would be more appropriate to first conduct some experiments at existing hydro-electric power stations.

*d. Environmental Effects:* At the November, 1988, ninth expanded meeting of the leading group, Ma Shijun, chairman of the Experts' Group on Ecology and Environment and a member of the Academic Committee of the Chinese Academy of Sciences, stated that an academy study of the ecological impact of the Three Gorges project concluded that the adverse effects would be greater than the benefits. Comrade Hou Xueyu believed the Three Gorges project would have a profound impact on the environment and natural resources and, therefore, argued that great caution should be taken in deciding whether to launch the project.

*e. Risks:* Since there are now many potentially dangerous spots around the Three Gorges area, the high dam may induce earthquakes which, in turn, would cause landslides. Furthermore, should the dam burst, several critical areas and cities located in the lower reaches, including the Jianghan plain, the Dongting lake area, Yichang city, Shashi city and Wuhan, would inevitably face disaster.

The dam could also become a possible target of strategic importance in time of war, since the reservoir would play a pivotal role in flood control, power generation, and navigation. Even in peacetime, it would be necessary to be prepared for a possible surprise military strike.

On December 24, 1970, Premier Zhou Enlai wrote a letter to Chairman Mao regarding the Gezhouba dam. Zhou stated: "When considering construction of the Three Gorges dam, it is necessary to take into account...the international situation and the progress of air defense capability, and the accumulation of experiences in building high dams."

On December 16 of the same year, while being briefed on the progress of the Gezhouba dam construction, Premier Zhou commented to Lin Yishan (who led the Yangtze Valley Planning Office in the late 1970s): "The Three Gorges project you are talking about is not our generation's business. Leave this project to our children in the 21st century." On this matter, we should also take a very cautious approach.

## II. Tributaries First and the Mainstream of the River Second

*1. Rather than an exclusive emphasis on the Three Gorges, an overall plan and a proper order should be established for the development of the whole river basin based on concrete conditions.* The Yangtze River has many tributaries, large and small, covering an extensive area of land. The big tributaries, such as the Yalong, the Minjiang, the Dadu, the Jialing, the Wujiang, the Yuanshui, the Xiangjiang, the Hanjiang and the Ganjiang rivers, have annual water volume equal to or greater than that of the Yellow, the Huaihe, and the Haihe rivers together. It is therefore necessary to give priority to the tributaries, so as to meet the needs of local economic development in a timely manner.

Overall planning for the Yangtze River's development should take into account the *Survey Of the Land Resources In the Southwestern Areas and Studies On a Development Strategy* recently proposed by the Investigation Group on Resource Development in Southwestern China. Overall planning should also take into account the proposal by Sichuan province for developing the waterpower and natural resources at the upper reaches, the plan by Guizhou province for developing the Wujiang River, and the plans for the development of tributaries proposed by Hunan, Hubei, and Jiangxi provinces among others.[8] Proper consideration of these local programs is important in the economic development of the areas concerned and absolutely necessary for environmental protection and improvement.

*2. Enhance work on harnessing the Yangtze River.* In order to be prepared against big floods in the next 10 to 20 years, the main channel must be dredged, dikes strengthened, and safety

---

[8] These other studies are significant because they propose alternative area development plans and other river tributary projects.

facilities consolidated in the flood storage and diversion areas. At the same time, dredging should be carried out in the tributaries to meet the growing needs of navigation as the economy progresses. Water and soil conservation should also be carried out to reduce increasingly serious soil erosion. We should avoid the tendency of waiting for the Three Gorges project and expecting it to solve all the problems.

*3. Carry out the development of the tributaries at the maximum possible speed so as to ease the acute shortage of electricity and make comprehensive use of water resources.* Presently, the following hydro-electric power stations are under construction on the tributaries of the Yangtze: the Tongjiezi on the Dadu River (600 MW), the Baozhusi on the Bailong River (700 MW), the Ertan on the Yalong River (3,300 MW), the Manwan on the Lancang River (1,250 MW), the Dongfeng on the Wujiang River (510 MW), the Geheyan on the Qingjiang River (1,200 MW), the Wuqiangxi on the Yuanshui River (1,200 MW), the Ankang on the Hanjiang River (800 MW), the Wan'an on the Ganjiang River (400 MW), and the Shuikou on the Minjiang River (1,400 MW), totaling 11,360 MW of installed capacity. The construction of these 10 large-scale hydro-electric power stations on the Yangtze's tributaries should be completed on or before their scheduled completion dates and in accordance with their work plans and investment schedules. At the same time, medium- and small-scale hydro-electric power stations should also be constructed.

There are also a number of hydro-electric power stations on the tributaries that have been assessed, or are in the process of being reviewed, but for which construction has yet to begin. Measures should be taken to ensure an early start for these projects, so as to bring them on line by the year 2000. These projects include: the Taipingyi and the Zipingpu on the Minjiang River (260 MW and 680 MW respectively), the Pubugou on the Dadu River (3,300 MW), the Hechuan on the Jialing River (500 MW), the Hongjiadu and the Pengshui on the Wujiang River (540 MW and 1,200 MW respectively), the Jiangya on the Lishui River(400 MW), the Fuxikou on the Zishui River (270 MW), the Pankou on the Duhe River (510 MW), the Taihe on the Ganjiang River (180 MW), the Tankeng on the Oujiang River (600 MW), the Shanxi on the Feiyun (240 MW), and the Tianhuangping pumped-storage hydro-electric power station on Tianmu mountain (1,800 MW). The total installed capacity for these projects will be 10,480 MW.

Most of the above-mentioned power stations can serve as multipurpose projects for flood control, irrigation, navigation, water supply, fish farming, and tourism. The local people concerned may provide a certain amount of financing, which would also make the job of population relocation easier. Besides, it would be a better idea to have different power stations run by a number of enterprises, rather than by a single one, so as to quicken the development of hydro-electricity. Therefore, in making an overall plan we must ensure that the aforementioned projects are not hindered by the debate over whether and when the Three Gorges project should be started.

As for structural reform of the hydro-electric construction system, we support the proposals by the Ministry of Power[9] to establish hydro-electricity development companies organized according to river basins and regions. In the initial stage of the formation of those companies, financial support might be granted by the state so as to help them become enterprises that ultimately bear responsibility for profit and loss in their operations. By selling surplus electricity to the national grid, they would become self-financing.

In addition, the leading group's assessment found that the preparations for the projects on the tributaries, including the Jinsha River, are far less advanced than those for the Three Gorges project. We therefore would like to bring to the attention of the Ministry of Power and the Ministry of Water Resources the fact that they should allocate more funds for the purpose of surveying and design since, we believe, the amount required for this purpose would not be large but the benefits would be substantial.

---

[9] Authority in the energy sector was greatly concentrated with the 1982 decision to transfer authority over local and regional power grids to the Ministry of Power at the central government level. See Thomas Fingar, "Implementing Energy Policy: The Rise and Demise of the State Energy Commission," in *Policy Implementation in Post-Mao China*, ed. David Lampton (Berkeley: University of California Press, 1987), p. 206.

## Location of Large Hydro Projects on the Main Stream of the Yangtze River and Tributaries of the Yangtze River Valley (Installed Capacity > 250 MW)

| | Project | Capacity | River |
|---|---|---|---|
| **Existing** | | | |
| (1) | Gongzui | 700 MW | Dadu R. |
| (2) | Bikou | 300 MW | Bailong R. |
| (3) | Wujiangdu | 630 MW | Wu R. |
| (4) | Gezhouba | 2715 MW | Yangtze R. |
| (5) | Danjiangkou | 900 MW | Han R. |
| (6) | Fengtan | 400 MW | Youshui R. |
| (7) | Zhexi | 447 MW | Zi R. |
| (8) | Dongjiang | 500 MW | Leishui R. |
| **Under Construction** | | | |
| (9) | Ertan | 3300 MW | Yalong R. |
| (10) | Tongjiezi | 600 MW | Dadu R. |
| (11) | Taipingyi | 260 MW | Min R. |
| (12) | Baozhusi | 700 MW | Bailong R. |
| (13) | Dongfeng | 510 MW | Wu R. |
| (14) | Ankang | 800 MW | Han R. |
| (15) | Geheyan | 1200 MW | Qing R. |
| (16) | Wujiangxi | 1200 MW | Yuan R. |
| (17) | Wan'an | 400 MW | Gan R. |
| **Under Design or Feasibility Study** | | | |
| (18) | Pubugou | 3300 MW | Dadu R. |
| (19) | Zipingpu | 680 MW | Min R. |
| (20) | Tingzikou | 900 MW | Jialing R. |
| (21) | Hechuan | 500 MW | Jialing R. |
| (22) | Tongzilin | 400 MW | Yalong R. |
| (23) | Jinping 2 | 3000 MW | Yalong R. |
| (24) | Jinping 1 | 3000 MW | Yalong R. |
| (25) | Hutiaoxia | 4000 MW | Jinsha R. |
| (26) | Xiluodu | 12000 MW | Jinsha R. |
| (27) | Xiangjiaba | 6000 MW | Jinsha R. |
| (28) | Hongjiadu | 540 MW | Liuchonghe R. |
| (29) | Goupitan | 2000 MW | Wu R. |
| (30) | Silin | 840 MW | Wu R. |
| (31) | Shatuo | 800 MW | Wu R. |
| (32) | Pengshui | 1200 MW | Wu R. |
| (33) | Three Gorges | 17680 MW | Yangtze R. |
| (34) | Shuibuya | 1500 MW | Qing R. |
| (35) | Jiangya | 400 MW | Lishui R. |
| (36) | Linxihe | 800 MW | Lishui R. |
| (37) | Wanmipo | 270 MW | Youshui R. |
| (38) | Sanbanxi | 680 MW | Qingshui R. |
| (39) | Fuxikou | 270 MW | Zi R. |
| (40) | Xunyang | 300 MW | Han R. |
| (41) | Pankou | 510 MW | Duhe R. |
| (42) | Huanglongtan | 490 MW | Duhe R. |

## Location of Large Hydro Projects on the Main Stream and Tributaries of the Yangtze River Valley

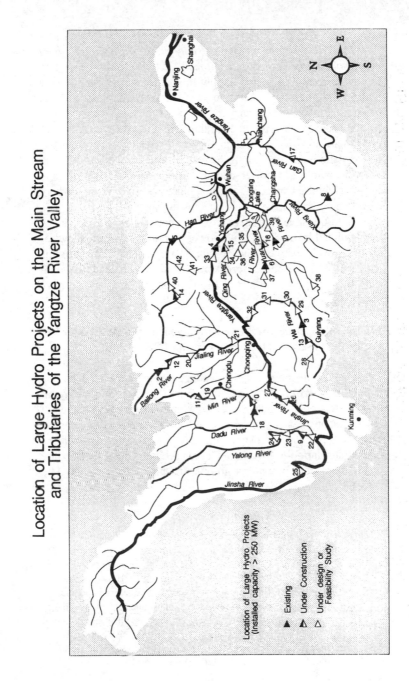

Location of Large Hydro Projects
(Installed capacity > 250 MW)

▲ Existing

△ Under Construction

△ Under design or
Feasibility Study

4. *The development of electricity plants according to local conditions in the respective regions.* Hydro-electricity generation is a main source of energy supply in southwestern China, as are hydro and thermal generation in central China and thermal generation in eastern China. In accordance with the natural distribution of water resources and coal and fuel deposits in our country, hydro-electric powerstations would mainly be concentrated in the southwest, with hydro-electric power and thermal generation stations and plants in central China, and thermal plants in eastern China where coal can be transported by land, or water, or through pipes (i.e., slurry) to this area.[10] In this part of the country, power peaks can be regulated by the local waterpower and pumped-storage hydro-electric power stations. Nuclear energy might be developed in this area as well. If the Three Gorges project were completed, it would only provide power to central China. Eastern China would have to rely on its own resources.

## III. Inappropriate Methods Employed in the Assessment of the Project Harmful to Democracy and Science

The 11 members of the leading group, appointed by the former Ministry of Water Resources and Electric Power, were all ex-ministers or ex-deputy ministers, former chief or assistant chief engineers, and heads of the Yangtze Valley Planning Office or the Three Gorges Project Development Corporation. All favor the immediate startup of the Three Gorges project. Under this leading group, there were 14 experts' groups, of which 10 were chaired by

---

[10] There are enormous costs of transporting millions of tonnes of coal from China's relatively remote regions in the north and west, where 90 percent of the deposits are located, to centers of power generation in the east and west. Low, subsidized prices for coal and electricity, plus the impact of highly outdated equipment, make for huge inefficiencies in energy use, especially in the industrial sector. Indeed, "China's energy consumption per unit of gross national product is the highest in the world." See He, *China on the Edge*, pp. 68-73, and Vaclav Smil, *China's Environmental Crisis: An Inquiry into the Limits of National Development* (Armonk, N.Y.: M. E. Sharpe Inc., 1993), pp. 117-124.

persons from different departments in the system (*xitong*)[11] under the ministry. The remaining four groups had vice-chairs from the ministry as well. Even in the enlarged session for the assessment, among the 177 participants, 103 were from the hydro-electricity system. This situation inevitably produced biases.

While many different views were expressed, and the assessment report was adopted in principle by a majority, in successive sessions an undemocratic atmosphere existed: Only those favoring the project could speak freely, while opposition views were immediately suppressed. We therefore consider that, so far, the assessment has been carried out by the department responsible for the project, and by no means is it an objective and comprehensive one.

In view of this fact, we suggest that the next step involving discussion of a feasibility study of the Three Gorges project be organized by all the departments concerned, such as the State Planning Commission, the State Science and Technology Commission, and the China International Engineering Projects Consulting Corporation. Moreover, we also suggest that more experts and specialists be invited from various departments, so as to solicit different suggestions and comments in a real and earnest atmosphere that respects democratic and scientific procedures.[12] After a careful and serious study, the report would be submitted to the State Council for examination and then to the Party Central Committee and National People's Congress for deliberation in order that a wise decision can be made.

---

[11] A key organizing principle in the Chinese bureaucracy, "system" refers to the vertical functioning hierarchies of bureaus and lower level bureaucratic organs that can span from the central government to the local level, and provide an enormous basis of bureaucratic power and decision-making influence. See Lieberthal and Oksenberg, *Policy Making*, p. 141.

[12] As noted by Sullivan in his preface, science and democracy are the two great ideals of the Chinese revolution; they were initially promoted during the May Fourth Movement in 1919.

# CHAPTER SIX

## PLEASE ATTEND TO THE OPPOSING OPINIONS ON THE THREE GORGES PROJECT
### A Letter to the Leadership of the Chinese Communist Party[1]
by
Li Rui[2]

To: Comrade Jiang Zemin and other Chinese Communist Party Politburo Standing Committee members:

According to press reports, the State Council has set up the Three Gorges Project Development Corporation. Preparatory work for the construction of the Three Gorges project has officially begun. Lu Youmei, the general manager of the development corporation, has indicated that the company will strive to push the project ahead, so that the damming of the Yangtze will coincide with the reunification of Hong Kong and China. Lu has also said: "I hope that the comrades in the preparation office will not be afraid and just do it [i.e., build the dam]. If they make some mistakes, I will take responsibility for them."

I wrote a letter to the communist leadership on January 1, 1992, in which I illustrated the many advantages and disadvantages of the Three Gorges project in great detail and explained why the project should not be started right away. This letter reiterates many of those points.

---

[1] This letter, submitted on March 12, 1993, was not included in the original Chinese edition of *Yangtze! Yangtze!*

[2] Li Rui, previously Mao Zedong's secretary on industrial affairs, was also vice-minister of the Ministry of Water Resources and Electric Power. He is currently an advisor with the Energy and Resources Research Institute of China.

The last paragraph of the "Resolution on the Construction of the Three Gorges Project on the Yangtze River" passed by the National People's Congress (NPC) in April, 1992, states:

> With regard to future work on the Three Gorges project, research shall continue towards the proper solution of the potential problems that have been identified. We must be cautious, treat problems very seriously and welcome the opinions of all interested parties. In so doing, the construction of the Three Gorges project will be made safer and more reliable.

Unfortunately these words appear to be only lip service. When the motion to pass the resolution was discussed in group meetings of the NPC, many delegates voiced opposing opinions. Delegates from Sichuan province, in particular, made impassioned speeches, expressing their grave concern about the project.

Several months before the March-April, 1992, NPC meeting, the Chinese media launched a massive campaign to publicize the view that the project had to be started right way. The campaign pointed out that the Central Party Committee of the Communist Party had already approved the project, and that the approval of the resolution by the congress was a mere formality. Despite such a massive media campaign, one-third of the delegates still did not vote in favor of the project. Such opposition was unprecedented in communist China. It should make the people in charge think carefully.

Since the resolution was passed, I have been exposed to many different ideas and viewpoints concerning various aspects of the project. The most important issue, for which there are many opposition opinions, is sedimentation. It is feared that the current plan for a 175-meter dam would cause significant sedimentation, adversely affecting the port at Chongqing and blocking navigation. In the 1970s, when we discussed the sedimentation problem at the Gezhouba dam project, Premier Zhou Enlai clearly stated that navigation should be the number one consideration in the development of the Yangtze River. Premier Zhou said harshly, "the dam should be destroyed if it blocks the waterway."

I have been told by comrades from the Ministry of Communication who were in charge of the navigation section of the assessment report, that technical problems concerning the construction of the shiplocks for a 175-meter dam are far from being resolved.[3] Although navigation problems may not appear to be as important as the possible collapse of the Jingjiang dikes (which may occur once every 1,000 years due to flooding),[4] navigation in the Yangtze waterway is of vital importance to the current economic restructuring in China and to the future development of Sichuan province.

The assessment report, which endorsed the current 175-meter dam, does not provide guaranteed and reliable solutions to the problem of sedimentation. In fact, many of the consultants and specialists argued against the project for this reason. They included Shi Jiayang, Tan Xiudian, Luo Xibei, Zhang Changling, Li Erding, Huang Yuanzhen, Zhang Qishun and others. Instead of a 175-meter dam these specialists proposed the construction of a 160-meter or lower dam, so that navigation on the Yangtze River would not be so adversely affected, and the number of people displaced by dam construction could be reduced. What I wish to emphasize here is that the sedimentation that will result from the 175-meter dam will create serious problems for navigation on the Yangtze. It is still not too late to "be cautious, treat problems very seriously and welcome the opinions of all interested parties."

In short, there are many disadvantages to the Three Gorges project. Its capacity to control floods is limited and, worse yet, it passes the problem on to neighboring Sichuan province. It will necessitate massive population relocation, and its resettlement plan is ridiculous. The dam is not the best option for generating

---

[3] The Ministry of Communication is responsible for navigation and shipping and has thus generally opposed the Three Gorges project, arguing that it would severely disrupt river traffic during the long-drawn-out construction period. See Barber and Ryder, eds., *Damming*, p. 17, and Lampton, *Policy Implementation*, p. 172.

[4] The Jingjiang River section of the Yangtze is located between Jiangning and Jianli, where protection from floods is provided by embankments that, it is argued, can withstand a flow not exceeding 60,000 m$^3$/s. In the event of a breach, it is estimated that at least 100,000 casualties would result. Debate over the sufficiency of these dikes is a key element in the larger debate over the Three Gorges. See Luk and Whitney, editors' Introd. to *Megaproject*, p. 8.

electricity, as there are numerous alternatives that would produce greater benefits. It would unnecessarily obstruct navigation and, finally, it goes against current wisdom, which states that large hydro-electric projects do not work and are often abandoned.

One must also remember that the environmental effects of such a large dam cannot be predicted accurately. At this time, there remain many unknown elements that make it difficult to give any definite answers and conclusions. (In this area, the viewpoint of Huang Wanli should not be ignored.)

Once again I would like to make my opinion known to the Central Committee of the Party—postpone construction of the Three Gorges project and bring all preparation work to a halt. This would reassure the public and prevent future troubles. In the past several years, I have attended many group discussions of the Central Advisory Committee of the Communist Party. Whenever the Three Gorges project was discussed, many veteran comrades expressed opposition opinions. However, they had no place to present these views. For example, last year a group of specialists with the Chinese Academy of Sciences undertook a field trip to the Three Gorges. Upon completing their study, they submitted a report with opposition opinions, but no one paid attention to it.

The leading group's assessment that chose the plan for a 175-meter dam was completely under the control of the ex-leaders of the former Ministry of Water Resources and Electric Power, and of Qian Zhengying in particular. The discussions were not founded on democratic or scientific principles. Briefly, there were two major problems with the assessment report:

First, the study did not follow recognized river planning procedures. Normally, river planning should take into account the characteristics of the entire river valley, and through comparison with alternate plans, draw its conclusions. The Yangtze planners, however, had already decided that the Three Gorges dam was the only option even before they started to collect data and formulate arguments to support their decision. In this way, the discussions on the Three Gorges project can be compared to an election with a single candidate. This is all the more disturbing as we have had a very successful case of alternative planning in the Yellow River Valley. Why should we not follow that example in the case of the Three Gorges?

Second, all of the discussions were controlled by a single organization. They were originally to be led by the State Planning Commission and the State Science and Technology Commission. But it is argued that Qian Zhengying later persuaded the State Science and Technology Commission to let the Ministry of Water Resources and Electric Power lead the study.[5] The leadership of the assessment group (including the members of the leading group and the heads of the experts' groups) was composed completely of pro-dam individuals. The director and deputy directors of the leading group were ex-ministers, ex-vice ministers, and leaders in charge of the Three Gorges project in the Ministry of Water Resources and Electric Power, while the 14 experts' groups were composed mostly of ex-department directors of the ministry.

The leading group approved and invited 412 specialists to be part of the experts' groups but very few of them had different opinions from those of the Ministry of Water Resources and Electric Power. Many dissident scientists and specialists were excluded, and the participation of specialists was limited to the subject matter for which their experts' group was responsible. The experts were permitted to approve or disapprove of only the section they were studying. None of them participated in discussions of the project as a whole and, as a result, many were unable to air their opposing opinions on the project overall. For these reasons, it is misleading to say that the plan for a 175-meter-high dam was approved by 403 of 412 specialists and opposed by only nine.

It is clear that the protracted nature of the assessment report was a result of an exclusive focus on the issue of dam height. The study concentrated on the comparative study of 185-, 180-, 175-, 160-, and 150-meter-high dams, but no comprehensive studies to compare the Three Gorges project with alternatives for achieving flood control, electricity generation, navigation and so on, were ever undertaken. In other words, the study was the verification of one option—the election of a single candidate. Can such approaches be considered democratic and scientific? This is simply a disguised form of the old tradition where the person with power lays down the law.

---

[5] For more on this event see Chapter 28.

The January, 1993, issue of the periodical *Party Documents* published a number of instructions or directives concerning the Three Gorges project by Chairman Mao and Premier Zhou. One of the instructions was Mao's written reply of April 10, 1966, to a letter by Wang Renzhong, in which Wang asked Mao's direction on a report on the Three Gorges project by Lin Yishan.[6] In his letter Mao wrote: "We need an opposition opinion."

More than 27 years have passed since that letter was written; however, Mao's instructions are not out of date. I request that the Central Committee invite a number of specialists who represent different points of view and oppose the immediate construction of the Three Gorges project (or the 175-meter-high dam plan) to a special meeting. Please pay careful attention to their opinions, and excuse me for using an old saying, "Listen to both sides and you will be enlightened."[7]

---

[6] In Chinese political culture, leaders usually write their opinions in short sentences on reports or letters submitted to them. These comments would then be considered directives for the lower ranks of the bureaucracy to follow.

[7] For a list of specialists whose views on the Three Gorges project differed from those of the leading group's report, see Appendix F.

# CHAPTER SEVEN

## A REQUEST TO THE NATIONAL PEOPLE'S CONGRESS TO HALT LU YOUMEI'S[1] INAPPROPRIATE ACTIONS ON THE IMMEDIATE START OF THE THREE GORGES PROJECT[2]
by
Tian Fang and Lin Fatang[3]


To: Comrade Qiao Shi,[4] and the Standing Committee of the Presidium of the First Session of the Eighth National People's Congress (1993):

We are very concerned about the recent propaganda campaign which argues that the Three Gorges project should start immediately, ahead of the scheduled date. We are making an urgent appeal to the National People's Congress (NPC) in the hope that it will pay attention to this matter and stop the project as soon as possible.

The *Economic Reference* reported, on February 28, 1993, that "Lu Youmei has initiated the preparatory work for the construc-

---

[1] General manager of the Three Gorges Project Development Corporation.

[2] This letter, written prior to the National People's Congress meeting in March, 1993, was not part of the original Chinese edition of *Yangtze! Yangtze!*

[3] Tian Fang is a former director of the Research Institute of Planned Economy, of the State Planning Commission. An expert on population relocation, his interest in Three Gorges began in the 1930s.

Lin Fatang is a researcher at the Research Institute of Planned Economy. He is an expert in the distribution of productive forces, including the overall planning for coal mining, electricity, oil, and transportation.

[4] Current chairman of the National People's Congress.

tion of the Three Gorges project, and it will be started right away." The story added: "Lu said that the Three Gorges Project Development Corporation will be officially founded after the National People's Congress holds its annual meeting in March," and quoted Lu as saying: "I hope that the comrades currently with the preparation office will not be afraid and just do it [i.e., build the dam]. If they make some mistakes, I will take responsibility for them."

These daring words indicate that Lu has strong backing, although they are not in keeping with the principle put forth by Premier Li Peng in his government work report outlined at the eighth NPC. There, Li said: "The displaced population should be properly settled, and favorable conditions should actively be created. The project should be started at an appropriate time." In fact, no one has yet set the exact date for the construction of the project. Nor is there a date for the project's completion. In making these statements, Lu placed himself well above the NPC and the State Council, especially in his claim that he would take responsibility for the mistakes of others.

We may ask whether Lu Youmei is capable of bearing the responsibility for mistakes made in such an important project, which is vitally important to both the national economy and the livelihoods of future generations.

The resolution to construct the project, which was passed by the seventh NPC, states:

With regard to future work on the Three Gorges project, research shall continue towards the proper solution of the potential problems that have been identified. We must be cautious, treat problems very seriously, and welcome the opinions of all interested parties. In so doing, the construction of the Three Gorges project will be made safer and more reliable.

The resolution also says that:

The State Council shall, by taking into consideration the realistic conditions of the national economic development and the financial and material capabilities of the state, seek to organize its implementation at an appropriate time.

These statements are absolutely correct. A number of major problems that have recently surfaced have been ignored by past studies. However, Lu has never paid attention to them. It is clear that the "appropriate time" is not simply an issue of starting the project one or two years earlier or later. Rather, the "appropriate time" must take into account the strategic planning of the national economy. The essential principle of economic development in our country, which was described by Comrade Deng Xiaoping in his two important speeches in the springs of 1992 and 1993, and by Premier Li Peng in his report on government work, is to take advantage of current opportunities to speed up the pace of economic reform, and to thereby promote the national economy to a new phase in the next five years.[5] The leaders of the Three Gorges project, however, have paid no attention to this development principle. Instead, they have insisted on the immediate construction of the project. They intend to draw the nation's limited financial and material resources into a super project, which will not generate income for more than 10 years. The desire to start the project immediately, particularly in the current over heated economic situation, is not in keeping with the development principle outlined above.

Lu Youmei's proposal to start the project immediately would constitute poor macro-economic decision making and would cause the nation to lose an historical opportunity to develop.

The Communist Party has long been seeking more democratic and scientifically sound decision-making processes. The leaders in charge of the Three Gorges project, however, have long followed different practices. They excluded experts with different opinions from the assessment report groups, and imposed a news blackout on opposition opinions. The major newspapers of the

---

[5] The Three Gorges project requires a planned, centrally controlled economy rather than a decentralized market economy to survive. In a centrally planned economy a small number of individuals would be able to force local economies to bear the costs of the project for the sake of the "higher interests" of the nation.

central government showed their bias by concentrating on one-sided stories, which promoted only the opinions favoring an immediate or early start to the project. Opposing ideas were not allowed to be voiced publicly.

At the first meeting of the eighth NPC, Premier Li Peng stated:

> We should establish and improve the democratic processes of work, and pay attention to the studies and consultant reports when making decisions. We should pay attention to the opinions of all interested parties. We should strive to achieve more democratic and scientifically sound decision-making processes.

Unfortunately, Li's instructions were ignored in the studies of the Three Gorges project.

We wrote and published in sequence three books on the Three Gorges Project in 1987, 1989 and 1992, namely: *On a Long-Range Strategy for the Three Gorges Project*, *A Second Look at a Long-Range Strategy for the Three Gorges Project*, and *A Third Look at a Long-Range Strategy for the Three Gorges Project*. These books analyzed, from many different perspectives, the reasons why the Three Gorges project, instead of being started immediately, should be constructed as late as possible. Since we presented these books to you and other leaders of the Party and state, we have been harassed, attacked and falsely accused of being opponents. The situation is now barely tolerable. On the occasion of the first session of the eighth NPC, we appeal to you—please stop the rash actions of Lu Youmei and his goal of starting the project immediately. Please remove the restrictions on airing opposition opinions on the project. This would bless the nation and its people!

We invite criticism and instructions if this piece contains any inappropriate wording.

Best regards,
Tian Fang, Lin Fatang
The Economic Research Institute of
The State Planning Commission

# CHAPTER EIGHT

## SUGGESTIONS ON THE CONSTRUCTION SCHEME OF THE THREE GORGES PROJECT[1]
by
Lu Qinkan[2]

According to the "Resolution on the Construction of the Three Gorges Project on the Yangtze River" passed at the March-April, 1992, fifth session of the seventh National People's Congress (NPC), the NPC has resolved to approve inclusion of the construction of the Three Gorges project into the Ten-Year National Economic and Social Development Program (1991-2000).

> The State Council shall, by taking into consideration the realistic conditions of the national economic development and the financial and material capabilities of the state, seek to organize implementation at an appropriate time; research shall continue towards the proper solution of the potential problems that have been identified.

This is a wise statement, which allows for the improvement of the Three Gorges project.

---

[1] This letter, written on March 9, 1993, was not included in the original Chinese edition of *Yangtze! Yangtze!*

[2] Lu Qinkan is a member of the Economic Committee of the Chinese People's Political Consultative Conference. He graduated with a degree in Civil Engineering from Zhejiang University in 1936 and obtained a master's degree in hydrology in the United States. Since 1949, he has been working in the field of water resources and hydro-electric planning and was deputy chief engineer in the Ministry of Water Resources and Electric Power. In 1988, he was one of 10 experts who refused to sign the leading group's assessment for the Three Gorges project.

During the assessment of the project, I concerned myself mainly with the subject of flood control and was unable to take a serious look at the issue of sedimentation. Having recently investigated the available data in this field, I now realize that it warrants further attention.[3] I hereby propose, in light of the NPC decision, that research continue towards the proper solution of the problems identified hereunder.

## I. Sedimentation as an Obstruction to Navigation

The sedimentation experts' research conducted during the leading group's assessment has produced valuable data and increased understanding with regard to reservoir sedimentation. In order to reduce sediment aggregation in the proposed reservoir, the assessment report proposes an operational system that would "store the clear water and flush out the muddy." This system, I believe, will be effective during normal times; that is, when there are no flood-control requirements for the middle and lower reaches of the Yangtze. However, flood control is one of the planned main functions of the Three Gorges project. During years of major floods, its reservoir must retain flood water, causing a tremendous amount of sediment to be deposited in the reservoir. In such situations the reservoir is unable to "store the clear water and flush out the muddy," and has to "store the muddy water" instead. Sediment aggregation will occur in the back end of the reservoir, namely at the Chongqing harbor reach, thereby jeopardizing navigation.

At this point, it is necessary to refer to the findings of the "Experimental Research on the Impact of the 1954 Major Flood on the Chongqing Harbor Reach," which the Institute of Water Conservancy and Hydro-electric Power Research (IWCHPR)

---

[3] At the 1992 National People's Congress meeting, Wang Demao, a delegate from Guizhou, saw a flaw in the proponents' argument: proponents claim that the Three Gorges dam would protect downstream Dongting Lake from sediment aggregation, but also that sediment would be flushed through the dam leaving the reservoir available for storing flood water. Wang contented that the project cannot do both.

# The Three Gorges Project & The Yangtze River Reaches

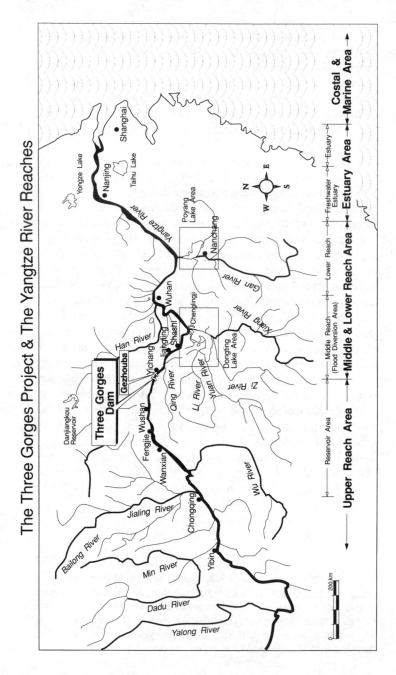

released in July, 1988.[4] If the Three Gorges reservoir were required to store flood waters of the magnitude of the 1954 flood[5] and ensure the safety of downstream areas by maintaining a maximum allowable controlled flood discharge at Chenglingji,[6] the water level in the reservoir would increase by six to eight meters in July, and seven to 13 meters in August. This would be a striking increase from normal flood years. The water level at the dam would increase from 145 meters (the flood-control level) to 175 meters, and the backwater level at Chongqing would increase from the normal flood level of 185.3 meters to 198.1 meters, causing a significant increase in sedimentation.

The IWCHPR study found that, at Jiulongpo port (the major upper port of Chongqing harbor) sediment deposition would concentrate along the wharf, causing the silted area to both increase in height and expand in area. The reservoir's post-flood depth would be 185 to 186 meters, or more than 20 meters higher than the normal pool level. The original main channel would be obstructed totally, and the main flow would divert itself to the original supplementary channels. Flushing in the following two years would be unable to fully reopen the original main channel (it is still unknown how much more time would be required to do so), and the conditions for navigation would remain unfavorable.

The study also found that significant sediment aggregation would occur at Chaotianmen port (the main lower port at Chongqing harbor) at the mouth of the Jialing River. This sedimentation would cause the river's main flow to change direction to Jinshaqi beach, where it would become rapid, shallow, and hardly navigable.

---

[4] The IWCHPR worked under the Ministry of Water Resources and Electric Power. This report publishes the experimental results from a hydraulic physical simulation model for the normal pool level of 175 meters.

[5] The 1954 flood devastated the middle and lower reaches of the Yangtze. 32,000 km$^2$ of cultivated land were inundated, 19 million people were displaced and 30,000 were killed.

[6] Various sections of the Yangtze are also known by different names. Chenglingji is a control section on the middle reaches of the river, north of Dongting Lake.

The IWCHPR report was released in July, 1988, and therefore was not considered in either the "Subject Report on Sedimentation Analysis" or the "Subject Report on Navigation Analysis" of the leading group's assessment, which were released in February and April of the same year. Nor was the IWCHPR report considered by the ninth session of the leading group that examined the "Subject Report of General Planning and Water Level Analysis" in November, 1988, the tenth session from February to March, 1989, or the reporting assembly held by the state government in July, 1990. I wonder whether the IWCHPR report was even submitted to the meeting of the State Council Examination Committee of the Three Gorges Project in 1991?

The IWCHPR conducted a mathematical simulation of the major 1981 upstream flood.[7] Although in 1981 the flow of flood waters in the middle and lower reaches was not large, had the Three Gorges dam been in place, the dam site water level would have risen from about 76 meters (the Gezhouba dam backwater level) to 147.25 meters (slightly higher than its flood-control level),[8] and Chongqing's flood level would have increased by 6.35 meters, to 199.05 meters. This level is higher than the 1954 flood backwater level of 198.1 meters, as described by the IWCHPR study. Compared with the physical simulation of the 1954 flood, the 1981 flood, though shorter in duration, had an even higher flood peak and a more concentrated sediment load; thus its threat to the Chongqing harbor reach was just as serious. These findings warrant a second physical simulation experiment.

Since the founding of the People's Republic 40 years ago, the Yangtze River has experienced two different types of major floods: the first type is represented by the 1954 flood (downstream flooding), and the second by the 1981 flood (upstream flooding). We must be fully aware that either type can cause sediment

---

[7] This large flood caused extensive damage above Yichang but none below it.

[8] The flood-control level is a low reservoir level proposed during flood seasons to provide storage for incoming floods. With a normal pool level of 175 meters the flood-control level of 145 meters leaves 221.50 x $10^6$ m$^3$ of flood storage capacity between the flood-control and normal pool levels.

buildup in the Chongqing harbor reach. In the case of a catastrophic flood on the scale of the 1870 flood,[9] (which is to be the major flood-control target for the project), the reservoir would play an even greater role in flood storage, accommodating an even greater sediment load. This would lead Chongqing's water level and level of sedimentation to grow to an even greater extent. Unfortunately, there has yet to be any research conducted on this issue.

During the assessment study, the sedimentation analysis was focused solely on making the concept of "store the clear water and flush out the muddy" operational. However, the analysis used only those years when the flood-control requirements were minimal and, therefore, when sedimentation of the reservoir was not serious. The analysis was preoccupied, in other words, with how, when small quantities of sediment accumulate at the Chongqing reach, optimizing reservoir management, undertaking harbor renovation, and improving navigation channels, could solve the problem. These efforts may have certain merits when the reservoir is filled only to the flood-control level. But once the Chongqing reach is turned into part of the Three Gorges reservoir and major floods occur, these efforts alone would be unlikely to serve as an effective solution.

The Ministry of Communication and the municipal government of Chongqing are pressing for the adoption of the higher pool level plan of 175 meters or 180 meters, so that Chongqing's Jiulongpo port will be accessible to 10,000-tonne cargo ships. But the 175-meter pool level plan is likely to cause so much sedimentation in the Chongqing harbor reach after a major flood that the navigation to both the Jiulongpo and Chaotianmen ports would be obstructed. The 180-meter pool level plan would affect navigation even more seriously. If the main channel, once silted up, remained difficult for navigation even after two years of flushing, Chongqing would likely become a "dead port." This would be an extremely serious situation, one which I am not sure the Ministry of Communication and Chongqing municipal authorities fully understand.

---

[9] The peak flow of the 1870 flood at Yichang, 40 kilometers below the Three Gorges dam site, is estimated to have been 105,000 m³/s.

## II. The Problem of the Two-Phase Storage Scenario

To reconcile the higher- and lower-pool level plans, a two-phase storage scenario has been proposed by the assessment, as stated in the "Subject Report of General Planning and Water Level Analysis."

In the initial period, the normal pool level would be set at 156 meters so that the backwater level would reach only the mouth of Tongluo Gorge (about 16 kilometers below Chongqing), thus relieving Chongqing harbor and the mouth of the Jialing River from sedimentation and allowing sediment deposition to be more easily monitored.

The subject report noted that: "A period would be made available for the survey and investigation of reservoir sedimentation at the lower pool level." However, this measure is aimed only at eventually raising the pool level to the proposed higher level.

The survey and investigation of the sedimentation situation must be conducted in all hydrological conditions (major floods in particular) over a period of a few decades. If the construction scheme allows for only a few years of study at the lower pool level, it will be impossible, I am afraid, to conduct investigations.

Based on the conclusion furnished by the Experts' Group on Sedimentation, the "Subject Report on General Planning and Water Level Analysis" declares:

The sedimentation problem to be incurred by the lower pool level plan (150 meters to 160 meters in depth) is relatively easy to grasp, and its solution relatively reliable, whereas it is already evident that the higher pool level plan (170 meters to 180 meters in depth) will cause so much sedimentation as to affect, to varying degrees, the city of Chongqing, the harbor, and the mouth of the Jialing River.

This statement is both theoretically and empirically grounded. By proposing to conduct surveys and investigations during a lower pool level period, the two-phase storage scenario illustrates a lack of confidence in the higher pool level. If the higher pool level is not recognized as unattainable until after the completion of the dam, many of the facilities of the Three Gorges project will be inappropriate or uneconomical. Moreover, a great number of households, resettled according to the plan for "population relocation for development,"[10] will also seek to return to their land.

Sediment deposits caused by the lower pool level plan and those caused by the higher pool level plan are different by nature. The former would be simple formations deposited in the river course, but the latter would be more complex formations deposited in the Chongqing harbor reach and at the mouth of the Jialing River. Even after a prolonged period of time, the survey and investigation of sedimentation caused by the lower pool level plan would still be inadequate for explaining the different and more threatening sediment deposits that will be caused by the higher pool level plan.

We should seek answers to these problems through scientific research and experimentation. Thus far, however, only one attempt has been made to simulate the 1954 flood. More flood simulation studies may be worthwhile. What is unacceptable is a gigantic field experiment on the Yangtze River. One trial experiment of this kind might well result in the suspension of navigation for several years. How can anyone risk such devastation?

The issue of navigation poses a dilemma: On the one hand, a lower pool level is preferable because it would cause less sedimentation. On the other hand, a higher pool level is preferable for enabling 10,000-tonne cargo ships to reach the Jiulongpo port facilities directly. If the 175-meter plan were subjected to scientific scrutiny, the results would show the extent of the sedimentation threat at Chongqing harbor, and those who now insist on a higher pool level would recognize it as unrealistic. Demands for

---

[10] This is a new concept, which came into being when the discussion of the Three Gorges project resumed in the early 1980s. The basic idea is that people relocated because of reservoir construction are no longer simply compensated, but are "rehabilitated," with their lives and jobs taken care of under a unified and comprehensive plan to realize long-term stability.

increased transportation capacity can be realized in other ways—for instance, through the construction of reservoirs on the Yangtze's upstream tributaries the depth of the river near Chongqing can be increased.

Another plus that those favoring a higher pool level often cite is the expectation of increased flood-control capacity. Important as this is, flood control should not compromise navigation to Chongqing harbor. Yangtze River floods can be enormous. Their control, therefore, cannot depend on only one facility (the Three Gorges dam), but must also be based on facilities built on the river's upstream tributaries. According to the "Main Points of the Yangtze River Comprehensive Development Program" (revised in 1988) by the Yangtze Valley Planning Office (YVPO), a number of reservoirs on upstream tributaries are slated for completion by 2015. At the same time, according to the "Report of Strategic Research on the Southwest China Hydro Power Energy Base" by the Hydro-electric Power Institutes of Sichuan, Guizhou and Yunnan provinces and organized by the Chinese Society of Hydro-electric Engineering, a number of large hydro power projects will also have been completed by 2020. These programs cover 70 percent of the drainage area of the Yangtze River Valley upstream of the Three Gorges, and include projects which, in terms of their total active storage capacity, will play a far greater role than the Three Gorges project in flood control both upstream and downstream.

### III. The Submergence Area and Resettlement

*1. Sedimentation.* According to the "Regulations for Design to Deal With Reservoir Submergence of Hydraulic and Hydro Power Projects," which the Ministry of Water Resources and Electric Power formulated in 1984,

> in defining the backwater submergence zone for reservoirs on rivers bearing high sediment content, the designer shall take into consideration the impact of sedimentation over a period of time, normally 10 to 30 years from the time the project goes into operation, and pay attention to sedimentation at the upstream reaches of the reservoir.

But the study, by not adequately examining the numbers of people forced to resettle because of sedimentation, has grossly underestimated the number of people who will be affected. Moreover, the study examined only the impact of sedimentation on backwater in the main channel of the Yangtze, but not in its tributaries.

In January, 1988, the "Subject Report on Resettlement Analysis," submitted to the leading group by the experts' group on resettlement, stated:

> The sedimentation-caused 20-year backwater level will not materialize until a few decades after the commencement of the project. With the construction of upstream reservoirs and improvements in soil conservation, the quantity of sediment discharge will change, possibly leading the backwater level to decline. Therefore, it is suggested herein that, for the time being, sedimentation-related resettlement be excluded from the resettlement investment budget during the assessment report.

In fact, the Three Gorges project will begin to cause sediment build-up in the reservoir in its 12th year, when the dam comes on line for power generation. By the completion of the resettlement plan, in the 20th year of the project, sediment will have been building up for eight years. Then, after only 12 years of the project's normal operation, the impact of sedimentation will be felt fully. It is true that by that time, more reservoirs will have been constructed in the upper reaches of the Yangtze to meet the rising demand for power supply. However, they will control, at most, 70 percent of the drainage area, and leave the rest of it unattended. At the same time, any soil conservation projects would take much longer to manifest their effects. Therefore, enough sedimentation will build up in the near future to raise the backwater level of the Three Gorges reservoir. By not anticipating the sediment aggregation of the reservoir, the plans to construct reservoirs on the tributaries have actually violated the "Regulations for Design to Deal With Reservoir Submergence of Hydraulic and Hydro Power Projects." They are inappropriate, and should be corrected in the subsequent process.

2. *The Reservoir Backwater Curve.*[11] According to the Yangtze River Scientific Research Institute (YRSRI) calculation, if the 175-meter normal pool level plan is adopted, a 100-year flood after 100 years of sedimentation would raise Chongqing's backwater level by 4.79 meters to 199.09 meters. Comparing this figure with the IWCHPR simulation, which indicates that after 109 years of sedimentation, a flood of the magnitude of the one in 1981 (equivalent to a 45-year flood) would be enough to raise the index by 6.35 meters to 199.05 meters, the YRSRI calculations appear to be conservative. The backwater curves of five-year, 20-year and 100-year floods, calculated by YRSRI, do not consider the corresponding sediment load carried by the flood, whereas the IWCHPR figures do. Every flood of the Yangtze carries a sediment load, and the greater the flood the more silt contained. Calculation of the flood backwater curve for a river with high sediment content, without consideration of its sedimentation impact, is not realistic, and cannot predict flood levels with any degree of safety. The backwater calculation of the Sanmenxia Gorge project, on the Yellow River, erred by using a "clear water" approach (not considering the sediment load of the flood). Its backwater calculation was that, based on the normal pool level of 350 to 360 meters above sea level, even a 1,000-year flood would not in any way affect Xi'an City. The fact is, however, that in the very first year of the project's operation, when the pool level reached 333 meters (substantially lower than the proposed normal pool level of 350 to 360 meters), the safety of Xi'an was already under threat even though it had only been a normal flood year.

3. *The Flood Submergence Standard for Chongqing.* According to the Ministry of Water Resources and Electric Power's "Regulations for Design to Deal With Reservoir Submergence of Hydraulic and Hydro Power Projects," the submergence flood standard for important cities shall be set for a 50- to 100-year flood. The State Council has agreed that the flood-control standard for Chongqing should be set for a 100-year flood.

---

[11] The water level in a reservoir will affect river height for a considerable distance upstream. The increase in height caused by the reservoir is referred to as the reservoir backwater curve.

Presently, however, the flood storage level indices furnished by the "Subject Report on Resettlement Analysis" have either excluded the 20-year sedimentation impact or have been derived from a "clear water" study for a 20-year flood, which falls far from the required standards of the above regulations. The results of the physical simulation and mathematical calculation of the 1954 and 1981 floods have already added 12.8 and 6.35 meters respectively to the natural flood level. These figures are much higher than is allowed by the above regulations. Also, based on these figures, the backwater level would be much higher than its present calculation, representing a substantial increase in the prospective submergence zone.

If the submergence zone of the project is defined according to the above regulations and by taking into account the above factors (such as sedimentation, reservoir backwater curve, and submergence flood standards), the resettlement population, which already exceeds one million, will increase by another several hundred thousand persons. This additional population will have an enormous effect on the resettlement plan, the natural environment and the investment budget.

What the foregoing discussion questions is whether the construction scheme for the Three Gorges project, namely of setting the normal pool level at 175 meters, of two-phase storage, and of population relocation for development, are ultimately feasible. I hope that these questions will be granted serious consideration.

By scaling down the normal pool level, the potential obstruction to navigation and the excessive resettlement requirements, the two most complicated problems facing the project, can be alleviated. This can, at the same time, contribute to reducing the budget, the intensity of the construction schedule, the complexity of technologies (such as the large shiplock cascade and the high shiplift) and the construction techniques required, environmental impacts, and safety hazards.

I hereby suggest that a comprehensive examination be given to the existing normal pool level plans. During the Three Gorges project assessment and the work of the State Council Examination Committee for the Three Gorges Project, many advisors and experts proposed, apart from the 175-meter plan, plans for 160-meter, 156-meter and even lower normal pool levels. Each plan needs to be tested in physical simulation analysis, for 1954, 1981, and 1870 floods assuming a 20-year accumulation of sediment. The same method should be applied to the study of five-year, 20-year, and 100-year floods with their respective sediment content, the sedimentation in the Chongqing harbor reach, and the prospective submergence zone. If any plan is adopted, the crest of the dam needs to be only five meters above the normal pool level. The plan for "over-storage" above the normal pool level (also the level of the resettlement zone) was strongly opposed in discussions during the assessment in every prefecture or county in the reservoir area. Taking into account the possible threat of sedimentation in Chongqing harbor, I would insist that the plans for over-storage should be officially dropped.

The 175-meter normal pool level plan was adopted by the leading group. Once the YVPO took it as the basis for its feasibility report, it was approved by the examination committee. Now, any attempt to restudy the subject must receive State Council approval. It is therefore suggested that the leading group and relevant experts meet to restudy this serious problem, then report their proposal to the examination committee and, upon the latter's approval, submit it to the NPC.

Criticism or correction to any improprieties in the above opinions will be appreciated.

# CHAPTER NINE

## OPINIONS AND RECOMMENDATIONS ON THE THREE GORGES PROJECT
### A Statement for the Third Session of the Seventh Standing Committee of the Chinese People's Political Consultative Conference[1]
by
Li Boning[2]

I am in full support of the Communique of the Third Plenum of the Thirteenth Party Congress, and the report by Comrade Zhao Ziyang, which emphasized controlling the economic environment, diminishing consumer demand and capital investments, and favoring major industries. At the same time, investments for non-productive construction projects and conspicuous consumption should be eliminated, a series of measures should be adopted to maintain necessary supplies, the momentum of economic development and the living standard of the people. In addition to the two measures put forth by Zhao to cope with the problems of food and grain supplies, I would like to stress in particular the issues of agriculture and irrigation. Here, the investment should not only be maintained but increased each year. The current situation, where since 1980 there has been a decline in agriculture and irrigation as well as in the enthusiasm of farmers for raising grain, should be

---

[1] This statement was included in the original Chinese edition of *Yangtze! Yangtze!* in order to present pro-dam arguments.

[2] Previously, Li Boning was the deputy minister of the Ministry of Water Resources and Electric Power. In 1989 he became deputy chair of the Economic Construction Group of the Chinese People's Political Consultative Conference. Presently, he is the director of the Population Relocation Bureau of the Three Gorges Project Development Corporation.

altered.[3] The stability of agricultural prices and the people's living standard depends on increasing the productivity of the land and the enthusiasm of the farmers. Without this, it will be very hard to achieve an output of 500 billion kilograms of grain by the year 2000.

Various discussions and speeches made in small groups and during the conference, as well as by members of the Chinese People's Political Consultative Conference (CPPCC) assessing the Three Gorges project, and in numerous articles and publications, were strongly opposed to construction of this grand project because of the need to reduce capital investment. It was felt that during the initial stages of our socialist society,[4] at least before the year 2000, this project should not be considered. In my opinion, this argument reveals a lack of knowledge about the real situation, and does not conform to the facts. Having been engaged in the field of hydro-electric resources for 38 years, ever since the establishment of the Ministry of Water Resources in 1950, I feel obliged to present a realistic picture of the current situation. While I am trying to contribute what I know, I would also like to hear your opinions and comments, and welcome criticism for any incorrect remarks.

Zhao's report called for a drastic reduction in "non-productive and redundant construction," "office-buildings and luxury estab-lishments," along with "conspicuous consumption" in favor of projects encouraging economic development and major industries. I believe the Three Gorges project is of strategic significance for the four modernizations (agriculture, industry, sciences and technology, and national defense). The project should not be reduced or eliminated, because it will add great momentum to economic development.

---

[3] The move away from grain production into more highly profitable forms of production, such as cash crops, including flowers, since the inauguration of economic reforms in agriculture in 1978, has been a major concern among more conservative-minded leaders such as Chen Yun.
[4] This is a concept of economic development relying heavily on market mechanisms introduced by Zhao Ziyang at the October, 1987, Thirteenth Party Congress.

The Three Gorges project is a great project, capable of producing enormous economic results of a comprehensive nature, promoting flood control, the generation of hydro-electricity, and navigation, thereby enhancing the economic development of the reservoir area and the economic prosperity of the local people. Experts on water resources from the Nationalist government and from the United States studied the Three Gorges project for many years before Liberation in 1949. In 1954, after the disastrous flooding of the Huaihe River in Anhui province, scientific research was carried out in the Yangtze River basin while the blueprint for the river's economic development was being formulated. In 1958, two resolutions on these matters were adopted at the meeting of the Party Central Committee held in Chengdu, Sichuan province. In the 30 years since that meeting, scientists and engineers have continued to study the project. Given that study has gone on for so long, how can the approach of the water resources and electric power departments and the scientists be considered rash? Although a final feasibility report has yet to be completed, an initial conclusion has been made based on the assessment report done by the 14 experts' groups. Basically, no technical problem is insoluble and therefore the concerns shown by many comrades can also be met.

There is no equally effective alternative to the Three Gorges project for flood control, navigation, and economic development in the reservoir area. As for the electrical supply for central and eastern China, including the eastern part of Sichuan, the construction of the Three Gorges project is relatively more economical than any other alternative. The number of people to be relocated has already been carefully ascertained through repeated investigations. The new policy known as population relocation for development has been welcomed in the area because it allows for stable production and livelihoods for the local population, in contrast to the earlier plan which granted a single lump-sum payment. Four years of experiments have proved that this is an effective and correct policy. The local governments have also promised to do their job in resettling their own populations. So it is groundless to say that population relocation, not being fully understood, could be a source of endless investment. As for the funds needed for this project, our economic situation as a whole would not be greatly affected if the revenues from the electricity generated by the

Gezhouba dam could be used for this purpose. In addition, state bonds could be issued, other financial resources mobilized and foreign loans solicited.

The Three Gorges project, therefore, should be approved. In order to improve the design and the plans of the project, studies could be undertaken without, however, influencing the 1984 decision already made by the Central Committee.[5] The earlier the project is launched, the fewer the resources needed, the smaller the economic losses will be and the greater the benefit to the four modernizations. This was the scientific conclusion of the majority of the experts who participated in the assessment of the project.

Some criticisms were leveled against the departments in the Ministry of Water Resources, and especially against the Yangtze Valley Planning Office (YVPO), alleging that for many years attention had been focused only on the Three Gorges to the neglect of the development of the tributaries, which is contrary to the principle of developing the tributaries first and the mainstream of the river second. This allegation is neither true nor fair. First of all, our national policy towards river management and control has never adopted such a principle. The priorities are given to the tributaries or to the mainstream according to the results of scientific evaluations of economic and technological situation. In fact, as far as the Yangtze River is concerned, the tendency over the past 38 years has been to treat the tributaries first and the mainstream later. Since the founding of the People's Republic of China, the state has invested heavily in capital construction projects along the Yangtze River basin. These projects are all on the tributaries, except for the ongoing Gezhouba dam project, which is situated on the mainstream of the river.

According to statistics from 1983, altogether 23 billion $m^3$ of earth and stonework went into the reinforcement of the river dikes, in order to regulate the rivers and control irrigation and flooding. As a result, 3,570 kilometers of river embankment and 30,000 kilometers of dikes have been repaired or strengthened. The height of the 182-kilometer embankment along the Jingjiang River has been increased by about 1.5 to 2 meters and some

---

[5] The Central Committee adopted a plan for a 175-meter dam with a normal pool level of 150 meters.

potentially vulnerable points have been reinforced. Quite a number of flood diversion and storage basins were completed, with a capacity of more than 50 billion m³. About 48,000 large, medium and small reservoirs were built with a total capacity of 122.2 billion m³, while the 105 large reservoirs on the tributaries have a combined capacity of 73.3 billion m³. They have played a significant role in flood control for both the Yangtze River basin and its tributaries. In addition they have met 62 percent of the irrigation needs, coping with the droughts of the past years, and ensuring good harvests in the areas concerned.

In terms of electricity generation, as of 1985, the completed or unfinished large and medium hydro-electric plants have a total installed capacity of more than 17 million kWh, with an aggregate output of electricity of more than 72 billion kWh. In addition, small power plants already constructed in the rural areas produce about 4 million kWh. Finally, pumped irrigation schemes with an installed capacity of 6.24 million kWh, as well as 7,000 small and large water drainage pipes and gates, have been installed. Up until 1985, about 56.72 million *mu* of land could be protected from flooding, which accounted for about 82 percent of the total land area affected by potential flooding.

Beyond this, in 1954 the YVPO called together a great number of technological personnel and started the comprehensive plan for the development of the Yangtze River basin while the initial stages of the Three Gorges project also began. The draft plan was finished in 1957. In March, 1958, at the Chengdu conference the Politburo of the Party Central Committee adopted a document entitled "Report on the Main Design Features of the Three Gorges Project." On the basis of this document, the planning office modified its draft, and in 1959 submitted "Report on the Main Points of Preliminary Design." In 1983 the State Planning Commission examined and endorsed the instructions for the revision and updating of "The Yangtze River Basin Development Plan." In March, 1988, the YVPO once again produced the "Supplementary Report on the Comprehensive Development of the Yangtze River Basin." In 1988, the Ministry of Water Resources and the Ministry of Power invited members of the State Planning Commission and the relevant departments from the State Council and the provinces to a forum for discussion and consultation, where unanimous agreement was reached on the content of the

Yangtze River Basin Development Plan. It was also decided at the forum that the YVPO would make further modifications to the supplementary report and produce a formal report by the end of 1988. That report would then be submitted to the departments concerned, and finally to the State Council for approval. In the past 30 years, the YVPO has carried out extensive scientific research, both academic and experimental, in connection with the Yangtze River and the Three Gorges project. As a result of numerous experiments and comparisons along with the urgency of the realization of the four modernizations, it is clear that there is no alternative to the Three Gorges project for flood control, electricity, navigation, economic development in the reservoir area, and extensive economic benefits. Construction on the tributaries alone could not meet the diversity of needs that the Three Gorges project can. Thus, harnessing the Yangtze River floods for the economic development of the lower and middle reaches can ensure the security of hundreds of thousands of human lives and millions of *yuan* worth of property. In addition, it can relieve acute electricity shortages and strains on the coal supply for the thermal power plants in central and eastern China. It can also realize the image of the Yangtze River as a golden waterway by permitting a fleet of 10,000-tonne ships to sail directly from Wuhan to Chongqing.

For these reasons, it is necessary to launch the project as early as possible. This is the scientific conclusion reached through repeated assessments and evaluations. Faced with all these facts, how could anyone say the YVPO has been concerned only with the Three Gorges while neglecting the tributaries? Some even accuse experts and specialists from the Ministry of Water Resources and Electric Power of trying by fair means and foul to launch a "long-and-dragged-out-project,"[6] in order to enhance their reputation while damaging national economic interests.

Some comrades favor the idea of "tributaries first and the mainstream of the river second" with regard to the construction of reservoirs and hydro-electric power plants along the Yangtze River. They contend that the tributary reservoirs require less

---

[6] These are projects that are said to need limited investment at the beginning, but require more and more funds once they are started.

investment and offer quicker results than the Three Gorges project, which would therefore make the Three Gorges unnecessary. This assumption has no scientific basis at all. In terms of flood control, there are only about a dozen tributary reservoirs serving that function and they are scattered on several tributaries over an area of 1,000,000 km². Because precipitation may be concentrated in particular areas of the drainage basin, not all of these reservoirs can fulfill their flood-control function at the same time. Moreover, further downstream from these reservoirs is an area of heavy precipitation, 300,000 km² in size, that is not yet under control and where if storms occur, flooding of the Yangtze cannot be avoided. So, in terms of flood control, the functions of the tributary reservoirs cannot compare with those of the Three Gorges reservoir.

As for hydro-electric power generation, a project with a water level of 175 meters, an installed capacity of 17.68 million kW, and an ultimate yearly output of 84 billion kWh, would solve the problem of acute energy shortages in central and eastern China foreseen for the beginning of the 21st century. Through the assessment and the repeated analyses by the hydro-electricity experts, the Three Gorges project is considered to be much better than the 118 large- and medium-sized hydro-electric power plants already constructed or the 31 planned or under construction, and the numerous water-power stations waiting to be developed in central and eastern China, eastern Sichuan and Guizhou. Those so-called alternative projects, which are mainly concerned with the generation of electricity, can neither play a significant role in flood control in the lower and middle reaches, nor improve navigation on the Chuanjiang River.[7] Therefore, none of them could replace the Three Gorges project. Even developing the Xiangjiaba and Xiluodu dams on the Jinsha River could not improve flood control and navigation, even though their installed capacity and electrical output might be about the same as the Three Gorges reservoir. Construction at these locations is more complicated because of the possibility of earthquakes.

Even if every possible effort is made in this respect, it would not be possible to start construction within a few years' time. In

---

[7] This section of the Yangtze stretches for 1,030 kilometers between Yibin and Yichang in the upper reaches.

addition, these two dams are about 800-1000 kilometers west of the proposed Three Gorges dam, increasing the distance for electricity transmission to central and eastern China. Why should we develop the more distant points and waste the closer one? In comparison with thermal plants of the same scale, the Three Gorges project could save 40 million tonnes of coal per year. Eastern and central China could only be provided with coal from Shanxi province where the lack of water prohibits the development of coal resources, the construction of power generating plants, and the transportation of coal by slurry. Given the present overload on railway transportation, relying on thermal plants to meet the demands for electricity in central and eastern China would necessitate laying more than 1,000 kilometers of additional track and opening up of several large-scale coal mines to ensure the supply for the thermal plants. This is not an economical use of time or money. Furthermore, the thermal plants create considerable pollution and coal is a valuable but non-renewable source of energy. Why should we refuse to develop hydro-electric power, which is cleaner and more cost-effective? The waters of the Yangtze are potential energy sources that should not be wasted.

Although nuclear power is a very promising energy source, we need some time to accumulate our own experience in this field, because of its belated development in our country. The funds required to install plants are much higher than for hydro-electric power stations; for instance, the construction cost of the Daya Bay nuclear power plant near Hong Kong is US$4 billion, $2,222 per kWh (about Y8,300-11,000 per kWh). It is therefore impossible to build nuclear plants within a decade or more to replace the Three Gorges reservoir. Besides, the nuclear plants cannot control flooding or improve navigation.

In calculating the budget, the figures provided by the YVPO and the leading group are all based on a realistic assessment of construction costs and a precise calculation of the number of people to be relocated, with due consideration given to various unpredictable factors. Estimates that the actual costs would be several billions, even Y20 billion more than the YVPO and leading group figures, have no scientific basis. Nor do they use the same criteria to compare the budgets for the tributary reservoirs with that of the Three Gorges project. How can anyone convince others without such a comparison?

Some cited the Gezhouba dam project as an example, claiming that it is a "rule" at home and abroad to quadruple the estimates to arrive at the final budget for a hydro-electric power construction project.[8] First, it is unrealistic to take the Gezhouba dam as an example in this sense. The proposed budget of Y1.35 billion for the Gezhouba dam project was drawn up in 1970 by the then Wuhan Military Region and the Revolutionary Committee of Hubei province without preliminary estimates or preparation. As such, it was an "ultra-leftist" product of the Cultural Revolution. This figure could not be treated as a realistic estimate of the project.

In November, 1974, after two years of planning and design by the YVPO, the initial estimated budget approved by the State Council was Y3.556 billion, of which the first stage of construction was set at Y2.3 billion. That figure was very close to the true cost of the first-stage ,Y2.471 billion, when it was completed in 1981. In 1983, the planning office reestimated the funds for the second stage of construction, increasing the original Y3.556 billion to Y4.848 billion, which was approved by the State Council after examination by the State Planning Commission.

How could anyone say that the estimate had quadrupled? The additional funds were due to an increase of 50,000 kW in the installed capacity of the generation units, to an increase in the voltage of the transmission lines, as well as to an increase in the price of construction materials. It is fair only to compare Y3.556 billion with Y4.848 billion, and to take into consideration the reasonable factors behind the increase. As for the figure of Y1.35 billion, it should never have been considered as an estimate.

Since it came on line seven years ago, the Gezhouba dam has already shown substantial economic benefits, having generated more than 52 billion kWh of electricity, which would have otherwise required 20.82 million tonnes of standard coal. On the basis of Y3.00 per kWh, it has generated a value of Y156.9 billion of industrial production value for the country. Therefore it has been

---

[8] Originally, a total investment of Y1.35 billion was estimated for the Gezhouba dam along with a construction period of five years. Ultimately, the dam cost Y5 billion and took 19 years to complete. See Luk and Whitney, editors' Introd. to *Megaproject*, p. 6.

highly praised by the state. Describing the project as a "historical error" and a "long-and-dragged-out project" does not respect the truth. As for the "rule" in foreign countries that the final budget is four times higher than that of the estimate, we have no concrete examples. In capitalist countries, budgets for electrical generating stations are usually bid upon by contractors. If the "four-times-more rule" were true, no one would dare to make a bid. The intention of those people is very clear. By citing the "rule" to show that the Three Gorges project was bound to fall into such a category, they hoped to kill this so-called "long-and-dragged-out project." This is not a scientific approach at all.

In terms of construction time, if one is talking about one or two tributary projects, construction might be less costly and yield faster results. But when it comes to the construction of more than a dozen dam projects as an alternative to the Three Gorges project, then I ask how much money would be needed and how long construction would last? As for some of the tributary projects that are envisaged, so far as I know, the geological and resettlement studies have yet to be completed, and preparations are still in the initial stages. Under such conditions, how could anyone calculate the actual budgets and the construction period for these dams? Conversely, all the basic data concerning the Three Gorges project has been assembled and present a fairly clear picture of the proposed project. With completion of the preparation work, the project will be ready to start at any time. If modern construction methods are employed, in a little over 10 years, the first group of hydro-electric generators will be functioning. (And during the course of construction, by resorting to temporary shiplocks and by using the low-head generating units on the cofferdams, it may take only nine years to produce power.) Then, subsequent construction work can be covered by revenue from the production of electricity. All these advantages are unavailable for the alternative projects on the tributaries. The allegation that in the next 20 years the Three Gorges dam could not be used effectively is totally out of touch with the facts.

As for the issue of our national financial strength, it is appropriate to take the state's financial difficulties and the critical state of our economic reforms into account when considering the huge investment required for the Three Gorges project. But the production of electricity is the vanguard of our entire national economic development. In order to assure a continuous supply of electricity for our four modernizations it is imperative to launch the project as soon as possible. In spite of the state's acute financial difficulties, the project can be managed through careful arrangements to ensure the funding.

A precedent can be found in the Baoshan Iron and Steel Complex in Shanghai, which cost about Y32.7 billion in its first and second stages of construction, with the third stage yet to begin. Although opposed by many at the beginning, it proved economically worthwhile and did not exceed the state's financial capacity. In fact, the first stages of the Daya Bay and Qingshan nuclear plants, together with the 1.2 million kWh nuclear power plants under negotiation with Germany, required about Y26.2 to Y34.5 billion, which is close to the amount required for the Three Gorges project. Since the state is able to offer such a large sum of money to build nuclear power plants in a short period of time with a production capacity of only 4.3 million kWh, then it is also well within the national economic capacity to raise Y29.8 billion—plus the cost of transmission lines—to invest in the Three Gorges project with an installed capacity of 17.68 million kW.

In reality, the Three Gorges project will not cost the state so much. With an annual output of 84 billion kWh, it will produce an annual income of over Y5 billion. The total output during the construction period of 11 to 17 years will reach 300 billion kWh, which means total revenue of Y18 billion, calculated on the basis of Y0.06 per kWh. (That is an unreasonably low rate for electricity and will inevitably change in the future, thereby increasing the total income.) Should the project be launched now, the electricity charges collected would allow the project to finance itself after the first group of generators goes into operation in 10 years.

The present Y11 billion estimated for resettlement was determined on the basis of a lump-sum compensation, not on the principle of population relocation for development. A four-year experiment using this principle showed it is more economical than lump-sum payments. For instance, on the basis of the plan for a 175-meter water level, 330,000 people in the rural areas should be relocated and 420,000 *mu* of land submerged, requiring compensation of more than Y1.6 billion. If the experience gained from the above-mentioned experiment were applied, only part of the 3.89 million *mu* of barren land on the hill slopes designated for the resettlement of 361 towns would have to be devoted to the cultivation of 800,000 *mu* of orange groves. (The income for every *mu* of orange grove is about four or five times that of fields of grain.) According to the calculation of Y500 per *mu* for cultivable land, the total comes to Y400 million. Allowing for hidden costs, let us say altogether Y600 million. It is still only a fraction of the Y1.6 billion, and this alone can save one billion *yuan*.

As far as social benefits are concerned, the output of 84 billion kWh a year would create a total output of more than Y250 billion in industrial production value for the state, assuming a production value of Y3.00 per kWh. The day construction is completed would coincide with recovery of the total investment in the project. This can be guaranteed. In addition, there would be significant benefits both for flood control and navigation. With so many advantages for society, the Three Gorges project should be started as soon as possible.

Some people have argued that it is inappropriate to construct such a large-scale project in the initial stages of socialist society. That argument is not tenable. Everyone knows that the large rivers of China, prone to flooding, have not yet been brought under control. Among them, flood control of the Yangtze River is weakest of all. The dikes along both banks of the Jingjiang River are not strong enough to sustain a 1,000-year flood. The safety of the Yangtze and Yellow rivers has an important bearing on the nation as a whole. Catastrophic flooding could disrupt our overall national economic planning and delay implementation of the four modernizations. At the present time, when the whole nation is working heart and soul to overcome economic difficulties, we could not sustain such a devastating blow.

Records for the past 2,000 years show that floods occur every 10 years on the Yangtze. Since the big floods on the Yangtze and the Huaihe rivers in 1954, the Yangtze River has not had a full flood throughout its entire basin. So it seems probable that a big flood will come soon. Nature does not care what stage of development a society is in. But a big flood could come precisely when we are in the initial stages of socialist development, and when economic reforms are in a very difficult period, making us unable to sustain heavy losses of human life and property.

The general industrial and agricultural output in the Yangtze River basin accounts for 40 percent of the nation's total, and it is at the heart of key development areas. Thus, removing the danger of floods as soon as possible is of great strategic importance to ensure further economic reform. Unless the Three Gorges project is launched at the earliest date possible, we will face such danger throughout our socialist economic construction.

We should consider the ability of our economy to sustain the construction of the project. But we should also take into account the fact that, without the project, the state and the nation could risk even greater losses—probably beyond the tolerance of the country's economy.

It is normal to have different points of view and concerns about such a huge project. Since the adoption of the plan for the 150-meter water level by the Party Central Committee in 1984, attention has been given to opposing opinions. After further investigations of the proposed reservoir area in 1986, instructions were given to the Ministry of Water Resources and Electric Power to organize experts and specialists from all scientific fields to reassess the project. The Central Committee has shown considerable democracy in the decision-making process concerning important issues and policies. In accordance with the decision of the committee, the ministry invited 412 experts and consultants from 40 specific fields within economics, science and technology to form 14 experts' groups.

These people came from 12 research institutes under the Chinese Academy of Sciences, 21 ministries, departments, and commissions under the State Council, 11 national associations or institutes recommended by the Chinese Association of Sciences, 29 institutes of higher learning, and eight provinces and cities along the Yangtze River basin. Among the experts were 15 members of the Chinese Academy of Sciences, 66 professors and associate professors, 38 researchers and associate researchers and 251 senior engineers, totaling 370 people, accounting for 89.9 percent of the entire assessment team. In addition, many supplementary studies were carried out by researchers in each field.

The whole process has taken about two years; but now, when the assessment is about to reach an affirmative conclusion, some comrades have started to criticize the decision by the Central Committee to let the ministry take charge of the assessment work. They have accused the ministry of not taking a democratic and scientific approach to the issue, alleging that most of the 412 participants were under the control of the ministry—48.3 percent were from the units engaged in the field of water resources and electricity, while 51.7 percent came from other sections of departments outside the ministry. They accuse the ministry of suppressing opposing positions, and of even having gone so far as to say, "submit false statements and data to create a long-and-dragged-out project."

This kind of accusation is difficult to understand. What was wrong with the decision made by the Central Committee? Would it be democratic and scientific to entrust the assessment of a project concerning water resources and hydro-electricity to a department that has neither responsibility nor expertise in this field, rather than to the Ministry of Water Resources and Electric Power, which has the best concentration of scientists and experts in this field? Both the experts and the others, whatever their opinions, had plenty of opportunities to express their viewpoints during the assessment. How could it be said that the experts were under the control of the ministry? Doesn't such an allegation amount to a personal insult? Moreover, it is inappropriate to dismiss the project in a hasty manner, since the assessment is still not fully completed, the feasibility report has not yet been written, and the Examination Committee on the project has not yet been formed.[9] And thus, to reject the conclusion of the assessment and the Three Gorges project would be unscientific.

Everything has two different viewpoints, the correct and incorrect. The opinion held by the minority could be correct or incorrect. As for the debate on the Three Gorges project, is it democratic and scientific to listen to the opinions held by the minority alone—to reject the project—without any sound scientific evidence? The debate has been going on for more than 30 years. Those who favor it, the scientists, technicians and departments concerned, have been working very hard night and day for the past 30 years—carrying out surveying and investigations, planning, completing scientific studies and research—and have achieved considerable results in this respect. But up till today, those who oppose the project, as far as I can see, have not been

---

[9] The committee was eventually set up in July, 1990, and was headed by Zou Jiahua.

able to present any new or convincing scientific evidence. They simply repeat old slogans of the 1950s, inventing more and more accusatory labels for the achievements made by the scientists and experts, and arbitrarily dismiss them with many irrelevant accusations. It does not conform with the values we have been promoting, that is, respect for knowledge, respect for science and respect for intellectuals.

Now, some have come out to say that "the Three Gorges project is a political issue," and one has to be "responsible to history." This in itself is not wrong, but those who say it are referring to the launching of the project as a "political blunder," as an act of "irresponsibility to history." I think the reverse is true.

From 1860 to 1870, there were two severe floods in the Yangtze River, which caused tremendous losses. The 1931 flood submerged 50.9 million *mu* of land with a death toll of 145,000. Flood waters remained in the city of Hankou for three months. Later, in 1935, another flood submerged 22.64 million *mu* of land with a loss of 142,000 lives. The flood in 1954, after the Liberation, inundated 47.55 million *mu* of land, drowned 30,000 people, and ruptured railway links between Beijing and Wuhan for 100 days, even though the Jingjiang River dikes and those around the main parts of the city of Wuhan were not affected. If a flood like that in 1954 occurred today, the human and economic losses would surely be much greater, because of the substantial increase in population and the significant development of industry and agriculture in the area. On top of the losses, considerable funds would be needed to restore people's lives and reconstruct the economy. The combined losses described above would far exceed the cost for the entire construction of the Three Gorges project.

The frequent occurrence of localized floods in parts of the Yangtze and the Yellow rivers may serve as a serious warning. In 1985 and 1986, floods occurred in the Liaowa River.[10] They caused damage of Y6-7 billion.[11] The 1988 flood in the Nenjiang

---

[10] Part of the Danjiankou reservoir.

[11] The massive floods that occurred in the summer of 1991 in Zhejiang and Jiangsu provinces were used by both sides in this debate. Proponents of Three Gorges asserted that the floods demonstrated the necessity for

(continued...)

River, in the northeast, cost Y2.5 billion. One in the Liujiang River in Guangxi Y900 million, and another in Dongting Lake in Hunan, more than Y4 billion. By historical standards, 1988 witnessed a medium level of flood disaster. According to statistics, 175 million *mu* were affected by flood in 1988: 81 million *mu* were destroyed, 1.14 million houses were washed away and 2,895 people died. The total economic loss was Y13.5 billion.

We must prepare for the floods in the Yangtze and the Yellow rivers both psychologically and materially. But this, in my point of view, is far from enough. "If you do not think of the future, then you are bound to have worries in the present," is a Chinese proverb that should remind us never to forget that we are constantly being threatened by natural disasters.

In view of this situation, I sincerely hope the Central Committee takes careful consideration of the Three Gorges project and reaches a decision that will benefit the overall economic situation in the long run. Even if the launching of the project were postponed for a couple of years, I believe it would still be necessary to find ways for the population in the areas concerned to develop their local economy and to start the work of resettlement as soon as possible. This includes relocating the 330,000 people in the rural area under the 175-meter-water-level plan, and within 8 to 10 years at the latest, transplanting 80,000 *mu* of orange groves so as to provide proper conditions for a stable and productive life. Because orange trees need so long a time to reach the fruit-bearing period, transplanting those trees would have to precede relocation of the population.

In 1986, while inspecting the Three Gorges area, Comrade Zhao Ziyang instructed the people in the reservoir area to take full advantage of the natural conditions by developing more orange groves along slopes of the river. Now the people are very enthusiastic about the cultivation of oranges there. If relocation were to be started several years later, then it would be difficult and more costly to expropriate land since it would have already been turned into groves by the local people. The same case can be made for

---

[11](...continued)
the project, whereas opponents noted that the dam would not have prevented this flooding because it occurred downstream of the dam site.

the resettlement of towns and cities, as early planning is needed to make sure public facilities such as highways, public bus lines, telephones, electricity, and water supplies, are ready beforehand. The economic development of the reservoir area has been delayed for several dozen years, the cities are very crowded and living space is limited, with outdated facilities.

Since preparation for the Three Gorges project began, although the government has time and again forbidden any capital construction in areas below the proposed water level of the future reservoir, construction has been going on all the time, resulting in the growth of the population, as well as of enterprises and factories. It is impossible to keep the area in a static state. This calls for the state to give overall consideration to the development of the area both in the long and short terms.

If the problem is not solved, then the state will have to pay more compensation later. According to estimates, the cost for resettlement will increase by 7 percent or more for every year the project is delayed. Each year, as the local population increases and, with the introduction of private property, the people's living standard rises, so do the prices for each of the items to be submerged. Also, it becomes more expensive to administer all the aspects of social organizations made more complex by the rise in literacy and economic development. The difficulty of resettling the population will also increase, resulting in huge waste that will aggravate the poverty of the masses in the reservoir area. All these factors should merit our serious consideration.

That is all I wish to say. Your opinions and comments are welcome.

# Part Three

## The Interviews

# CHAPTER TEN

## AN INTERVIEW WITH HUANG SHUNXING[1]
by
Dai Qing

*Dai Qing:* In 1985 you returned to China by way of Japan. Were you, at that time, aware of the ecological crisis confronting the mainland and the detrimental impact of the Three Gorges project on the environment?

*Huang Shunxing:* For 40 years or so, people in Taiwan have been deprived of information about the mainland. Therefore, to tell you the truth, I was not well informed about the situation here. The available information was of two extremes: on the one hand, there was the anti-communist propaganda of the Nationalists, for example, "the red bandits are vicious and the masses live in bitterness"; on the other hand, there was the news carried through the grapevine by leftist youth—describing that the mainland was an ideal society. No one ever raised the issue of the environment. It reminds me of what happened in Taiwan years ago, when everyone was so enthusiastic about economic development that they ignored the environmental impacts of unbridled economic growth. Even those who thought about the environment did not dare mention it, nor point out the inevitable destructive effects of focusing solely on growth at the expense of the environment. At

---

[1] Huang Shunxing was born in Zhanghua, Taiwan. From 1964 to 1969, he was a freely elected county executive in Taiwan and from 1972 to 1980 a freely elected member of the judiciary. Since 1988, he has been a member of the Standing Committee of the National People's Congress. He is founder of the magazine *Life and Environment*. His major works include: *A Journey Around the Globe, Testimony to History, The Future of Agriculture in Taiwan, A View of the Mainland, Endless Road,* and *What I Saw in Beijing*. This interview, conducted in 1993, was not part of the original Chinese edition of *Yangtze! Yangtze!*

a 1985 environmental symposium held by the Center for East Asian Studies at the University of Chicago, I met Professor Lin Junyi, a native of Taiwan residing in the United States. He first brought the serious environmental problems in China to my attention. From that point on, I became very concerned and once I had the opportunity to visit the mainland I saw the severity of the problems right away.

*Dai Qing:* Since you reside in an area far from where forests are disappearing and rivers are drying up, why are so concerned with these issues? They have little impact on your daily life?

*Huang Shunxing:* The environment is an issue that affects the entire planet. It knows no national boundaries. I myself am Chinese, and mainland China is part of the motherland. No matter how long I have been away from her, I am always part of her.

*Dai Qing:* Soon after you arrived you began to tour the country. When did you begin to be concerned about the Three Gorges project?

*Huang Shunxing:* Not long after I arrived. At that time, the assessment of the project had already begun and both the National People's Congress (NPC) and Chinese People's Political Consultative Conference (CPPCC) were debating the project's launch. In order to ascertain the truth, I began to collect data.

*Dai Qing:* How did you feel at that time? Did you feel that this grand project would bring glory to the Chinese people?

*Huang Shunxing:* It is hollow words like "grand and magnificent" that cause us problems. In terms of "grandness," no matter whether we are discussing the Aswan dam in Egypt or the Mississippi river project in the United States, dam projects lacking serious analysis and done in haste should not be undertaken. It usually takes a million years for a river to cut a channel and establish its drainage. In China, where the population density is high, the impact of a large dam collapse or a nuclear power station failure would be beyond our imagination. Therefore, in principle, I absolutely oppose such "grand" undertakings.

There is no question that we must develop our economy. However, before we build such a grand project we must first ask whether we need so much electrical power. Second, we must examine all possible alternatives. Third, even if no alternatives are available, we must first consider the environmental and social impacts of the project.[2] The Three Gorges project should be considered from these three perspectives.

*Dai Qing:* As a member of the Standing Committee of the NPC, were you provided with easy access to materials and information by the NPC, the Ministry of Water Resources, and the Yangtze Valley Planning Office (YVPO), to aid you in assessing the project at the 1992 NPC meeting? Prior to this meeting, the NPC sent a Three Gorges Project Inspection Group to inspect the project area. Since your concern about the dam is well known, were you invited to participate in that tour?

*Huang Shunxing:* Prior to the NPC meeting, I knew absolutely nothing about the inspection tour. In fact, I didn't learn about it until the group returned and announced on television its support for the proposed early launching of the project. A few other members of the Standing Committee who have expressed similar concerns about the project have also indicated that they were not informed of the inspection group's existence. Hearing the news, I telephoned the Secretariat of the NPC and was told that they had not informed me of the tour because they assumed that I was not in good health. I asked how they knew anything about my physical condition. The person at the Secretariat only mumbled an incomprehensible reply. Later, I heard that all of the members of the inspection group had been appointed. The majority of them were non-specialists and therefore, naturally, did not come up with any opposition views.

*Dai Qing:* At the NPC meeting in 1992, the resolution on the Three Gorges project was on the agenda. Is it correct to assume that this helped you to gain an understanding of the project?

*Huang Shunxing:* Absolutely not. They set up various obstacles to my learning about the project and were unwilling to provide the most basic data on the assessment. Over the past few decades, few project proposals, large or small—from breweries to nuclear power stations—have been submitted to the NPC for

---

[2] For an extensive discussion of environmental impacts of large-scale dams, see E. Goldsmith and N. Hildyard, eds., *The Social and Environmental Effects of Large Dams*, 3 vols. (Cornwall, U.K.: Wadebridge Ecological Centre, 1984-92).

approval. Why was this particular project singled out for NPC consideration? This was peculiar.

At the meeting, they tried every which way to get the project approved. I told the Secretariat of the NPC that since I had read all the "positive" materials in support of the project, I wanted to see data concerning the other side of the argument. Both sides, I emphasized, should be examined. They replied that the Taiwan delegation had a copy of the material delineating the opposition views, but that I could only borrow it. I then pointed out the elaborate effort made to promote the positive side of the argument. Each delegate was presented with several pounds of materials supporting the project! Yet the materials outlining the opposition views consisted only of a few pamphlets that had not been made available to all of the delegates. I noted that it is the delegates who vote and must therefore understand the over all situation. Perhaps some were willing to give up that right, but I told them that I would never do so. I demanded my own copy of the opposition materials and told the Secretariat to do everything possible to secure me a copy.

Since I was afraid that they would ignore my request, I made a few copies of the pamphlets on my own and distributed them to delegates who had expressed an interest in learning about the opposition views, including Liu Caipin, a Taiwan delegate. Later, when I showed up at another session of the meeting, a member of the Secretariat gave me a copy of the opposition pamphlets that I was told had been especially prepared for me. I indicated that I didn't want such special treatment: "Understanding the overall situation is the basic right of every delegate," I stressed.

*Dai Qing:* Without written materials how could the opposition's views ever be given due consideration? Or had experts holding such views been invited to the meeting?

*Huang Shunxing:* The experts invited to introduce the project were all from the Ministry of Water Resources and the YVPO, all of whom, of course, support the dam. Although members of the Taiwan delegation did not raise that many questions, they did express their opposition views. Fan Zengsheng, vice-director of the Shanghai Area Port Facility, mentioned that once the project was completed, the sedimentation problem at the mouth of the Yangtze River would intensify. He also raised the possibility of longer waiting periods for ships to pass through the Three Gorges shiplocks. Liu Caipin noted the inadequacy of scientific data garnered in the assessment, the closed nature of the debate, and the problem of inaccurate budgets. After studying all the available data from the assessment, I also asked a few questions. Why don't the budget figures (Y57 billion) include interest costs, I asked. If these costs are incorporated, what does the total budget for the project come to?

In addition, I also posed questions concerning the life-span of the reservoir, ways for dealing with earthquakes or other natural disasters, the threat to rare species, and the submersion of important historical relics. Although these questions were directed to the entire body, only one person responded, the director of the YVPO. Some of my questions he did not answer, especially those on the budget and fund raising. Others, he responded to simply by reading from the agenda items. Still others he simply ignored.

*Dai Qing:* Under such conditions was it possible for the project to be approved? Of course, I assume that people like yourself who are willing to pose questions and take action do not constitute the majority of the delegates.

*Huang Shunxing:* You're quite right. During the panel discussions, I tried to contact other delegates as much as possible to help them understand the entire issue. I also made copies of the opposition pamphlets that the NPC Secretariat refused to distribute. However, it turned out that I could not even give out these materials since, according to the rules of the meeting, delegates from different regions were prevented from having mutual contact. All materials had to be channeled through the Secretariat assigned to each delegation and so there was no question where they would end up.

*Dai Qing:* Although Deng Xiaoping has stated that to avoid making mistakes, the Party should be more open, listening to the masses' opinions, and Zhao Ziyang emphasized that important issues must be discussed by the people, it appears that the abstract "people" have been kept in the dark. At that time, did you feel there was any opportunity to get opposition views across to the majority of delegates through legitimate channels?

*Huang Shunxing:* Many years ago, during the Mao era, I would have thought it difficult. But given that during my first two years as a member of the NPC Standing Committee, I drafted several proposals for the Bureau of the NPC Secretariat to ensure that opposition views could be voiced, including the proposal at the second session of the fifth NPC Standing Committee to allow journalists to enter the conference hall to conduct interviews, I no longer felt that way. At that time, I argued that the NPC was China's supreme legislative organ similar to deliberative bodies in other modern countries. Whoever heard of a legislature that refused journalists the right to conduct interviews? Does it make sense for issues that are discussed by the legislative body not to be broadcast to the public? And, why is it that delegates are kept ignorant of the views of the people? Without such procedures, how can we say that the NPC is truly representative? In order to establish such give and take, media people are definitely needed. Why is it that almost all the countries in the world, including the Chiang K'ai-shek regime on Taiwan, allow journalists to interview delegates, and the People's Republic does not?

When Zhao Ziyang was still in charge he proposed "transparency" for the people's representative bodies. At that time, Wan Li was also quite open-minded. In fact, he passed on my opinions to the higher authorities. And indeed, from the third session of the fifth NPC onward, they allowed journalists to enter the NPC conference hall.

During an adjournment of the third session, a journalist came to me and asked if I would like to talk with him. I asked if he was requesting an interview and if so, would it be publicized. He said no, for although a few newspapers were allowed to send observers to the meeting (without conducting interviews), reports would still be under the control of the NPC. I replied that if that was the case, then there was no need for me to talk with him. But he insisted, indicating that his report would be published in the *Internal Reference*. When I told him that I had never heard of this publication he explained that it was so important that only VIPs had access to it. I replied: "I am the people. And the people are supreme. We serve the people. The external reference is more important than the internal one. I'm sorry but I simply cannot accept such interviews."

*Dai Qing:* Your proposal of allowing journalists to enter the conference hall and conduct interviews had a great social impact. Did you make other proposals?

*Huang Shunxing:* Another proposal was the procedural regulations approved in 1989. Originally, NPC meetings did not allow speeches at the conference level (i.e., to the entire legislative body). I argued that no matter what happened at the smaller panel discussions, giving speeches at the conference level was the last opportunity for the delegates to express themselves. That right must not be taken away. I remember that I was very persistent, and a few other members also supported my proposal. At that time, Zhao Ziyang was still in power, and so eventually it was approved.

*Dai Qing:* Did the regulations play a role at later meetings? For instance, at the meeting held in March, 1992, at which the Three Gorges resolution was voted on?

*Huang Shunxing:* According to item 54 of the regulations, delegates who wish to give a speech at the meeting must first register with the Secretariat, and then the chairman sets aside time for the speech. Delegates who wish to make impromptu speeches from the floor can do so once they are recognized by the chairman, first for 10 minutes, and then a second time for five minutes. The chairman is obligated to allow those who register ahead of time to speak. Only those who decide to speak from the floor can be ignored and kept from speaking. I was determined to speak and registered to speak on March 31. I hoped for the best but prepared for the worst.

*Dai Qing:* How did things go at the meeting?

*Huang Shunxing:* Seeing that the first and second items on the agenda had already been approved, I knew the Three Gorges project would be voted on next. At this point, I took a dose of my medicine—you see I am not in particularly good health as I have a pacemaker and it's dangerous if I get too excited. I was not allowed to speak before the voting. I raised my hand, requesting to speak, but was ignored by the chairman. I stood up anyway and at this point, I heard a journalist from Taiwan shout: "No sound! No Sound!" At first, I didn't know what had happened, but later I learned that the entire sound system in the meeting hall had been shut down, with the exception of the chairman's microphone. How dare the NPC cut off the power to prevent delegates from exercising their rights? It was then that I decided to protest by walking out of the meeting. I walked to the lobby and in no time, I was surrounded by journalists. I gave them the materials I had prepared and talked just as if it was a press conference.

*Dai Qing:* Why were you treated that way? Hadn't you simply reminded the government to take adequate precautions for the sake of both the nation and the people in carrying out such a huge project?

*Huang Shunxing:* Indeed, I myself didn't understand it, either. How could the government and the NPC, in order to stop a delegate from speaking, blatantly violate the constitutional right in front of the entire country and the world? I assume that certain people were afraid my speech would be detrimental to their project. But if their motive was really to serve the interests of the nation and the people, then what would it matter if they listened to other opinions? There was no need for them to act like that! Most opposition was raised on technical points. If you are confident on these matters, why fear others speaking out?

*Dai Qing:* You hit the nail on the head: their greatest insecurity is in the technical area.

*Huang Shunxing:* Then, what was the purpose in having the project approved by coercion if they were so unsure of it? As far as I am concerned, their aim is to hold the NPC responsible, especially if anything goes wrong in the future. It was, after all, the NPC that approved the project. And what's their motive for doing that? Do they really think they can avoid responsibility? Everybody and every matter will be judged by history.

*Dai Qing:* Later, I heard that in great anger you made a decision regarding your position with the NPC.

*Huang Shunxing:* Yes, in the lobby one of the journalists, asked: "Do you intend to continue as a member of the Standing Committee of the NPC?" "No," I replied. "I want to resign now!" As soon as I said it, I sensed the question was asked on purpose. I asked: "Which newspaper do you work for?" He refused to tell me. I assume that he was from the Xinhua News Agency.

*Dai Qing:* Your public announcement was the outcome some were hoping for, while it leaves the common people with a sense of pity. Did you say it out of anger?

*Huang Shunxing:* No. In fact, I thought of resigning long ago and I had actually submitted my resignation on several occasions.

*Dai Qing:* Did you feel that what the Party did was too outrageous or have you just lost hope in the system?

*Huang Shunxing:* From my own perspective, I am disappointed in the system. No matter how hard I try, after 50 years, the situation is the same, for all the troubles I have encountered stem from the system. And such problems cannot be solved by one person. I feel that I should no longer waste my time here. I am 70 years old, and it is time that I resigned from public positions. I had planned to resign when I fulfilled my term this year; thus my resignation was not simply out of anger.

*Dai Qing:* The resolution on the Three Gorges project has been passed, and according to the propaganda in the newspapers, things are now being accelerated. What can you say about the future of this project?

*Huang Shunxing:* The environmental situation in China is extremely dicey and the Three Gorges project is only one of many problems. Projects whose impacts will be even more serious are being promoted and developed. If efforts are not made to rescue the situation now, it will soon be too late.

Overpopulation is the most serious problem facing China today. With overpopulation come low levels of education, and these, in turn affect the quality of government. Poorly educated people form governments composed of corrupt officials who seek only personal privilege. Also, the system of government is key. Without a legal system and a proper separation of powers, the Chinese nation will soon die.[3]

There have been some small but interesting developments in the Three Gorges project recently. A report was published (in June) in the *People's Daily* based on interviews with the soon to be relocated people of Sandouping. There was another article published in *Metropolitan Youth* describing how funds for population relocation from the Three Gorges area had been used for socializing and entertaining. Also, a sub-project of the Three Gorges dam was supposed to receive Y800 million in funding this year. But by the end of June only Y100 million had been allocated. Without adequate funding, how can the project be launched? Since pro-dam officials are so supportive of the project, it seems that the only reasonable thing to do would be to print as much money as possible.

---

[3] In *China on the Edge*, He Bochuan makes essentially the same argument.

These two situations (the use of project funds for recreational purposes and the inadequate allocation of funds to a Three Gorges sub-project) occurred after Li Peng fell ill early in 1993, when he reportedly suffered a heart attack. That, to me, was no coincidence. With things under tight control, the information contained in the two newspaper articles could not have been reported. How can you plan a project and then not provide adequate funds? To me, this is a very important sign, indicating that certain changes have taken place within the internal power structure.

Have you noticed that Three Gorges project bonds are no longer being issued? Why did this effort at fund raising apparently fail? In my opinion, once the bonds are issued, the bond holders should have the right to be informed about the over all budgetary situation. This knowledge will make it more difficult to suppress the voices of opposition. Then, because the opposition can express its views, the potential bond buyers will be scared off. Dam proponents have created a vicious circle.

Some Taiwanese companies wanted to join in financing the project, but they hesitated when they became aware of the opposition's views, including my own direct admonition: "Don't make evil money, let alone money that will never be made." Thus, with the various difficulties involved in fund raising, this project will be blocked for a period of time in which we can make our opposition more explicit. So, to answer your question regarding the future of the project, I think that there is a bit of hope. If people in positions of authority are wise and follow the principle of seeking truth from facts, and if officials in the financial sector are hesitant to take risks, then the Y100 million fund will be left dangling there, and will be little used. It is still not too late to halt the project, especially now that public opinion has become more averse. If the inadequate funding and the exposure of the truth about the project are part and parcel of one message, I feel there is still hope that we can halt this disaster.

# CHAPTER ELEVEN

## AN INTERVIEW WITH LI RUI[1]
by
Dai Qing

*Dai Qing:* On November 30, 1988, the assessment by the leading group of the Three Gorges project, which had lasted for 2 ½ years, proposed "starting the construction early." For the sixth time in more than 30 years, this has moved the project forward on the national economic agenda, which has inevitably drawn the concern of citizens who will assess the project through its impact on their shopping bag. From the very beginning, you have been involved in the debate over the project, and have already participated in decision making at the highest level. In fact, half of your career has been concerned with the fate of the Three Gorges. Could you tell us under what circumstances the proposal for this grand project was put forward?

*Li Rui:* In early 1954, I was visiting the Soviet Union with an electric power delegation from the Ministry of Fuel Industry. A telegram arrived from home, saying that the Ministry of Water Resources was considering starting a dam project at the Three Gorges. After discussing the matter with Liu Lanpo,[2] I sent a reply, which said that we were not presently able to undertake such a project. I understood that the people at the ministry were anxious to start the project in order to control floods along the Yangtze River. Later that year, Wuhan was besieged by floods that lasted for 40 to 50 days, so the people from Hubei province in which Wuhan is located wanted desperately to launch the

---

[1] This interview was included in the original Chinese edition of *Yangtze! Yangtze!*

[2] Liu Lanpo was, at this time, with the Ministry of Fuel Industry. In 1978 he was appointed minister of Electric Power. See Lieberthal and Oksenberg, *Policy Making*, pp. 51-54.

project. Three Gorges would not, however, provide effective flood control for Wuhan.

*Dai Qing:* As far as floods are concerned, isn't it true that people were more worried at that time about flooding of the Yellow River than the Yangtze River?

*Li Rui:* Yes. In those days the General Bureau of Water Resources and Electricity under the Ministry of Electric Power was working closely with the Ministry of Water Resources in formulating an overall program for the Yellow River valley. Here, I would like to emphasize that it was not a project concerned only with flood control, but also with many other elements influencing all the reaches along the Yellow River. True enough, flood control is much more urgent in the Yellow than the Yangtze River. We can certainly say that the life of the Chinese nation, from its very origins, has been deeply involved in the struggle to control rivers such as the Yellow, Huaihe, and Yangtze. Innumerable historical cases involving flood diversion and dike construction fill the annals, from Dayu[3] to the Nationalist era (1927-1949) when three resource committees were set up for the Yellow, Huaihe, and Yangtze rivers.

Since 1949 and the founding of new China, flood control has been a serious concern of the state, which began constructing reservoirs on a large scale. In the 1950s, Lin Yishan proposed a scheme involving a normal water level of 235 meters and a reservoir that would hold 100 billion $m^3$ of flood water for the Three Gorges. Obviously, he had been influenced by the Russians during his studies in the Soviet Union, where there are world-famous reservoirs and water-power stations.[4] But the situation in China is very different from that in the Soviet Union, where flooding results from melted snow, making the flood peak relatively low. In China the monsoon rains cause floods with high peaks. Furthermore, the Soviet Union has more land with a

---

[3] A legendary figure from the Xia dynasty (2200 B.C.) who saved China from catastrophic floods.

[4] For a study of Soviet dam construction in the 1930s, see Anne D. Rossweiler, *The Generation of Power: The History of Dneprostroi* (Oxford: Oxford University Press, 1988).

smaller population, whereas in China, the opposite is the case, resulting in greater human losses when the floods occur.

*Dai Qing:* Building reservoirs for flood control is something new. So, isn't it good to learn new methods after all? In fact, the Sanmenxia Gorge dam plays an important role in flood control, right?

*Li Rui:* Right. But the Yangtze River is different from the Yellow River. The Sanmenxia Gorge dam, which is situated at the lower reaches of the Yellow River, can control over 92 percent of the watershed, while the Three Gorges dam, which would be located at the end of the upper reaches of the Yangtze River, has control over only 55 percent of the watershed. Moreover, floods from the many large tributaries at the lower and middle reaches of the Yangtze often cause serious damage. Comparatively speaking, floods are less serious along the Yellow River, the largest of which was in 1843 when the river flow peaked at only 36,000 $m^3$/s and the total flood volume over 30 days reached 16.7 billion $m^3$. As for the Yangtze River, the highest flood peak on record was three times as much, and the flood volume 10 times as much as that of the Yellow River. So I think it is of little use to rely on reservoirs to control floods along the Yangtze. We should not forget that the sedimentation problem at the Sanmenxia Gorge dam became so serious that within two years of its completion sediment had accumulated in the Weihe River and was rapidly extending towards the upper reaches, causing great alarm in the city of Xi'an. As a result, the reservoir had to be reconstructed.[5]

*Dai Qing:* As I understand it, the control of large-scale floods requires large-scale reservoirs. I have the impression that your argument confirmed the proposal first put forward by Lin Yishan at the end of the 1950s emphasizing the enormous capacity of the

---

[5] "In 1965-1968, two parallel side tunnels, each eight meters in diameter, were excavated on the left bank [of the dam]. In 1970-1973 eight bottom sluices, formerly used for diversion, were reopened, and three unused penstocks were modified into conduits for sediment flushing. In the meantime, the elevation of the remaining five inlets of the powerhouse was lowered by 13 meters, and low-head water turbines were installed instead of high-head ones; the plant was turned into a run-of-river type." Wu Xiutao, "Environmental impacts of the Sanmen Gorge project," *Water Power & Dam Construction*, November 1986, pp. 23-24.

proposed reservoir to finally solve flooding problems. This view was reconfirmed in the leading group's assessment, which said: "The role of the Three Gorges reservoir in flood control is irreplaceable, and only when the reservoir is built can the floods along the Yangtze River be harnessed."

*Li Rui:* I have to make it clear that I believe there are many other ways to control floods, and the flood-control capacity of the Three Gorges project should not be exaggerated. Because of the unique conditions of the Yangtze River, priority should be given to strengthening dikes, setting up flood storage basins and diverting water from lakes and low-lying land, constructing reservoirs along the tributaries and carrying out soil- and water-conservation projects. In support of an immediate start of the project, some people cite the major floods in 1870 and 1954, claiming that any recurrence would kill thousands or even millions. In my view, these people do not seek truth from fact.

*Dai Qing:* But what if the Jingjiang River dikes burst at Shashi City?

*Li Rui:* I'm afraid this argument doesn't hold water. Before the Tang (7th-10th centuries) and Song (10th-13th centuries) dynasties, big floods were quite unknown along the Jingjiang River, where there were a number of outlets such as Yunmeng Lake to the north and Dongting Lake to the south that served very well as natural flood-storage areas and diverted the water flow. During the Ming Dynasty (14th-17th centuries) Zhang Juzheng, a prime minister from Hubei, blocked the Haoxue diversion channel, the only outlet on the northern bank of the Jingjiang River, to ensure the safety of the north against floods, but only at the expense of the south. In 1870, a 1,000-year flood occurred in the upper reaches of the Yangtze. Because the southern bank was then lower than the northern one, the flood broke through at Songzikou on the southern bank and rushed into Dongting Lake. However low and weak the Jingjiang River dikes seemed, they withstood the flood above Jianli.

Today, after years of reinforcement, the Jingjiang River dikes are much stronger than before; therefore it is misleading to presume that the dikes would break again causing millions of deaths. The 1870 flood was from the upper reaches and the water level in Chongqing at that time was four meters higher than that of the flood in 1981. If a flood as serious as that in 1870 occurred again, the water level in Chongqing would be even higher due to the construction of the Three Gorges project, because it would store the flood waters and cause sediment to accumulate. Obviously then, Chongqing will be in danger if a flood occurs in the upper reaches instead of in the lower ones.

I remember well the big flood in 1954. The flooding in the lower and middle reaches was not very serious. At Yichang, the heaviest flow exceeded the security limit only by several thousand cubic meters per second, which was easily handled by the existing flood diversion network on the Jingjiang River. But, along the Xiangjiang, Zishui, Yuanshui, and Lishui rivers in Hunan province, the flood was ferocious, increasing the flow above Chenglingji to over 100,000 $m^3$/s. Dikes along these rivers were not strong enough and finally burst, causing severe damage.

In 1980, (then premier) Zhao Ziyang gave instructions to the effect that flood-control methods along the Yangtze River should be undertaken but should not be delayed by the Three Gorges project. In response, the Ministry of Water Resources drew up a plan to build higher dikes, install dredgers for sediment management, and arrange flood-storage and diversion networks in the low-lying areas along the lower and middle reaches. This was not the first time this approach had been suggested. In 1972, similar programs had been put forward. But this approach does not interest those in decision-making positions. Therefore, we should not be surprised to learn that two of four dredgers at Shashi[6] were removed, and the remaining two were working at a snail's pace. Why does a plan that was formulated 10 years ago remain neglected? Let me remind you that the volume of the 1954 flood was about 100 billion $m^3$. If the dikes along the lower and middle reaches were raised and strengthened, 50 billion $m^3$ of flood waters could be channeled by the river itself. If the flood-storage basin and diversion network were set up as planned and safety facilities provided to the local people, the other half of the flood waters could be handled too. We should be quite confident that floods like that in 1954 could be successfully dealt with without the Three Gorges reservoir.

---

[6] Shashi is a town just downstream of the proposed dam site.

*Dai Qing:* But one might argue that once the Three Gorges reservoir is available, the other storage and diversion network at the lower and middle reaches will no longer be needed.

*Li Rui:* The point is that we have already built these storage basins and channels for this purpose. Why should we still think of building another big one to leave these existing ones idle? We have already imported dredgers. Why were they taken away for other purposes? Dikes that require constant, arduous work have proved to be the best way to control floods. Of course, dikes are not as grand as dams are and, hence, do not constitute a glorious testimonial to the builders. I firmly believe that the role of dikes is irreplaceable in taming irritable rivers. For the past 30 years, while the Three Gorges project has been frequently encouraged, the Ministry of Water Resources and Electric Power has not worked hard enough on dike construction and the establishment of flood-storage basins and diversion channels. As for the 1980 Ten-year plan, eight years have elapsed but less than half of the job has been completed.

As early as 1958, Premier Zhou Enlai warned that we should not wait for the Three Gorges reservoir to achieve flood control and we should guard against the illusion that it could solve all of our flood-control problems. Sun Yueqi, who is now over 90, once remarked that the first mistake was made when Zhang Juzheng blocked the outlet to guard the north against floods at the expense of the south; the second was when some lakes were turned into farms after 1949,[7] which caused the flood-storage basins and diversion networks to be reduced by half; the third will be if the Three Gorges reservoir is built.

*Dai Qing:* It seems that the reason for starting the Three Gorges project in the 1950s was flood control, while in the 1970s and 1980s the major concern is power generation.

*Li Rui:* That's right. In 1956 Lin Yishan wrote a lengthy report that barely mentioned power generation. But today, dam proponents cite electricity generation as a top priority. For instance, in the leading group's assessment, investments in the hydro-electric aspects of the project account for 75 percent of the

---

[7] A reflection of the heavy reliance in China on extensive rather than intensive agriculture.

total budget, while flood control accounted for 21 percent and navigation 4 percent.[8] At this conference, according to the proposed scheme of a 175-meter normal pool level the installed capacity would be 17.68 million kW and the annual electricity production could reach 84 billion kWh, solving the problem of an electricity shortage in central and eastern China and in eastern Sichuan. But it should be noted that it will take 12 years for the dam to generate power, and a total of 20 years to complete construction and resettle the people who are displaced. How then can the immediate problem of acute electricity shortage be solved? Li Boning, the former vice-minister of water resources and electric power, calculated that the cofferdam can generate power three years earlier than the reservoir. However, I resolutely oppose this idea of sacrificing a major navigation channel to install a few low-head power generation units. Premier Zhou Enlai once criticized this idea, calling it "tyranny on the waterway."

*Dai Qing:* In the leading group's assessment, isn't it mentioned that the tributary development program should be encouraged according to the needs of local conditions and that the Three Gorges project will not replace the local program? Rather, they will complement each other.

*Li Rui:* This is merely wishful thinking. Given the present economic situation, it is impossible to do everything at the same time. After 1979, when I took over responsibility for the water-power construction program,[9] I saw that many projects were being delayed because of the Gezhouba dam, which cost one-third of the total state budget for capital construction. In 1984, after the feasibility study on the Three Gorges project was basically approved by the State Council,[10] the project preparation work began. As a result, the program for the Wuqiangxi power station in Hunan (1.2

---

[8] Similar shifts of priorities occurred in the construction of dams in the Soviet Union. See Rossweiler, *Generation.*

[9] After being politically rehabilitated.

[10] This earlier study was undertaken in 1982–1983 by the YVPO. It envisaged a normal pool level of 150 meters, and was approved "in principle" by the State Council. The plan, however, came under attack from the Ministry of Communication and from Chongqing because it could not guarantee access for 10,000-tonne ships to Chongqing harbor. These criticisms led to the establishment of the leading group's study.

million kW) and the Geheyan Power station in Hubei (1.2 million kW) had to be put off along with the Ertan Power station in Sichuan (3 million kW). Then, due to disagreement about the Three Gorges project, the preparation for the Three Gorges had to be stopped for reassessment by the leading group. Only then were these smaller-scale projects carried out. This has proved that it is impossible to undertake the Three Gorges project and those on the tributaries at the same time. There are currently a number of tributary power stations under construction, such as Tongjiezi (600,000 kW), and Baozhusi (640,000 kW) in Sichuan, Dongfeng in Guizhou (510,000 kW), Ankang in Shaanxi (800,000 kW), Wan'an in Jiangxi (400,000 kW), along with the aforementioned Wuqiangxi, Geheyan, and Ertan, with total power generation reaching 8.45 million kW. I believe that these medium-scale power stations are very effective in meeting the urgent demand for electricity, because they can be built relatively quickly. Their budgets should be guaranteed. But, in reality, the budgets are far from enough and some of them are still waiting to be initiated.

Other hydro-electric stations on the tributaries that have undergone either an initial preliminary design or a feasibility report, include: the Taipingyi in Sichuan (260,000 kW), the first stage of the Tianshengqiao (1.2 million kW) and the Hongjiadu (540,000 kW) in Guizhou, the Jiangya in Hunan (400,000 kW), and the Fankou in Hubei (510,000 kW). They are all awaiting financing. Given this, how can one say that the Three Gorges project does not conflict with stations on the tributaries? As everyone knows, projects on the tributaries are similar and do not involve complicated problems such as sedimentation, population relocation, and environmental degradation. It is not right to delay urgent and more realistic projects on the tributaries for the sake of the Three Gorges project that has yet to be decided upon. Just as flood control on the Yangtze River requires dam consolidation, a series of stations must be constructed on the tributaries to solve electricity shortages as soon as possible.

What a terrible waste it is that these effective smaller projects have to give way to an extensive one that even after years of discussion has produced no results at all! I was engaged in the field of hydro-electric construction for more than 10 years and tirelessly argued this point. Somebody was always occupying center stage with grandiose but impossible and impractical plans forcing the good but small players to wait in the wings. Isn't that ridiculous? I retired from my post six years ago, but this painful situation still concerns me.

*Dai Qing:* At present the masses of Chinese who have experienced hunger have very few romantic notions. When they stand in long lines at crowded airports and train stations and at embarkation points for several days on end, they worry that after this life-line (the Yangtze River) is cut in half, the already seriously overtaxed transportation system will be even worse. However, it is said that the Three Gorges project will improve navigation, thereby allowing 10,000-tonne ocean-going vessels to reach Chongqing directly.

*Li Rui:* The Ministry of Communication is responsible for navigation. But I have yet to hear them suggest that the Three Gorges project will improve navigation. In fact, the Gezhouba dam has caused troubles for navigation. You misused a key term in your previous question. It is "10,000-tonne ships" not "10,000-tonne ocean-going vessels." The latter term was used by Lin Yishan in his report to Mao at the 1958 Nanning Conference. The term was changed when it was discovered that ocean-going vessels could not clear the bridges at Wuhan and Nanjing.

I don't think raising the water level with reservoirs is the only way to improve navigation. Waterway dredging has proved more effective, and thus, has been favored worldwide. For example, before the Mississippi River was dredged, the shallowest part was a mere 1.37 meters deep while that in the middle reaches of the Yangtze River is 1.8 meters. After dredging, the shallowest part of the Mississippi is now 3.63 meters, enabling fleets of 50,000-60,000 tonnes to navigate all year round.

*Dai Qing:* Here is a point that I don't understand. For the sake of navigation, the Three Gorges reservoir needs to keep a high water level with a minimum depth of four meters in the section between Yichang and Chongqing. But in order to control floods and sedimentation, the water level must be lowered in the high-water season. So, should the water level be raised or lowered?

*Li Rui:* Well, that is exactly the dilemma this supposedly faultless project faces. One possibility exists for solving it. That is to keep a high water level for half of the year and to lower it to its natural level for the other half, which would keep the waterway safely open. However, when the high water level is maintained, many technical problems remain unresolved. As suggested in the leading group's assessment, the shiplocks and the shiplift required will both exceed international standards. If any of the locks breaks down, navigation will have to be stopped in at least one direction. In the assessment report, the carrying capacity of the shiplift is estimated at 11,500 tonnes, and the highest elevation at 118 meters, both of which surpass world standards, and are far above the domestic record. (One in Belgium has a carrying capacity of 8,800 tonnes with an elevation of 23 meters; and the one at Danjiangkou carries 450 tonnes up 50 meters). Theoretically, one would like to believe that all of these difficulties can be overcome. But as for the actual problems, one cannot be too careful. Haven't we had enough lessons in this respect?

*Dai Qing:* Sure. A recent lesson is the Gezhouba dam. There has been much praise for the dam. But we should not forget that, in order to coincide with the birthday of Chairman Mao Zedong,[11] the Gezhouba dam was started in such a hurry that the whole project had to be stopped and redesigned. Apparently many people have forgotten this lesson. The *Xinhua* news agency has stated:

> After completing the Gezhouba dam project, our domestic teams in charge of investigation, design, equipment and manufacturing, and construction and installation are now capable of carrying out the important task of development projects on any river in the country

*Li Rui:* High-sounding words like these have been common in the past 30 years. At the opening ceremony for the Gezhouba dam, Chairman Mao sent the following instructions: "I approve the construction of the Gezhouba dam. Designing the project is one thing. Unexpected problems and difficulties that might arise are another. Therefore, we must be ready to modify the design of the project." These instructions, I am afraid, are not scientific in

---

[11] An aspect of the Mao cult, which Li Rui and others in post-1978 China believed led to highly distorted and grandiose projects during Mao's lifetime.

that they violated the normal working procedures of a construction project.

Certainly, we see that the Gezhouba dam has made some technical achievements, which, however, should not be over-estimated and used in the hope of facilitating the immediate launching of the Three Gorges project. The Gezhouba dam is just 47 meters high while the Three Gorges dam will be at least 150 meters in height, and some plans even foresee a height of 235 meters. Therefore, the Three Gorges project will be more complicated than the Gezhouba dam, which has already proved to be no easy job.

The budget for the Gezhouba dam, when approved by Chairman Mao in 1970, was Y1.35 billion, and it reached Y4.8 billion in real terms; the planned construction period was five years, and turned out to be 18 years. At one session of the Chinese People's Political Consultative Conference (CPPCC), Qian Jiaju pointed out that the Gezhouba dam construction was a typical case of a "long-and-dragged-out project." That accusation was denied by those who denounced Qian's remarks as being irresponsible, arguing that what had happened during the Cultural Revolution should not count. Yet, there are cases of smaller power stations, such as Fentan and Wujiangdu, which were built in 1970 during the Cultural Revolution, whose budget and construction schedule were all kept as planned.

Here I have to add that the quality of the Gezhouba dam is far from satisfactory. Because of navigation requirements, the Gezhouba dam cannot adequately regulate the water peak and, as a result, the power generated is erratic—more when there's more water, less when there's less water. During construction, navigation was stopped for seven months. After its completion, the follow-up work, including the testing of the locks and sediment removal, also caused frequent halts to navigation. The activities interrupted navigation in the area of Chongqing, Peiling, and Wanxian county, the economic loss reaching Y30 million.

Since the Three Gorges project will be much more extensive, involving flood control, power generation and navigation, problems of sedimentation, population relocation, and environmental damage will arise. Therefore, it is very important to tell the truth to the departments concerned, to the Party Central Committee and to the mass media. Decision makers and policy consultants should call a spade a spade.

*Dai Qing:* The sedimentation of reservoirs is a worldwide problem. In terms of silt content, China's rivers are rated among the highest in the world. In seven years, sediment deposited in the Gezhouba dam has swallowed up 44 percent of its storage capacity. For the dams of the Yanguo and Qingtong gorges, the situation is more serious. But the assessment of the project has stated that the sediment problems can be handled by such methods as "storing the clean water and flushing out the muddy." Isn't it over optimistic to say that the sedimentation problem can be solved?

*Li Rui:* It is true that the annual volume of sediment in the Yangtze River ranks fourth highest among the world's rivers. The method of "storing clean water and flushing out the muddy" was first adopted after the reconstruction of the Sanmenxia Gorge dam on the Yellow River, which involved lowering the water level and clearing away the muddy sediment in the reservoir during the flood season and then raising the water level again during the low-water season by storing up the clean water. But in fact, this method will not be practical for the Three Gorges reservoir, which will be over 600 kilometers in length, and the sediment deposited at the backwater reach of the reservoir will not be effectively scoured. What's more, this particular method is totally contrary to the reservoir's flood-control function, that is, to store flood waters during the high-water season.

Anyway, we should not forget the lesson of the Sanmenxia Gorge dam, which had to be reconstructed because of a serious sedimentation problem. As a result of the reconstruction (which lowered the reservoir's water level), a hydro-electric power station of 1.2 million kW has now turned into a run-of-the-river power station of only 250,000 kW. If this happened to the Three Gorges reservoir, which is supposed to be 15 times larger than the Sanmenxia Gorge reservoir, the economic losses would be very serious!

*Dai Qing:* Just now, you mentioned that the important lesson we should draw from the Sanmenxia Gorge dam is that people did not have adequate knowledge about sedimentation patterns.

*Li Rui:* Right. If we look back on history, we will see that it is not a technical issue. When the Sanmenxia Gorge dam was constructed, the Soviet experts made it clear that they had no

128

experience in this respect. But based on the data provided by the Chinese, they predicted the life expectancy of the reservoir would not exceed 50 years, due to sedimentation. Unfortunately, we didn't take them seriously. Hotheaded and overoptimistic, we believed that the "mass campaign" of soil and water conservation—"the sage has emerged and the Yellow River is cleansed"—carried out in the upper reaches would surely "turn the Yellow River into a clean stream." This kind of unrealistic and unscientific attitude still dominates some of our people's thinking. As far as I'm concerned, the severity of the sedimentation problem is still unknown today. I do not trust the tests (either complete or still in progress) physically modeling sedimentation build-up I don't think it's reliable to extrapolate from a small-scale model to a large-scale project. Regarding the mathematical calculations used in the simulation, the disparity that results from averaging and relying on probabilities in examining complicated phenomena is much greater than is realized. In dealing with the sedimentation problem of the proposed Three Gorges dam we must be very cautious and clear-headed.

*Dai Qing:* Recently Li Boning made a speech to the CPPCC suggesting a new program of population relocation for development, which has been supported by the leading group's assessment. It now seems that this problem can perhaps be resolved. What do you have to say about that?

*Li Rui:* In that speech, Li Boning mentioned that if the scheme for a 175-meter water level for normal storage is implemented, there will be an additional 300,000 people to relocate. According to his calculations, if the compensation payments are distributed as early as possible to encourage people to plant orange groves, Y1 billion will be saved, which means the cost will be only Y400 to Y600 million, instead of Y1.6 billion as originally budgeted.

Well, I'm afraid this whole idea is very unrealistic. Based on the census by resettlement experts, the total population relocation will reach 1.13 million with a cost of no less than Y1.1 billion by the year 2008, when the Three Gorges project is expected to be completed. Afterwards, with the water level in the reservoir raised due to sedimentation, more people will have to be moved. It is estimated that 20 years after the completion of the reservoir, another 300,000 will have to be resettled, which will bring the total number up over 1.4 million.

In the assessment, it is suggested that around the hilly areas of the reservoir some 13 cities and 657 factories can be resettled, the land can be cultivated and orange groves can be developed. But this is already an overpopulated area where food is insufficient and the land depleted. To resettle a population as large as that of a small European country will certainly exceed the local environmental capacity of this mountainous region.

*Dai Qing:* According to Li Boning's speech, a four-year pilot project of population relocation for development has been completed and has been welcomed by the people around the reservoir area and supported by the local government as well.

*Li Rui:* Wherever there is resettlement due to reservoir construction there has always been enormous difficulties. It is surprising to see that the local population in the Three Gorges area is so willing to cooperate. Of course, there is a reason for all this. Due to the long delay in the final decision on the project, all of the development plans for the area are almost at a standstill, just as was the case in the 1950s with residents in Fujian in the areas of coastal defense. Today, the assessment has promised them Y11 billion in compensation, which is one-third of the total project budget. It appears as if each person would get Y10,000,[12] with the money to be paid in advance. This sounds attractive to the local people. However, it may be a case of government officials engaging in wishful thinking.

Population relocation has always proved very difficult, no matter what the scale of reservoir construction. In 1979, when I resumed my job in the Ministry of Water Resources and Electric Power, the first task was to relocate 20,000 people from the Xin'an River reservoir construction area. I should say that I have quite a lot of experience in this field.

It is said that around the time of the Cultural Revolution, among those who presented petitions to the government, the majority were cases involving resettlement problems due to reservoir construction. Among them there were several tragic incidents, such as the murder of the person in charge of relocation

---

[12] Approximately US$1,800.

by furious petitioners. China has never before attempted to resettle more than 300,000 people.

Most efforts at resettlement occurred during the 1950s, when the Party and government enjoyed greater popularity, the people followed Chairman Mao's every word and "charged forward" in accord with his commands, cadre work style was much better, and the farmers were easily persuaded. In addition, a commercial economy and inflation were virtually unknown.[13] But even then, there were problems.

It is by no means an easy job to resettle one million people in narrow mountain valleys. Qian Zhengying, the minister of water resources and electrical power, once said: "Population relocation is a key problem of both economic and political importance." Why not let the local people stay and encourage them to develop the local economy?

*Dai Qing:* In fact, population relocation is far more than a political and economic problem. It is directly related to environmental and social issues. Unlike previous reports, the recent assessment has paid considerable attention to this aspect. Apparently, great progress has been made in standards compared with when the Sanmenxia Gorge dam was built.

*Li Rui:* Attention is only the prerequisite to a good decision and they are by no means the same thing. Of course, the Yangtze Valley Planning Office has conducted a large number of investigations and calculations on environmental issues. I would like to emphasize that one should not overlook the problems of sedimentation, soil erosion, induced earthquakes and landslides, as well as resettlement. I agree with Ma Shijun, an environmental expert, who said that the Three Gorges project will do more harm than good to the environment. I also support Hou Xueyu, an ecologist, who warned that in the Three Gorges area, which constitutes one of the unique subtropical climates in China, large tracts of fertile arable land and unique tourist areas will be destroyed by the construction of the reservoir. Even with today's modern equipment, it is still difficult to predict what environmental chain reactions could be triggered by the construction of the reservoir.

---

[13] As a result, compensation payments did not lose their value.

Therefore, it is unconscionable for people to assert that the project will have little or no impact on the environment.

*Dai Qing:* But why do some people still insist on this project, since it will bring so many disasters, rather than benefits?

*Li Rui:* This is exactly what has puzzled me, too, for the past 30 years. Here I can state again that my point of view is the opposite of the leading group's assessment. I suggest canceling the whole project, or at least putting it off till a later date. If I once agreed to the plan for a relatively low 150-meter dam, it was because I had heard that it was approved by the Central Committee of the Party and I found it difficult to take an opposition stand.[14] But I have to admit that my agreement was merely a trick to gain time. I knew then that this low dam would need another dam on the upper reaches, which was a whole new idea. It meant that time for the upper reaches was needed; as a result, the start of the project had to be delayed.

I would like to say a few words about decision-making procedures. For many years, we have been accustomed to the concept of rule by one man whether in politics, economics, science and technology, or culture.[15] In other words, everything is controlled by one person who has unrestricted power, whether it is starting the Cultural Revolution or the construction of the Gezhouba dam. Those who favor certain projects exploit this patriarchal system by "contacting the very top" to gain approval rather than relying on facts. But as far as I know, Chairman Mao and Premier Zhou Enlai never agreed to the launching of the Three Gorges project. On December 26, 1970, (Mao's birthday), after hearing a report on the project, Premier Zhou said to Lin Yishan: "The Three Gorges project you are talking about is not our generation's business. Leave this project to our children in the 21st century."

Even though Chairman Mao showed great interest in the project by composing a poem that contained the line "Build a

---

[14] A political situation once exploited by Mao Zedong but no longer the case with less obedient Chinese officials.

[15] This has been a major complaint of political reformers in China from the Mao era onward, but the system has been preserved by Deng Xiaoping and other hard-liners.

Stone Wall in the River," he was still prepared to listen to different views. At the January, 1958, meeting in Nanning, where Mao strongly opposed the "anti-rash advance"[16] policy and where he proposed the Great Leap Forward, he supported my view and criticized Lin Yishan's unrealistic plan. (The farce is that someone twisted that fact in the archives, in which it is recorded that Chairman Mao adopted Lin's plan.) Two months later, the Politburo held a session in Chengdu, which was supposedly a meeting to inaugurate the "Great Leap Forward." But the document on the Three Gorges project and Yangtze River development was the only one approved by the meeting, which was in fact not in accordance with the "spirit of the Great Leap Forward." The writing of the document was presided over by Premier Zhou (I participated in the writing), and later modified by Chairman Mao. Even in those days the Three Gorges project was still regarded as an important program which needed a great deal of consideration.[17]

*Dai Qing:* Although the document approved the construction, it gave a timetable of 15 to 20 years before the preparations for construction were to be completed.

*Li Rui:* That's right, yet it didn't mean counting from the year 1958, but from the time of the project's survey and design. As you mentioned at the beginning of our interview, it is now already the sixth time since 1957 that the Three Gorges project has been given priority on our national economic agenda. Each time, when the national economic situation appears stable, support for the project reaches a climax. Today, the Central Committee has just put forward a plan to improve the economic order in order to further deepen the reform.

The next two years will be critical for the national economy, which could either slip into chaos or move onto a broader road towards prosperity. Under these circumstances, the proposal to

---

[16] A reference to Mao Zedong's sudden shift in favor of advancing toward collective agriculture, a policy previously criticized as a "rash advance."
[17] In other words, Li Rui is noting that at a time when the most grandiose Communist programs were inaugurated, such as backyard steel furnaces, the leadership was aware of the difficulties and obstacles of the Three Gorges project.

start such a huge project in 1989 is very inadvisable. Even in 1992, it will all depend on the situation then. Personally, I think it better, over the next 10 years, to give priority to existing projects and to start a new series of power stations on the tributaries so that the acute energy shortage can be relieved by the end of the century.

I agree with Zhou Peiyuan's letter of November 9, 1988, to the Party Central Committee that the Three Gorges project be postponed until the national economic goal is achieved. At that time there will be greater economic and technological resources to support it. The Central Committee should decide as soon as possible to delay the project so as to assure the local people that they can start their own development programs and revitalize their economy, which has been delayed for more than 30 years.

I also fully agree with the article "Views and Suggestions on the Assessment Report of the Three Gorges project"[18] by Sun Yueqi, Lin Hua, Wang Xingrang and seven other members of the CPPCC where the authors suggest:

1.   It is advisable to delay construction of the project.
2.   The huge amount of money required for the project far exceeds the capacity of our national economy.
3.   Some intractable problems remain unsolved. They include sedimentation, population relocation, navigation, environmental damage, the risk of earthquakes and landslides, and threats to national defense.
4.   Development projects for the Yangtze River should be implemented on the tributaries first.
5.   Work on dike reinforcement, flood-diversion networks and water and soil conservation should be strengthened.

In order to meet the urgent demands for energy resources, construction of the power plants on the tributaries should be sped up: for example, hydro-electric power plants should be built in the southwest, thermal plants should be built in eastern China and a combination of these two in central China.

---

[18] See Chapter 5.

Further assessments should be presided over by government agencies, such as the State Planning Commission, the State Science and Technology Commission or the China International Engineering Consulting Corporation. More specialists should be invited to participate, since, until now, the assessment group has been composed only of people from the Ministry of Water Resources and Electric Power, who are all on the same side favoring an immediate start of the project.

*Dai Qing:* A project that has undergone assessment for 30 years is still undecided. This is quite a rare situation. What lessons can we draw from it?

*Li Rui:* If we put aside questions of fame and grandiosity, it is understandable to see people in charge of hydro-electric construction so eager to control floods and harness troublesome rivers. But one should always be realistic and act according to the laws of nature. It is true that the Three Gorges project has been through so much assessment over the past 30 years that it is difficult to reach a decision. The reason is that some of the people responsible for the project have been greatly influenced by rash emotions of a "leftist" nature. Instead of following democratic and scientific methods, they relied on directly contacting the very top, administrative means, and "the arbitrary will of officials."

*Dai Qing:* Yes, you actually stressed this point some 30 years ago when you emphasized that only by overcoming subjectivism can the Yangtze River plan be carried out well.

*Li Rui:* I continue to stress this point today. I believe in a philosophy that perceives the world objectively and realistically and from all possible angles. One should consider not only the technical problems of the project but also the whole issue of national economic development; one should not just plan for a huge 235-meter dam, but, instead, work out more accessible options; one should take into account not only the mainstream of the river but also the tributaries; one should realize that reservoir construction is not the only solution to flood control.

Developing the Yangtze River requires a comprehensive, overall program, of which flood control is just one part. In planning for the future, one should take into consideration present and future advantages and disadvantages.

*Dai Qing:* This reminds me of what Wan Li[19] said in 1985, at a meeting on soft sciences. He said, when making decisions, some leaders have a tendency to rely on the assessment provided by the project research office as the only theoretical basis for policy. Because researchers may not be able to act independently, and may produce a biased assessment, this can be both deceiving and dangerous and is worse than no assessment at all. Soft science research work should be done by independent institutes free from the direct influence of decision makers, and can only be verified by practice, the judgment of the people, and history.

*Li Rui:* Unfortunately, the people in charge of the Three Gorges project do not listen to such advice and they still stick to their "leftist" ideas, singing the same subjective tune over the years. Another lesson is that due to the practice of relying on the leader's personal experience and will in decision making, we have yet to establish a complete scientific and democratic decision-making process. Progress has been made in this respect over the past 10 years despite the fact that the project has been dominated by one school of thought and "self-assessment."

There are, however, some encouraging signs of improvement, such as when different views can be seen in the newspapers and many more scientists and specialists have the courage to voice their different opinions.[20] But we are still in a transitional period between "rule of men" and "rule by law."

*Dai Qing:* To many of our readers, you are not only known as a Party official and an organizer of hydro-electric development, but also as a poet and essayist. Although you have already left your post in the hydro-electric department, you still show a great deal of concern over the Three Gorges project.

*Li Rui:* The Three Gorges project is such an important issue, how can I remain silent? I will conclude with what Premier Zhou once said: "Leave this project to our children in the 21st century."

---

[19] A senior leader on economic and financial affairs.

[20] This greater openness of the press on controversial issues such as the Three Gorges in the mid-to-late 1980s, as supported by then General Secretary Zhao Ziyang, has all but disappeared since the 1989 Tiananmen Square massacre, which led to the purge of many officials opposed to the Three Gorges project.

# CHAPTER TWELVE

## WE ARE VERY WORRIED, WE ARE VERY CONCERNED[1]
### A Conversation on the Three Gorges Project Among Zhou Peiyuan, and Lin Hua[2]
by
Qian Gang[3]

*I. If decision makers are exposed only to positive arguments for the project, how can they make sound decisions? We have suffered greatly because of this one-sided approach. It should not be allowed to continue any longer.*

*Lin Hua:* Less than 5 percent of the water resources in the Yangtze River have been developed. Some blame this situation on the endless arguing over the Three Gorges project. Who is to blame? Those who support the project have submitted some misleading information to elicit the backing of the leadership.

*Zhou Peiyuan:* Those people are dishonest and show little respect for the scientific method and for factual evidence. Let's take the project's budget, for example. They told the public that the estimated cost of the project would be Y30 billion, but amongst themselves it was known that Y36.1 billion would be needed. The missing Y6.1 billion in the publicized figure is not due to careless calculations but to careful pruning of the figure so as to rush the start of the project. The project's costs will then be

---

[1] This discussion took place in 1989, and was part of the Chinese edition of *Yangtze! Yangtze!*

[2] Lin Hua is a member of the Economic Committee of the Chinese People's Political Consultative Conference and former vice-chairman of the State Planning Commission.

[3] Qian Gang, a journalist and writer, is editor-in-chief of *Life (Shenghuo)* magazine.

increased later on some other grounds, which they will argue is beyond the scope of their responsibility. (The Gezhouba dam construction is a case in point.)

How can we not be worried when the Three Gorges project is in the hands of people who show so little respect for the truth?

Once I was on a boat going through the Gezhouba dam. Accompanied by a person who worked at the dam, I asked how long it took to go through the shiplocks. "Forty-five minutes," he replied. Later, I went into the pilot's cabin, and was told by the captain that it should actually take four hours because the locks do not normally open until there are several ships waiting to pass. Of course, our boat was allowed to go through immediately, as we were members of Chinese People's Political Consultative Conference (CPPCC). So, you see, there is quite a difference between the reality of the situation and what is said.

*Lei Shuxuan:* (vice-counselor of the Research Institute of Energy Resources, who also happened to be present, interjected.) Please allow me to cite another example. We all know that one of the problems of the Three Gorges project is population relocation. But the Yangtze Valley Planning Office (YVPO) knows how to avoid the problem when it comes to reporting to the Party Central Committee. Since a dam of 170 to 180 meters would lead to the resettlement of about 700,000 to 800,000 people, it lowered the height, so that only 200,000 to 300,000 people would be involved in the relocation as the YVPO reported it. But, if the dam were lowered, the storage capacity would be decreased by tens of billions of cubic meters. How, then, could this dam fulfill its flood-control function?

So somebody came up with the terrible idea of building the dam 175 meters high, while keeping the normal pool level at 150 meters, thereby leaving 25 meters of the storage capacity unused during non-flood seasons. But if floods come, the remaining storage capacity would be filled up, otherwise the lower reaches would be affected by the flood waters. Yet, if the 25-meter capacity is filled up, several hundred thousand people would be submerged in the upper reaches. But the authorities in Peiling and Wanxian counties won't agree to such an idea. They cannot let the people of their counties suffer because of administrative convenience. This is how the YVPO cheats the Central Committee on the one hand, and on the other, makes promises to the people concerned: If you want to have a comfortable life, then you must move and resettle as soon as possible; and once you move out, you will receive good compensation for it. All the old houses along the river will be demolished, and very soon you will see high-rises and modern roads winding up the hills.

*Lin Hua:* When I asked officials at Wanxian county and Peiling, they all urged an early start of the project. They asked for their compensation first before the land is submerged, so they could improve their life with state funds. How can the state afford to offer such a huge amount of money?

In 1985, Li Boning, former director of the Preparation Group for the Three Gorges Province,[4] lectured me for three hours on the subject of population relocation for development. I told him afterwards that I didn't understand what he meant by the term, and asked for more details. He went on talking about "less investment" and "faster profits." I still pressed for more details. He argued that relocation could provide economic opportunities: "Take Peiling for example. There are natural gas resource deposits there, where we can set up a synthetic ammonia factory with a production capacity of 300,000 tonnes, and in Wanxian county, there are salt resources, where an alkaline factory can be built...." Frustrated, I just said "OK," and clammed up.

Afterwards, at a meeting of the assessment group, I told Li:

Since I have been involved in the chemical industry for most of my life, I understand your plans in this respect very well. These two plants will cost about Y1 billion, but can only employ at most 6,000 workers. Some may say that since I work with chemicals, I am not familiar with hydro-electricity; but, as I have some knowledge of industry, I am quite sure that it costs more to equip a factory worker than a farmer. So I am not yet convinced that it is more economical to carry out a program of population relocation for development, as you claimed.

---

[4] This involved a 1986 proposal to carve out an entire new province in the Three Gorges area that Li Boning had hoped to head. It is no longer seriously under consideration.

According to Li's plan, there are two approaches to population relocation for development. One is to transform farm land into groves, which in itself is no easy task. Experts have indicated that the orange trees will not survive at more than 400 meters above sea level. The other way is to develop industry, which, as I have already noted, will not solve the problems of resettling hundreds of thousands of people.

In order to convince Zhang Wei, vice-chairman of the State Association of Sciences and Technology,[5] to speak in favor of the project, dam proponents set up a slide show on a boat, to show the results of experiments in transplanting orange trees from the future submerged area. The slides showed trees bearing beautiful fruit. As far as I know this experiment had only been carried out for about a year. From my visiting the Orange Research Institute in Chongqing, I learned it takes three to four years for an orange tree to bear fruit. So I ask, how could the pictures shown on the slides possibly have been taken of the particular groves involved in the experiment? Chinese people have suffered a great deal from such falsehoods, like Dazhai,[6] for example. Why should we continue to repeat this time and again?

*Zhou Peiyuan:* It's not uncommon to see things of this kind in the YVPO. Regarding sedimentation, the office submitted a report to the CPPCC inspection groups for Hubei and Sichuan in September of last year. The report noted that, according to a discussion chaired by Yan Kai, president of the board of China's Water Resources Association, and Zhang Wei, experts believed the sediment load in the Yangtze River showed no signs of increasing. I know Comrade Zhang Wei is not an expert on this particular subject, and when I asked him if he had participated in the meeting with Yan Kai, he answered "no." He said that, although he had been invited by the leaders of the Ministry of Water Resources and Electric Power, he was not in Beijing at that time

---

[5] A non-governmental organization, not part of the state structure.
[6] A reference to a "model" agricultural brigade promoted during the Cultural Revolution which, contrary to its propagated ideal of self-reliance, had actually received considerable economic inputs from the state sector. Chinese, and many visiting Westerners, were successfully hoodwinked by this Maoist propaganda for years.

and was therefore unable to take part in the meeting. People ignored this fact and still put his name on the report, which was issued to the members of the CPPCC.

*Lin Hua:* Dam proponents argue that the Gezhouba dam provides two power transmission lines, one to Shanghai, and the other to Wanxian county. This is sheer propaganda! All the state funds have been wasted. A transmission line of 500,000 volts from the Gezhouba dam to Shanghai was completed last year, at a cost Y1.1 billion, only to discover that there is no electricity to transmit! Because the installed capacity of the dam is only 2,715 MW, and because Hubei province is demanding the power, Gezhouba can only guarantee one-quarter of what Shanghai needs. The governor of Hubei province has said that the transmission of electricity to Hubei would have to be stopped if the power were sent to Shanghai. As for the transmission line to Wanxian county, its construction has been canceled altogether, because of insufficient electrical output.

It is incorrect to say that the Three Gorges project can transmit power to east China. Its installed capacity is 17,680 MW, of which more than 4,000 MW are guaranteed. By the year 2000, electricity consumption in central China alone will reach 200 to 250 TWh[7] with a total load of 35,000 MW, which means that the total output will be used up there. How could it have power to transmit to Shanghai? In the assessment, taking an extra Y0.02 per kWh from the east China area to add to the budget for the Three Gorges project was suggested. But the people from the YVPO are well aware they will not be able to pay back the debt. Nevertheless, they keep telling lies for the sake of propaganda.

Another falsehood concerns the advantage of "channeling water from the south to the north." Many people have been enthusiastic about the idea. But when asked, at a meeting chaired by Luo Xibei, just what those advantages were, the same people couldn't give a definite reply and finally had to admit there were no advantages at all. If this plan of channeling water from the south to the north were implemented, the dam would have to be higher than 200 meters, which was, in fact, a proposal put forward in the 1950s. In the later schemes, the height of the dam has been

---

[7] 1 terawatt hour (TWh) = $10^9$ kilowatt hours.

reduced to 160 and 175 meters, which has effectively destroyed any plans to transfer the water from the south to the north. Yet, they still keep talking about it as if it were possible.

In 1985, when we visited the Three Gorges on an inspection tour, Li Boning told us that:

> The Jingjiang River dikes are so old and dilapidated, that without the Three Gorges dam there would be tremendous losses should floods come. The economic losses from these disasters would easily cover the cost of the Three Gorges project.

But on the way from Yichang to Wuhan, by bus, we paid a special visit to the "dangerously dilapidated" Jingjiang River dikes. To our surprise, even though it was the flood season, the dikes were holding without any additional activity to shore them up. A deputy official with a hydrology background told us that he had been working on the dikes for 20 years, and they were certainly not in a "dilapidated state." Here we see another example of how people have distorted the truth by exaggerating the seriousness of the floods along the Yangtze in order to get the project approved.

One of the major reasons for our failures in national economic construction since 1949 has been an unhealthy lack of respect for the truth. We often say that it was Chairman Mao who was responsible for the "Great Leap Forward." Yet, to be frank, those who provided Chairman Mao with false information were also responsible. Today, some claim that Deng Xiaoping also supports the Three Gorges project; but how can these leaders make good and sound judgments when they are provided with one-sided information? For these reasons, we old hands from the CPPCC are responsible for speaking the truth and presenting different perspectives on this matter.

*II. There should be a general strategy for the development of the Yangtze River basin. We suggest that the priorities be given to work on the tributaries. That is, "the tributaries first and the mainstream of the river second."*

*Zhou Peiyuan:* In November of last year, I presented a report to the leaders concerning my views about the project. Zhao Ziyang then gave the following instructions:

> Inform Old Zhou[8] that all of the issues raised in the report should be given serious consideration, and an adequate assessment must be made before any decision can be made on the basis of possibilities and necessities.

These instructions beg two important questions: What is the meaning of "possibilities," and what is meant by "necessities?"

For the YVPO, the major issue concerning the project has not been whether it should be built, but how to start it.

Before the Central Committee's final decision, several opinions should be presented for comparison. It is impossible to come to a decision with only one option, that of launching the project.

The Jiu San Society[9] and the provinces of Yunnan, Sichuan, Guizhou and Guangxi recently adopted the principle of "the tributaries first and the mainstream of the river second" for the development of the Yangtze River. This leads to the question of whether it is necessary to construct the Three Gorges project at all. If the tributaries at the upper reaches were developed in ways that dealt with the problems of power generation, flood control and sedimentation, what is the point of the Three Gorges project?

When people from the YVPO said they had attached great importance to the development of the upper reaches, I replied they had done a lot in this respect but had not given priority to it.

*Lin Hua:* It is, in any case, preferable to develop the tributaries in the upper reaches, whether for the sake of flood control or power generation, rather than the mainstream of the Yangtze.

---

[8] A term of endearment.

[9] One of eight lawful democratic parties under the Chinese constitution, composed primarily of Chinese scientists and academics. The Society was outspoken in its criticism of the Three Gorges project in March, 1992, when member Chen Mingshao noted publicly, "There are very many scientific and technical problems that remain unresolved and require further study before the project can go ahead." See Barber and Ryder, eds., *Damming*, p. 18.

Since 1984, we have conducted nine inspection tours along the Yangtze, including investigations of the tributaries. In the past two years, we have investigated the Wujiang River Valley in Guizhou province and the middle and lower reaches of the Lancang River in Yunnan; and this year we will investigate the Yalong, Dadu, Jinsha and Minjiang rivers, all in west Sichuan. Among those rivers, the Wujiang and Lancang have a hydro-electric potential of 34 million kW, making conditions for future power stations along these tributaries much better than those of the Three Gorges reservoir. The Three Gorges project is not the only solution to the hydro-electric power shortage in China. Many other locations have more advantages.

From our past inspection tours, we know that all the tributary provinces have shown great enthusiasm for tributary development, as well as a willingness to contribute their own local budgets to construction. Although very poor, Yunnan province has laid aside Y300 million for the tributary project, and Guizhou province has provided funds for the initial stage of the program. These development projects, which are separate from the Three Gorges, must wait for central government financing. Once profits are connected with local interests, enthusiastic cooperation will be ensured. Furthermore, the development of the water resources of any river by stages reduces the funds needed by 20 to 30 percent. Once the upper reaches are brought under control, then it will be easier to work on the lower reaches.

*Lei Shuxuan:* The reason the Gezhouba dam was so costly was that it had been planned to shift the construction machinery to the Three Gorges project after it was completed. So, among the Y4.8 billion invested in the Gezhouba dam, Y800 million was spent for construction machinery, including huge trucks and dredgers useful only in the Yangtze River. Since this equipment was imported, 20 years have elapsed, and there is still no sign of the Three Gorges dam. Some Y200 million has been depreciated from the equipment, and the remaining investment of Y600 million has gone to waste. What an enormous loss!

*Lin Hua:* All in all, the development of the upper reaches can enhance the tapping of more natural resources and promote both industry and agriculture, making rapid progress possible for the minorities in those areas and improving the environment at the upper reaches.

*III. It is not appropriate to let the ministry in charge conduct the assessment of the project instead of the state. The "debate on the Three Gorges project" reflects the essence of the problem: whether or not we respect the demands of the sciences and of democracy.*[10]

*Lin Hua:* In 1985 the Leading Group for the Assessment of the Three Gorges project was set up in cooperation with the State Planning Commission and the State Science and Technology Commission. After June, 1986, however, it was handed over to the Ministry of Water Resources and Electric Power, thereby transferring responsibility for the assessment from the state to a ministry. Many were unhappy with this change. Within the Ministry of Water Resources and Electric Power, some leaders claimed that the project was indispensable, ending all discussions on whether the project was necessary, focussing only on discussions of how to carry out the construction. This is one of the drawbacks of allowing the ministry in charge to undertake the assessment of such an important project. The technological aspects of the project only account for, at most, 30 percent of the whole. Moreover, they must be viewed in the context of the overall situation of our national economy and social environment. Thus, the assessment should be carried out in a comprehensive manner involving all the departments concerned.

*Zhou Peiyuan:* It is inappropriate to change a state assessment into a ministerial assessment, presided over by the leaders of the Ministry of Water Resources and Electric Power. How could different opinions and views from within the ministry be made known to all the others involved?

*Lin Hua:* It seems that it really takes time to realize democracy and show genuine respect for the sciences. The feudalistic influence of thousands of years is definitely deep rooted, making

---

[10] Obviously, the hard-line leadership in China ascendant since 1989 wants to avoid the kind of public outcry and demonstrations that were mobilized in other Socialist countries, as occurred in Hungary against the Nagymaros dam. See Virginia Fairweather, "Hydro on Hold," in *Civil Engineering*, Vol. 59, No. 8 (August 1988), p. 54.

it difficult to implement the values of "science and democracy" as was put forth in the "May Fourth Movement"[11] in 1919.

The controversy over the project is related to our overall system and to the guiding principles of our industrial development for the past several decades. In the past, international pressures made it reasonable for Stalin to put great emphasis on heavy industry. At the beginning of the New China, in the early 1950s, it was also reasonable to carry out 156 large industrial projects and to mobilize the whole nation for the construction of the Anshan Iron and Steel Complex. But things have changed now. It is not always possible for the state to concentrate the efforts of the whole nation on one single job. At the assessment meeting, someone put out a slogan: "Total support for the Three Gorges project." What will the consequences of this be? There are always some people who are unaware of the real economic situation, never considering the financial results, and blindly seeking something grandiose. In the final analysis, this is an old method suited to the old system. I therefore predict that modernization will never become a reality without economic and political reforms.

*Zhou Peiyuan:* The controversy over the Three Gorges project questions whether we want to respect science and democracy. The proposal to develop the tributaries should be adopted as soon as possible. We can no longer delay the decision on the project. The present hesitation will only bring greater economic losses to the populations of Wanxian and Peiling counties, in which there are 14 million people, many of them poor and waiting for relocation. The state and the provinces cannot put funds into the tributary projects in these areas because they are projected to be submerged. Moreover, in the upper reaches, there are many electrical power resources, much more than in the Three Gorges

---

[11] On May 4, 1919, thousands of students from Beijing took to the streets protesting the Paris Treaty that the North Warlord government was about to sign. The demonstration was dispersed by force but students in Beijing, Shanghai, Guangzhou and Tianjin started boycotting classes and soon they were joined by manufacturing workers from Shanghai, Nanjing, Tianjin, Hangzhou, Wuhan, Anhui and Shandong who went on strike. This nationalist movement caused the North Warlord government to reject the treaty and release the jailed students.

area. There is no coal in the area of Sichuan province where the energy shortage is very acute. The people in Sichuan truly hope that the Central Committee can quickly make a decision on the Three Gorges issue and authorize development of the upper reaches as soon as possible.

*Lin Hua:* For the past 30 years, over the course of the anti-rightist movement[12] and the Great Leap Forward we have suffered culturally and politically by not speaking the truth. Today, the only way to find a solution to the issue of the Three Gorges project is to enhance political "transparency,"[13] democracy, and respect for the sciences. We have to work hard for the "Spring of Sciences" and struggle for democracy because it will not come automatically.

---

[12] A brutal 1957 attack on Chinese intellectuals that followed their outspoken criticism of the Communist Party, prompted by Mao Zedong's call to "let a hundred schools of thought contend." This persecution effectively silenced intellectuals and scientists for years.

[13] Party General-Secretary Zhao Ziyang's version of a Chinese *Glasnost* that, before the disturbance of 1989, produced greater openness in the Chinese press and decision-making bodies such as the National People's Congress.

# CHAPTER THIRTEEN

## EQUAL TREATMENT FOR DIFFERENT OPINIONS AND PERSPECTIVES
### An Interview with Sun Yueqi[1]
by
Zhang Aiping[2]

*Zhang Aiping:* Old Sun, as a specialist in mining and metallurgy, when did you begin to do research on the Three Gorges project?

*Sun Yueqi:* During the War of Resistance against Japan, I was running four coal mines in Sichuan province and had already received some information about the Three Gorges. As chairman of the Natural Resources Committee, I could not but show my concern for this matter.

*Zhang Aiping:* Is it true that Dr. Sun Yat-sen came up with the idea of building a dam across the Three Gorges 70 years ago?

*Sun Yueqi:* Yes. Sun Yat-sen had suggested a dam across the Three Gorges in his National Development Plan. Later, when I was in charge of the Natural Resources Committee, I invited J. L. Savage, an American dam expert, to come and study the Three Gorges project with us. At that time, the plan was to build the dam in the Nanjinguan pass in Yichang, about one or two kilometers away from the present Gezhouba dam. The Three Gorges project is a project of an unprecedented scale, both economically and technically. I therefore have read much material concerning it and

---

[1] Sun Yueqi is from Shaoxing, Zhejiang province. He has held government positions specializing in the economic and financial sectors. He is now a member of the Standing Committee of the Chinese People's Political Consultative Conference and chairman of the Economic Construction Group of the consultative conference. This interview was included in the original Chinese edition of *Yangtze! Yangtze!*

[2] Zhang Aiping is a journalist with the *Enlightenment Daily*.

have consulted many experts on the subject. You are never too old to learn.

In 1985, together with seven experts from the Chinese People's Political Consultative Conference (CPPCC) and the Three Gorges Project Inspection Group, I took a 38-day trip from the Dujiangyan dam in Sichuan all the way down, to investigate the upper and middle reaches of the Yangtze River. We rode on boats and in buses and visited many places, some of which were very dangerous, in order to conduct surveys, make inquiries, and listen to popular opinion. Although I was 92 then, I did not tire. After our return, I reported to the CPPCC on the results of our investigation and subsequently wrote four proposals.

*Zhang Aiping:* I have read articles by Qian Jiaju and others suggesting that a proposal concerning the Three Gorges project was made under your suggestion at the CPPCC in June, 1988. Did it have any impact? Or was it just "more water over the dam"?

*Sun Yueqi:* I drafted that proposal together with nine other experts.[3] There was considerable publicity about the assessment of the Three Gorges project conducted by the Ministry of Water Resources and Electric Power. But we think the way the assessment was conducted was neither democratic nor scientific. At an enlarged meeting of the Leading Group for the Assessment of the Three Gorges Project, I gave two long speeches on the subject along with other members of the CPPCC. Although many different views were expressed at the meeting, nothing appeared in the summary of the proceedings, except the names of the speakers. Some experts presented different points of view, but none was accepted and the assessment reports on various subjects were adopted by the majority. The structure of meetings only reinforced "the single opinion" of the Ministry of Water Resources and Electric Power. We therefore suggested that since the Three Gorges project would have an important impact on national economic strategy, the assessment should be conducted under the auspices of the State Planning Commission and the State Science and Technology Commission, with the participation of some establishments that are not closely related to the ministry, such as the China International Engineering Projects Consulting Corpora-

---

[3] For this document, see Chapter 5.

tion, the Bank of China, the Construction Bank and individual experts and specialists from many fields. Only by making decisions in a genuinely democratic and scientific manner can we reach a conclusion on the basis of truth and facts. The proposal was handed over but nothing happened, and there was no reply at all. We should let the different ideas and opinions contend.

*Zhang Aiping:* What do you think we should do about the Three Gorges project? (Although Sun Yueqi is nearly 100 years old, he is still high-spirited and clear-minded. Taking out a sheet of white paper, he drew a picture of the water flow of the Yangtze River with a few simple strokes.)

*Sun Yueqi:* I believe that it is not yet time for the construction of the project. Priority should be given to small-scale projects that produce quicker economic results and which can improve flood control, electricity generation, and navigation within this century.

Some people say the major objective of building the Three Gorges reservoir is to control floods. In fact, the reservoir cannot handle this job effectively. Along the Three Gorges there are many valleys, so the dam would have to take the shape of the gorges. Because of problems with population relocation, the level of water storage in the reservoir cannot be very high. According to the present plan for a 150- to 180-meter water level, the storage capacity is not large enough to contain heavy floods. As a result the dam could not play a significant role in reducing the effects of floods on the lower reaches.

Originally, it was envisaged that the Three Gorges dam could take over the flood storage function of Dongting Lake and the Jingjiang River flood-diversion network in the middle reaches, thus transferring flood-control capacity to Sichuan in the upper reaches. I am afraid this plan of sacrificing the upper reaches in order to save the lower and middle reaches is just "shifting one's trouble onto neighbors."

The Yangtze River is more than 6,000 kilometers long, and the lower and middle reaches account for 1,800 kilometers. What about the upper reaches? Are they less important? Because of the project, more flooding disasters would befall Sichuan, where there have already been serious floods, such as the one that occurred in 1981. Regarding the middle and lower reaches, since the flood sources along the Yangtze River are from the Chuanjiang, Hanjiang, and Ganjiang rivers and four rivers in Hunan province, the Three Gorges, limited by geographic conditions, can only control floods from the upper reaches of the Chuanjiang River and would be powerless when confronted with those from other tributaries at the lower and middle reaches.

There are two facts that I think worth mentioning. In 1931 and 1954, heavy floods hit the Wuhan and Nanjing areas, while Sichuan province was unaffected. Conversely, in 1870, Sichuan suffered from the most severe flood since the time of Dayu, 4,000 years ago. The 1981 flood in Sichuan was also severe, but it was clear and calm in Wuhan. For the two flood types that I have mentioned here, we have the data and their study has been scientific, based on real historical practice. Practice is the sole criteria for verifying the truth.[4]

*Zhang Aiping:* What would you suggest to control floods?

*Sun Yueqi:* A comprehensive plan should be developed for all the reaches of the Yangtze River. It is unscientific to assert that "the project is the only one for the development of the Yangtze River." The Three Gorges project will cost hundreds of billions of *yuan*, submerge 350,000 *mu* of arable land and 70,000 *mu* of orange groves, and necessitate the resettlement of one million people. Yet its flood-control ability is very limited. So we say, this is not the best plan. Although some people admit that generating power is the major aim of the project, flood control will be a more acceptable reason to start it, as flooding worries more people.

*Zhang Aiping:* It is said that the generation of electricity is one of the major advantages of the project. I wonder if this has been scientifically proved.

*Sun Yueqi:* According to the plan, the installed capacity of the Three Gorges power stations would be 13 to 17.68 million kW with an annual production of 67.7 to 84 billion kWh, which could satisfy the electric energy needs of central and east China and eastern Sichuan province. The Itaipu power station on the Parana River between Brazil and Paraguay, presently the world's largest hydro-electric power station, has an installed capacity of 12.6

---

[4] A phrase popularized in the late 1970s, as part of China's reform, that was aimed at injecting more scientific and realistic data into government decision making as opposed to the leftist and subjective dogma dominant during the Mao years.

million kW with an annual output of 71 billion kWh. So, the future Three Gorges hydro-electric power station would be the largest in the world. But is it the best choice? We must be realistic and scientific and consider the project in the context of national power development.

I believe there are many other smaller projects that can be more effective and profitable. I suggest that power stations be constructed on the tributaries first, and then on the mainstream, and that both thermal and hydraulic power plants be built according to local conditions. It will take only four to eight years at most to build a number of thermal and water power stations on the tributaries of the upper reaches of the Yangtze River as well as in the areas of central and eastern China. Compared with the Three Gorges project, which needs at least a decade before generating power, these smaller stations can meet the urgent demand for energy in order to fulfill our national economic goal by the end of the century.

What's more, considering that the Three Gorges project is higher and more complicated than the Gezhouba dam, which took 18 years to complete, I think it is unrealistic to claim that 17 years would be enough to build the world's largest dam. Even if the project started now, it would not generate electricity until the beginning of the next century, thus leaving the country unable to meet its immediate energy needs. In addition, it will result in the needless diversion of materials from other projects. This is one of the reasons that it is inadvisable to start the project right now.

*Zhang Aiping:* Another advantage of the project is said to be navigation. What is your view on this?

*Sun Yueqi:* The Yangtze River is the third-largest river in the world, next only to the Nile and the Amazon. It is also the most important river course for navigation, connecting southwest, central and eastern China and serving as the main transportation route for the provinces of Sichuan, Yunnan and Guizhou. If anything happens to this river course, it will affect the economy and future generations. For many years, the upper reaches of the Yangtze have suffered from deforestation and indiscriminate wasteland reclamation, both of which have contributed to serious water and soil erosion and increased sedimentation in the river, making the Yangtze the third most silted river in the world, up from its previous position—fourth. To build a high dam on the

Chuanjiang River would inevitably increase sedimentation in the Three Gorges reservoir area and thus badly affect navigation and reduce the efficiency of power generation.

We can say that the success of the Three Gorges project lies in the resolution of the sedimentation problem. We should draw a lesson from our past experience with the Sanmenxia reservoir on the Yellow River, where unsuccessful attempts to deal with sediment resulted in great losses. To this day, we must admit that there is still no satisfactory solution to the sedimentation problem of the Three Gorges reservoir. Can smooth navigation be guaranteed, even though the office in charge of the project has plans to employ huge shiplocks and a shiplift with an 11,500-tonne capacity and a 100-meter height? These standards are already beyond international levels.

*Zhang Aiping:* You have mentioned the problem of population resettlement. In such an overpopulated country, this will indeed be a problem

*Sun Yueqi:* Yes. Because of this project, 13 towns and cities will be submerged and over one million people will need to be resettled. Where will they go? The answer from the office in charge is to move back from the river. Well, we made exploratory trips to the target areas, which are all hilly, steep, rocky and barren. It will be very difficult to resettle a large population in such an environment. It is terribly irresponsible to start this project without a proper solution to these serious problems.

*Zhang Aiping:* Considering the overall economic situation, what do you think the principal strategies should be?

*Sun Yueqi:* I would say that one should be truthful, honest and realistic: one should act according to the actual circumstances and deal first of all with easy projects and then gradually proceed to the difficult and extensive ones. There should be a comprehensive plan for overall development; work should proceed step by step. I believe the budget for the projects should be within our national capacity.

When the state is reducing its funds for capital construction, a project as vast as this will surely cause other more urgent projects to be delayed or canceled. If other smaller projects are implemented at the same time as the Three Gorges, it will be extremely difficult for the state to bear the tremendous financial burdens, and

153

consequently, it would set back our national economic development. We have to give earnest consideration to these facts.

The price to be paid for the poor decision making will be extremely dear. Take the Gezhouba dam as an example. The decision to begin this big project was hurried. It was started by the Hubei Revolutionary Committee and the Wuhan Military Region, based on a report of a few pages. In the original plan, the cost was to be Y1.35 billion. It was to take 3½ years to generate electricity and five years to complete. As it turned out, the funds poured into this project reached Y4.8 billion, the dam took 11 years to generate power and 18 years to complete.

If we once again make a decision in an undemocratic and non-scientific manner, the laws of nature will mercilessly punish us and we will have to pay even more dearly. Unfortunately, the present organization of the assessment of the Three Gorges project is far from democratic and scientific. As I indicated earlier, this must be changed. A reassessment of the project should be conducted by the State Planning Commission and the State Science and Technology Commission.

*Zhang Aiping:* What else would you like to add?

*Sun Yueqi:* Though I am already an old man of 95, I will continue to be a faithful friend of the Communist Party. I sincerely wish all the best for the Party, the country and the generations to come.

# CHAPTER FOURTEEN

## THE BOTTOMLESS PROJECT BUDGET FOR THE
## THREE GORGES DAM
### An Interview with Qiao Peixin[1]
by
Li Shuxi[2]

*Li Shuxi:* When did you begin to take an interest in the Three Gorges project?

*Qiao Peixin:* In 1984, at the sixth session of the Chinese People's Political Consultative Conference (CPPCC), the Economic Construction Group started to study the Three Gorges project. In May, 1985, together with Sun Yueqi and several other CPPCC members, I participated in a field survey of the Three Gorges. The more I came to know about the issue, the more I thought about it. Gradually, I became one of the dissidents on this subject.

*Li Shuxi:* I have read the article titled "The Three Gorges Project: More Losses Than Gains" written by you and eight other CPPCC members. Afterwards, it was learned that some departments involved in the Leading Group for the Assessment of the Three Gorges Project asserted that the project is necessary and that an early start is better than a late one. Could you comment on this in terms of budgetary concerns?

*Qiao Peixin:* The leading group was inclined at the outset to minimize the actual cost. The original calculation for the total

---

[1] Qiao Peixin has held leading posts in the field of finance. In 1981, he retired from the post of vice-director of the Chinese People's Bank. He is now president of the Chinese Banking Association, and a member of the Chinese People's Political Consultative Conference. This interview was included in the original Chinese edition of *Yangtze! Yangtze!*
[2] Li Shuxi, a journalist and writer, is deputy editor-in-chief of *Economics Daily.*

project investment was Y15.9 billion, which has grown to Y36.1 billion today. In fact, there are still considerable costs that have not been taken into account in the budget prepared for the assessment report.

*Li Shuxi:* What major items have not been accounted for?

*Qiao Peixin:* In calculating the total investment required, some items can be estimated, such as the funds needed for basic construction: other figures, however, cannot yet be determined. These unknown costs, which could turn out to be huge, were not included in the budget. Moreover, the assessment did not consider the possible effects of inflation.

*Li Shuxi:* What is the current cost estimate?

*Qiao Peixin:* Based on the Yangtze Valley Planning Office's (YVPO) estimated budget in 1985, the Investment Investigation Department of the Construction Bank made a very careful account: the investment for the construction of the key projects is Y12.4 billion; power transmission projects, Y4.9 billion; resettlement costs, Y11 billion; plus Y2.5 billion for the price increase index. The total amount comes to Y30.8 billion. According to the time limit proposed by the YVPO for the loans and repayment, the aggregated figure for the interest, calculated on an annual rate of 10.8 percent as set by the state, comes to Y45.8 billion, which exceeds the total amount of the investments, the combined sum of the two being Y76.6 billion (i.e., Y30.8 + Y45.8).[3]

*Li Shuxi:.* This is already four times that of the original estimate, isn't it?

*Qiao Peixin:* Much more than that! This calculation was conducted in the way the YVPO wanted. If it had been done according to our[4] method and that of the Construction Bank, the total required investment would have been at least Y30.7 billion. If you add the interest on the loans calculated over a 33-year period to the total amount for the entire project, it comes to Y107.8 billion, which is six times the original estimate!

*Li Shuxi:* How about the hidden costs? How many items of this kind are there?

---

[3] In fact, recent estimates put the cost of the project at Y75 billion. See Appendix E.

[4] The Chinese Banking Association's method of calculation.

*Qiao Peixin:* There are six items that can be foreseen but not clearly calculated at present:

1. The regulation of the water level in the Three Gorges reservoir has to be linked to the navigation requirements. In order to ensure a steady flow of electricity, a thermal power plant of a corresponding scale must be built. Of course, it would not have to be close to the Three Gorges reservoir area, but it would be a supplementary installation related to the Three Gorges reservoir, and its budget would certainly have to be covered by the state.[5]
2. If floods occurred raising the water level to between 150 and 170 meters, 300,000 people would have to be temporarily removed and a number of factories and residential buildings would be submerged. The compensation for all these losses would also be the responsibility of the state.
3. An emergency budget must be set aside in the event of earthquakes.
4. After the construction of the reservoir, sedimentation would form at the upper reaches of the reservoir, while clear water would erode the banks of the river at the lower reaches, thereby changing the course of the river. Funds would be needed to maintain the main channel.
5. Because of the need to import generators, price and possible price changes constitute another unpredictable factor.
6. Since the construction period has been underestimated, the state must set aside extensive additional funds for possible prolongations of the construction time.

In a word, the total budget should include both the fixed and the contingent expenses. If the state cannot afford the expanded budget, project construction should not begin.

*Li Shuxi:* Since the summer of 1988, inflation in China has increased, and people are now complaining that the *Renminbi*[5] is becoming worthless. Will that have any impact on the budget estimates?

---

[5] *Renminbi* is commonly referred to as the people's money. Up until late 1993, it could not be exchanged for foreign currency, and therefore its value on the black market dropped.

*Qiao Peixin:* In the leading group's assessment, the total investment is estimated to be Y36.1 billion, which was calculated on the basis of the price index at the end of 1986. If the project were to be started in 1989, the price increase in 1987-1988 could not be ignored. To do so would violate common sense.

*Li Shuxi:* It is said that the state has given project loans favorable treatment by granting an annual interest rate of 9.36 percent,[6] minus the interest on investments in flood control and navigation projects. Other favorable treatments include the investment of the revenue produced by the Gezhouba dam power plant in the construction of the Three Gorges project. Will these factors in some way reduce the total cost of the project?

*Qiao Peixin:* Let's look at the following table based on the favorable interest rate of 9.36 percent and see how the increase of the price index affects the investment:

| | Price increase index | Interest on the loans | Repayment per kWh (*yuan*) | Duration of the repayment (years) | The total amount of the loans & interest (billion) |
|---|---|---|---|---|---|
| | 0 | 9.36% | 0.10 | 25 | 78.71 |
| | 4% | 9.36% | 0.12 | 32 | 157.46 |
| Budget Y36.1 billion | 6% | 9.36% | 0.17 | 30 | 202.44 |
| | 8% | 9.36% | 0.22 | 28 | 231.39 |
| | 10% | 9.36% | 0.27 | 30 | 320.33 |

*Li Shuxi:* You estimate the highest increase in the price index at 10 percent, which is obviously a conservative estimate.

*Qiao Peixin:* Yes. What I am emphasizing here is that it is impossible to have such a low interest rate. At the moment, the

---

[6] As opposed to the official state-set rate of 10.8 percent.

interest rate for investment in capital construction is 16 percent. Let's look at another table using this interest rate:

| | Price increase index | Interest on the loans | Repay-ment per kWh (*yuan*) | Duration of the repay-ment (years) | The total amount of the loans & interest (billion) |
|---|---|---|---|---|---|
| | 0 | 16% | 0.16 | 38 | 286.1 |
| | 4% | 16% | 0.25 | 31 | 293.9 |
| Budget Y36.1 billion | 6% | 16% | 0.30 | 33 | 396.1 |
| | 8% | 16% | 0.35 | 36 | 567.6 |
| | 10% | 16% | 0.45 | 32 | 584.3 |

*Li Shuxi:* Could you make an estimate based on the present price increase index? As far as I know, according to the State Statistical Bureau, the price increase index in civil construction has reached 18.1 percent in 1988.

*Qiao Peixin:* Given present trends, it seems unlikely that prices will drop. If we have confidence in the efforts of the Central Committee of the Party to redress these economic trends, we might expect the price index for 1989 to be lower than that of 1988. Therefore, in my calculation, the highest price increase would be less than 10 percent. In fact, this is the traditional means of calculation used by the Construction Bank. Whatever the methods used[7] the figure of Y500 billion is an underestimation, which is already 10 times over the Y36.1 billion of the initial estimate of the assessment.

*Li Shuxi:* If people insist on starting the project, what will the economic results be?

---

[7] Either the Chinese Banking Association's or the Construction Bank's method was used.

*Qiao Peixin:* The state's scale of construction must be in keeping with its financial and material capacity, which directly affects economic stability and the balance between expenditures and revenue in the budget and in bank loans. From the present economic and financial situation, starting the project would only worsen inflation.

*Li Shuxi:* Can you give more details of the financial situation?

*Qiao Peixin:* There has been a financial deficit for quite a few years, and banks have issued too many notes, making the financial situation very serious in my opinion. That is why the Central Committee of the Party has taken a series of measures to straighten out the economic situation and curb inflation.[8] Today, the investment for ongoing capital construction has reached Y420 billion, and none of these construction projects can be easily canceled. Under such circumstances, starting the Three Gorges project would only result in the issuing of even more bank notes, thereby encouraging inflation.

*Li Shuxi:* I hear that half of the investment is self-financing.

*Qiao Peixin:* This so-called self-financing refers only to investing the revenues from the Gezhouba dam into the Three Gorges project. Under the present system, no matter what means you may employ, everything comes out of state funds in the end, therefore "self-financing" has no practical significance. I have made some inquiries at the Chinese People's Bank and the Construction Bank. There, I was warned of the gravity of the present inflation rates since neither the state nor the banks have any money. As for accounts protected against inflation, the interest rate has been more than 20 percent, whereas the interest rate on loans is only 16 percent and has to be subsidized by the banks.[9] If the interest rate on loans is kept at the rate of 16 percent, then the banks will suffer more losses. The only solution then will be to print more notes, which inevitably brings about increased prices which affect salaries as well as investment in construction. All of them keep increasing by turns, producing a vicious circle. The financial results would be disastrous.

---

[8] 1993 saw renewed efforts in this direction as China's inflation rate hit 14 percent.

[9] As the banks are state owned, this subsidy is ultimately a state subsidy.

*Li Shuxi:*. Has anything of this nature ever happened elsewhere?

*Qiao Peixin:* Yes, the Brazilian military government started the construction of the Itaipu hydro-electric power station with a budget of US$18 billion. Such a costly project, combined with an acute shortage of funds at home, meant that the Brazilian government had to borrow from abroad. This resulted in a three-digit inflation rate: 110.2 percent in 1980, 223.8 percent in 1984, and 365.95 percent in 1987. Under such circumstances, the government had no choice but to call for a drastic reduction in public expenditures, including the suspension or cancellation of large-scale projects.[10]

*Li Shuxi:* I have interviewed some of the delegates of the National People's Congress and of the CPPCC and listened to some of the debates on the Three Gorges project. One of the arguments was that to put the investment figure so high would only cause chaos regarding the advisability of the Three Gorges project. Would you comment on this?

*Qiao Peixin:* (indignantly) Who is causing chaos? A project costing the state billions of *yuan* over dozens of years before it makes a profit causes chaos. Today, inflation has become so serious that both the people and the state find it hard to tolerate.[11] If this project were approved, it would ruin political stability and the plans for economic reform even before its construction could begin. I remember Premier Zhou Enlai said on November 8, 1972: "Should any trouble occur at the Yangtze River, it will be the trouble of the state and the Party as a whole rather than that of any individual."

*Li Shuxi:* The Three Gorge project has become a focus of attention both at home and abroad. As the debate over this project continues, could you say something about the decision-making

---

[10] Then Party general secretary, Zhao Ziyang, visited Brazil in 1985 where he reportedly carried out extensive discussions on this issue. See Lieberthal and Oksenburg, *Policy Making*, p. 337.

[11] Popular reaction to high levels of inflation in China was, in fact, a major cause of the 1989 pro-democracy movement in the country's urban areas.

process as it relates to the issues of democratization and centralization?

*Qiao Peixin:* Of course, some progress has been made in the direction of democracy in our country. But as for the debate over the Three Gorges project, I am afraid there has not been enough democracy; the affirmative voices are allowed to be heard while the negative voices are often suppressed. Though the decision-making process seems to be democratic, this is not the case in reality.

Last year, during the session of the CPPCC, I was asked by the *People's Daily* to present an article for the next day's paper. Of course, I wrote what I thought about the project. In the interim, however, the editor received word from above, instructing him not to publish my article. As a result it had to be withdrawn.

I really wonder why different views cannot be published in the newspapers, especially when the issues involved are too important to be ignored. I believe in the saying that everyone has a share of responsibility in the fate of his country, and I therefore have taken a scientific approach to the issue of the Three Gorges project. As a matter of fact, it took me two years to write "The Three Gorges Project: More Losses Than Gains."

We should all feel responsible for the state of the nation, for its present population as well as future generations. This is precisely the key point of difference between my position and that of the assessment report. It all boils down to one's primary responsibility to speak nothing but the truth.

# CHAPTER FIFTEEN

## NEVER DAM THE THREE GORGES
### An Interview with Professor Huang Wanli[1]
by
Dai Qing

*Dai Qing:* We know you were the only person who contended in 1957 that damming the Sanmenxia Gorge on the Yellow River should not be allowed. Now, you hold the same view on the Three Gorges project. May I ask, then, whether you oppose damming any river?

*Huang Wanli:* No. As a hydraulic engineer, I've never opposed the idea that a flood-control project should, wherever possible, combine such functions as irrigation, navigation, and power generation. However, in designing a major project, we cannot be concerned solely with engineering calculations. We must have insight into the many fields of science and the humanities, and have sufficient understanding not only of engineering, but also of hydrology and geomorphology. As far as the Yellow and Yangtze rivers are concerned, I maintain that damming the deposition reach of a main river course, such as at the Sanmenxia Gorge project, should not be allowed. The Three Gorges project, however, is located in the scouring reach of the Sichuan Basin. It

---

[1] Huang Wanli has been a professor in the Hydraulic Engineering Department of Qinghua University, Beijing, since 1953. He obtained his doctorate in engineering from the Engineering Institute of Illinois. He returned to China in 1937, after having worked at the Tennessee Valley Authority, and has held various positions including: chief advisor in water engineering technologies at the State Commission of Economic Affairs, chief of the bureau of water resources of Gansu province, and chief advisor to the Northeast China General Bureau of Water Resources. This interview, conducted in August, 1993, was not part of the original Chinese edition of *Yangtze! Yangtze!*

could be constructed if the bed-forming material of the reach were not so coarse. Such coarse material will not pass through the dam and will block Chongqing harbor after the dam is constructed.

*Dai Qing:* What do you mean by the "deposition reach"? Isn't it the case that the Yellow River's sediment builds up mainly in the alluvial plain[2] at its lower reaches? Why do you call Sanmenxia Gorge a "deposition reach"?

*Huang Wanli:* Sanmenxia Gorge's situation is rather complicated. From the town of Mengjin upstream, the Yellow River does have a deposition reach. But only at Sanmen (Three Gates) has the base rock of the river bed been lifted up due to igneous intrusion. This is a deposition reach inserted into the middle of the scouring reach of the Yellow River—a very irregular topographic formation. In 1957, it had yet to be studied; water engineers couldn't appreciate its peculiarity. It was said that once water conservation was improved in the upstream areas, there would no longer be sediment flushed down from the Yellow River. In the feasibility study for the Sanmenxia Gorge dam project, I was alone in insisting that the dam should not even be considered. Furthermore, only one engineer argued for a smaller dam. To reconcile with the majority opinion, I suggested that, if the dam must be built, then the sluice gate at its base should be left open in order to flush out sediment. For when we were dealing with the Yellow River, at least we knew it was a river with extremely high sediment content. Everyone agreed with my idea, except the Soviet experts, who insisted that it be blocked. As a result, the upstream course was silted up in barely two years, and the project had to be reconstructed.

*Dai Qing:* Is the silting pattern of the Yangtze in any way different from that of the Yellow River? Do you believe that no dam should be built on the deposition reach of a river?

*Huang Wanli:* In the Yangtze Valley, from Chongqing upstream, there exists the Sichuan Basin, which experiences high rainfall. There, ground vegetation cannot totally absorb the abundant volume of water, so the surplus rainfall flushes down to the lower positions, creating thousands of creeks and streams which are eventually gathered in the Yangtze's upstream tributaries. For

---

[2] Flood plain created by deposition of sediment from river floods.

the last 100,000 years this water has been reshaping the surface of the earth and deepening the river course, creating the gorgeous scenery along the Yangtze Valley from Sichuan downstream to Yichang. The topographic formation determines that the debris of igneous rock and sand created by weathering is carried by the river all the way through Chongqing and Yichang to the mouth of the Yangtze, where it is deposited on the slope of China's eastern continental shelf. The debris deposited on the continental shelf by this process is several kilometers deep. This continuous process has left us with the Yangtze's alluvial plains, which support the livelihoods of 500 million Chinese people.

The scouring and deposition process is the reason why the Sichuan Basin—which is on the scouring reach—has never silted up. The Yangtze and its tributaries upstream of Chongqing scour large amounts of gravel mixed with coarse sand which is flushed down river when floods occur. All of this sediment—from the Yangtze and its upstream tributaries—must pass through the Three Gorges. Once the Three Gorges is dammed, the river's flow will slow and the sediment will deposit in the backwater reach where it will block Chongqing harbor.

While a dam should not be built on a deposition reach, one may be constructed on the scouring reach. The Gongzui Reservoir on the Dadu River is a successful example. The Dadu Valley is small but the flow of the river is strong. In the 16 years since its completion, the dead storage of the reservoir has completely silted up. Although it can no longer perform its flood-control function, we do not have to remove it by blowing it up; its power plant still works. So what I mean is that, as long as a dam does not obstruct navigation upstream, nor claim arable land, it may be constructed on a scouring reach. Once it becomes silted up, let it be.

There is a German practice however, that as a small dam is built, a sluice gate is left underneath, so that the sediment can be removed at a later date.[3] Most dams built in this manner remain in good condition, and can be used for power generation, flood regulation, and irrigation.

---

[3] The debris may be flushed through the sluice gate by manipulating the river flow by upstream reservoir operations.

The focal point of the present controversy over the Three Gorges project is whether or not the Yangtze has a significant amount of coarse sand and gravel (i.e., bedload) and whether such material moves downstream. The Yangtze Valley Planning Office (YVPO) considers the movable bedload immovable, remaining constant at one spot. A simulation test under this assumption is meaningless. According to basic hydrogeologic theory, all of the rocks in this area may move downstream. This of course constitutes a huge amount of sediment, and it is from here that I start my argument. Do not forget that I have witnessed this movement. When I headed a survey team in the 1940s I saw rocks rolling in the flow with my own eyes.

*Dai Qing:* Is it possible to measure the movement of the rocks and gravel that the water carries down? What factors determine this movement?

*Huang Wanli:* It is measurable upstream. For instance, the Gongzui Reservoir was silted up in 16 years. Therefore, it is possible to measure the river's annual sediment load from this point upstream. From the Dujiangyan dam, it is reported that the river's annual sediment load is about 2 million m$^3$. If we add the sediment of each tributary, we will get the aggregate amount that goes through the Three Gorges. In principle, it is hard to investigate this factor in a deposition reach, because there the river may drop some of the load it carries before it moves it along again. But it is feasible to measure the amount of rock from the Yangtze that the river carries past Yichang each year, by synthesizing data derived from the small valleys upstream, in proportion to the total area to be investigated. My own estimation of that amount is in the neighborhood of 100 million tonnes.

*Dai Qing:* Do you mean to say that, in the past few decades, a geomorphic perspective has never been derived from the research of so many engineers?

*Huang Wanli:* This is a lesson that rivers and mountains continue to teach human beings even though we think we are knowledgeable in the area. Eighty years ago, an American engineer said that a dam builder must be well versed in two areas. One was hydro-engineering, which meant you had to understand how to construct a dam. The other was natural geography and geomorphololgy—in order to tell what impact the dam construction, once complete, would have on nature. This was his advice to

166

the U.S. government. It is also why, in the Tennessee Valley Authority, chief responsibility was shifted from J. L. Savage, an engineer, who knew only how to build dams, to Arthur E. Morgan, a specialist in comprehensive river planning from Ohio. Morgan invited S. M. Woodward, a professor from the University of Iowa, to join him. At that time, geomorphology researchers were dissatisfied with engineers, saying they often made mistakes, whereas the engineers involved in the concrete work were dissatisfied with scientists, saying that they couldn't solve problems. Few people were well versed in both methodologies.

When I arrived in the United States in 1934, I had already had two years' experience as a railway and structural engineer; then at Cornell University, the University of Iowa, and the Engineering Institute of Illinois, I branched out to astronomy, meteorology and topography. This has enabled me to really know whether a dam should be built, and where it can be built. A water engineer does not have to be a geomorphologist, but with a basic understanding of the field, he can gain a deeper insight and a broader view. In other words, any engineering project must involve both comprehensive and technical understanding; you must have the former before you can start the latter.

*Dai Qing:* But many distinguished scientists were also involved in the leading group's assessment of the Three Gorges project. Why, in your opinion, did their theoretical expertise have little influence on the project's key technological issues?

*Huang Wanli:* I don't mean scientists should be used to design a dam's operational processes. What I recommend is that engineers be informed of the findings of scientific research. To ask a geomorphologist to choose a location for a water engineering project is to ask him to do something for which he is not trained. On the other hand, to ask a water engineer to learn some geomorphology is a much more reasonable request. Scientists have their domains, their theoretical approaches, and are preoccupied with the most fundamental issues. In the field of application, it is up to the engineers to grasp the theories that scientists have provided and develop their own operational processes. One of the remarks that led me to be labeled as a "rightist" in 1957 was made exactly on this relationship. Mao Zedong proposed to relate theory to reality in the 1940s, saying that doctrines were useless and that only the kind of Marxism-Leninism that was produced in the rural hinterland[4] could solve China's real problems. In the 1950s, following this "great teaching," a batch of people started to use "reality" as an excuse for theoretical ignorance. I said: "There is no theory that cannot be related to reality, only realities that one fails to explain in theory." Now, 35 years have passed, and we still have different views and estimations of the Yangtze's sediment.

*Dai Qing:* Why has it been decided to build the dam at Sandouping, where the river is about two kilometers wide, when there are so many narrow gorges in the Yangtze? Wasn't the building of a two-kilometer-long dam decided, I'm afraid, just for the project to look magnificent?

*Huang Wanli:* For all water engineers, the narrower a dam is, the more cost-efficient it is from an economic point of view. Otherwise, why build a dam in a valley? But the Three Gorges is a complete reversal of the ideal: The dam designed for Sandouping only has a reservoir width between 500 meters and one kilometer. But it expands to two kilometers at its crest length, creating a winding reservoir 600 kilometers long. This is unprecedented. The rationale for this design, which the YVPO does not seem to want to address openly, is that there is actually no other alternative. For in the entire reach of the Three Gorges, only at Sandouping is the river bed made of igneous rock. But they seem to have forgotten that there is still about 35 meters of gravel on top of the base rock. During construction, this deposit is to be totally excavated, and 35 meters is to be added to the height of the dam, which will contribute nothing to the reservoir's storage capacity—uneconomic indeed. In addition, the resettlement of more than one million people, which will cost one-third of the entire budget, is unheard of. In my calculation, the combination of these factors will produce total costs seven times more than that for a power plant of the same capacity! The design is absurd, and overpriced. By contrast, just look at the Wujiang River hydro power station. On the narrow watercourse, there is just an arch dam to let the flood spill over it, with the power plant fixed within, combining its three functions perfectly. And at the

---

[4] Marxism derived directly from the experience of guerrilla warfare not from bookish readings of Marx. Implicit is a lopsided emphasis on practice and contempt for theory.

Guanting Reservoir in Beijing, the body of its earth dam extends only 100 meters. Of course, half of the space above the dam is silted up, and so a large part of its flood-control capacity has been lost. But it has been there for 40 years.

*Dai Qing:* If, according to the present plan, a 175-meter-high dam is built at the Three Gorges, how long will it take before things begin to go wrong upstream?

*Huang Wanli:* In terms of sedimentation, the Yangtze is different from the Yellow River. The silt head of the Yellow River has passed Chang'an and reached Xi'an. It will stop only when it meets with an upstream slope. The Yangtze's alluvial reach is originally steep enough to eliminate sedimentation. But if the flow of the river slows down, and drops the gravel at Chongqing, that would be equivalent to erecting a new dam, making it possible for the sediment to build up. This is unavoidable unless the river bed is somehow lowered. But who can do that? There is no chance for the sediment build-up to travel very far; it will stop where the slope becomes abrupt. But this is enough to raise the flood levels at Jiangjin and Hechuan (Sichuan), and cause frequent flooding. The affected area will not exceed one-fifth of Sichuan. But, think of it, one-fifth of Sichuan subject to floods—what a catastrophe!

The most serious problem is that once water storage begins, Chongqing harbor will silt up in less than 10 years. Under these conditions, in order to ensure upstream navigation, the dam will have to be blasted off. But the dam is deep in the valley. Where can the debris be put when there is no level ground? This would be extremely costly. To the east of Sichuan will be the reservoir's submergence zone, to its west will lie the destruction of Hechuan and Jiangjin, and with the obstruction of navigation will come problems with external communication. The residents of Sichuan will naturally begin to ask why, for no reason at all, they must make such sacrifices: I would not be surprised. You must know of the "Road Protection" movement[5] toward the end of the Qing Dynasty. It was when local interests were compromised in 1911

---

[5] A reference to the outbreak of violence in Sichuan as local elites resisted the efforts of the central government to take over the province's railroads and run them with foreign financial assistance.

that an opportunity for the Republican Revolution to topple the imperial regime occurred.

*Dai Qing:* But how can the Three Gorges project, now already under way, be stopped? So many years have been spent on its assessment, and so much has been done for its preparation. If it is stopped at this point, does it mean that all the previous efforts are totally wasted?

*Huang Wanli:* My view is different from many others. They are concerned with whether, according to the state's economic capabilities, the project should be started somewhat earlier or somewhat later. But I insist that never should the deposition reach of a river be dammed. The scouring reach may be dammed, provided it's not navigable, and the project does not claim arable land. The Three Gorges project is on a scouring reach; it is on a golden waterway, as it is commonly called. This project would also involve the submergence of 500,000 *mu* of farmland and the resettlement of more than 1 million people—it should not be taken lightly. Unfortunately, even if I tried to explain this point to my students, they might not accept it. The people who have devoted so much work to the project and have spent so much money will try anything to defend their project. Until 1986, when its publicity campaign began, I never really thought that someone would try to build a dam at the Three Gorges. So, I declared my point of view in the newspaper, *Science and Technology Tribune.* I hoped that there would be a public debate so I could elaborate on my concerns. Damming the Three Gorges might well have been Dr. Sun Yat-sen's grand view of the future, and it might well have fit Mao Zedong's poetic fantasy, but we engineers must treat the issue with a sense of responsibility. I have never been given a chance to speak out.

The construction of the Three Gorges dam (to follow the present preparatory works for the project) has not yet begun. What has been done so far is of no major consequence. It does not do serious harm to the river valley to relocate some local residents, to plant some trees on higher ground, and to build some bridges. This work would not be a total waste even if the dam project was canceled. However, the sooner it is canceled, the better.

# CHAPTER SIXTEEN

## ONCE THE GOLDEN WATERWAY IS SEVERED, CAN ANOTHER YANGTZE RIVER BE DUG?
### A Conversation with Peng De[1]
by
Fang Xiangming and Li Weizhong[2]

### I. The Three Gorges Project Will Produce Sedimentation That Will Hinder Navigation

Connecting the three biggest economic zones of eastern, central and southeastern China, transportation on the Yangtze has an annual volume that accounts for 76 percent of the total water transportation in China, which explains its name, "The golden waterway."

*Peng De:* Since the transportation capacity of the Yangtze River is approximately equal to that of 14 railway lines, the development of the river should give more emphasis to shipping than to flood control. Premier Zhou Enlai once pointed out emphatically: "If a dam in the Yangtze River hinders navigation, this dam must be blown up."

*Fang and Li:* At present, there are two schemes for the Three Gorges project: One plans to maintain a water level of 150 meters for normal storage conditions, and to create a 300-kilometer waterway between Wanxian county and the dam, improving navigation. The other scheme would maintain a water level of 175

---

[1] Peng De is former vice-minister of the Ministry of Communication. At the 1985 Chinese People's Political Consultative Conference, he warned of the danger of starting the Three Gorges project hastily, but his views were never made public. This interview was included in the original Chinese edition of *Yangtze! Yangtze!*

[2] Fang Xiangming and Li Weizhong were journalists with *China Youth News*.

meters, which would improve navigation conditions all the way to Chongqing, Sichuan.

*Peng De:* This is an illusion. What worries me is that the sedimentation caused by the project would block the waterway. The Yangtze is the third-largest river in the world, with the third-largest annual flow. Its sediment load at present is the fourth highest in the world. Due to deforestation along the river banks, the total sediment load has now reached 680 million tonnes per year, and the Yangtze will soon rank as the third most silted river in the world.[3] Dealing with the problem of sedimentation associated with damming such a river would be a difficult problem anywhere in the world. In 1980, an American group of experts conducted a field survey at the Three Gorges site. The chief representative considered sedimentation to be the most difficult problem that would result from the construction of the dam. In its report, issued in June, 1986, the Three Gorges project expert group for the World Bank agreed that sedimentation was one of the major problems facing the entire project.

Some Chinese experts regard sedimentation as the cancer of the project, which would become incurable if discovered too late; so they are now trying hard to make their point known. According to many experts, if the 150-meter-water-level scheme were employed, a backwater reach would form, stretching 300 kilometers from the dam. This area would be most susceptible to huge deposits of sediment. When the water level was lowered in the reservoir, navigation would be even worse than today. If the 185-meter-water-level scheme were used, the backwater area would be closer to the Chongqing port and the mouth of the Jialing River, threatening navigation even more seriously.

Under present conditions a natural balance is achieved, as sediment deposited in the waterway during the flood season is washed away afterwards. But after the construction of the Three Gorges project, sediment would continue to increase during each flood season; little would be washed away and the reservoir would gradually lose its capacity to generate power. Consequently, the

---

[3] Despite efforts at reforestation, "damage caused by deforestation in the [Yangtze] basin has already far outstripped what soil erosion control can restore." Smil, *China's Environmental Crisis*, p. 62.

sediment problem would increase in severity as time went by. In 50 years, 10 billion m³ of storage capacity would be taken up by sediment. If the water level at the reservoir were lowered, shoals would appear everywhere.

The Indus and the Nile have the most sediment of any rivers in the world, but their dams were not constructed to ensure navigation. Navigable rivers, such as the Danube and the Rhine, contain little sediment and their dams are built at the upper reaches to block sediment there. Today, the Itaipu power station in Brazil on the Parana River, the biggest in the world, has an annual sediment load of only 45 million tonnes, less than one-tenth of that of the Yangtze River.

Nowhere has such a large power station been built on a navigable river with such a high sediment content. Yet similar cases are not rare in China and instances of sediment blocking navigation have occurred around the reservoirs at the Danjiangkou, Xijin, and Huanglongtan rivers, among others, causing ships and boats to capsize.

Sedimentation in the Yangtze River would cause unpredictable damage to navigation. Can humans totally control nature? Some experts are trying to work out ways to solve this problem, but I think such efforts are only wishful thinking. Let's look at some examples. The storage capacity of the Liujianxia reservoir is 5.7 billion m³. After 17 years, one billion cubic meters have been filled up by sediment. The Ministry of Water Resources and Electric Power employed the method of "storing the clean water and flushing out the muddy" in an effort to clear out the sediment. But only two kilometers away from the dam this flushing method ceased to work. Yet, according to the scheme for a 150-meter water level for the Three Gorges reservoir, the area where sediment is deposited would stretch 300 kilometers away from the dam. Under these circumstances flushing sediment is clearly unrealistic.

At the Sanmenxia Gorge reservoir, after only two years of service, sediment deposits reached the town of Tongguan, Hunan province, and became so serious that the dam had to be rebuilt, without, however, resolving the sediment problem. At the Three Gorges, the procedures for dealing with sediment would be much more complicated and difficult than at the Sanmenxia dam, where the sediment is fine in texture. The Three Gorges area contains a mixture of fine and coarse silt and pebbles which are more difficult to wash away. Some experts who are eager to start the project are experimenting with models to show that the problem can be solved. Others believe that the results gained from using models are unreliable. Even those who are busy testing models are a bit worried that the Three Gorges reservoir might become another Sanmenxia Gorge dam.

## II. Improving Navigation on the Yangtze River Does Not Require the Three Gorges Project

Apart from the sediment problem, the project also involves many navigational difficulties, such as shipping channels whose technical standards of design, manufacture, construction and operation must all exceed current international standards.

The construction of the Three Gorges dam is to last for nearly 20 years. How, over this period of time, could navigation on the Yangtze River be guaranteed? How should the docks, which must adapt to the water levels needed for navigation at both the beginning and the end of the reservoir construction period, be built? And how much will all of this cost?

Because the regulation of the water level by the Three Gorges project would result in unstable water flow between the Gezhouba and Three Gorges dams, navigation would be seriously endangered. What's more, the Three Gorges reservoir would retain sediment and empty out clear water. This would deepen the riverbed at the lower reaches of the Gezhouba dam, lower the water level of the dam and thus result in an insufficient water depth at the threshold of the shiplocks.

If the scheme for a 150-meter water level for normal storage conditions were adopted, the 80-kilometer waterway near Chongqing would still remain an unimproved natural watercourse.

Yet, if the scheme for a 175-meter water level were used, the area submerged by the reservoir would undergo greater losses, which would definitely increase the project's costs and the population needing resettlement. These, and many other more detailed technical issues, pose difficult problems for which the experts concerned have no satisfactory answers. However, I believe that navigation along the Yangtze River can easily be improved without resorting to the Three Gorges project. After the dredging of the Yangtze, at a cost of Y100 million, the annual shipping volume has reached five million tonnes. If this process were continued using explosives to clear away the dangerous shoals, and extending the docks, the shipping volume could reach 15 to 30 million tonnes. These measures would cost only a fraction of the budget for the Three Gorges project.

*Comments by Fang and Li:* If the project is indeed carried out on the basis of the need for flood control and power generation, the upper reaches and the tributaries must be harnessed first in order to block the flow of sediment into the proposed Three Gorges reservoir. Unfortunately, despite the fact that other experts agree with Peng De, their opinions have not been given adequate attention.

## III. There Should Be More Democracy, Rather Than Rule by the Voice of One

The Three Gorges project has been an ambitious undertaking by well-known Chinese leaders over several generations, from Dr. Sun Yat-sen to the late Chairman Mao. During the early days after the founding of New China in 1949, the project was designed to implement the saying: "We will achieve what foreigners have achieved, we will get what foreigners haven't got!" Soon surveys and plans for the project proceeded to the marching rhythm of the "Great Leap Forward" campaign.

*Peng De:* Some 30 years have gone by. Each time the national economy has improved, the project is brought up again even though its problems have not been adequately addressed. The project viewed as "the second Ten Thousand *Li*[4] great wall" has stirred the hearts of many people. Those who support the project often try to remove those opposed to it from the departments or units involved, in some cases even by resorting to political persecution. In the newspapers, the one voice that is for the project drowns out different opinions and contending views. Over these 30 years, the assessment meetings for the project have not reached any agreement because, I think, the key issues concerning the project have not yet been fully discussed.

---

[4] 1 *Li* = 500 m.

At a session of the State Council in 1984, the project had the support of the leading people from the Central Committee of the Party. During the Chinese People's Political Consultative Conference meeting of 1985, several members from the Ministry of Communication wished to discuss the project. It was argued, however, that the decision for the project might already have been reached by the Party Central Committee. If so, why should they bring trouble on themselves, as there was no point in raising the issue at all. However, at the first group discussion, I spoke out anyway, suggesting that the project be delayed, as too hasty a start would leave many issues unsettled. My suggestion was supported by all 72 members of the group. I was asked to speak at the conference. Some even encouraged me by saying: "You go ahead and speak out. If you are stripped of Party membership, we will all stand up for you." I had then already retired from all my former positions so there could be no danger of being dismissed, and therefore I made my speech at the conference. Later, Comrade Yang Jingren passed down the opinion of the State Council that the project had not been finalized and was still open for discussion by the experts concerned. We were quite happy with this response. This meeting again impressed upon me the importance of democratic procedures of decision making.

During the Second World War, scientists from the United States developed the atomic bomb, hoping to quickly bring peace to the world. But they were naive, and later saw that what the bomb brought to mankind was the ruthless destruction of Japan. Albert Einstein, together with about 100 scientists, submitted a petition to President Truman, demanding a stop to the manufacture of atomic bombs, but the White House refused to listen because of its need to maintain supremacy in the world. More and more atomic bombs appeared, followed by hydrogen and neutron bombs as well. Here we see the defeat of science by politics, which resulted in the deadly risk of worldwide nuclear war.

In the history of hydro-electricity in China, cases of science being defeated by political need and public feelings are not at all rare. The Sanmenxia Gorge dam is a case in point. During those days, this project was used as a criterion for judging one's political stand. Those who supported the project were for the Party, while those who had different opinions were against the Party. As a result, the Sanmenxia Gorge dam was completed, but it has had to be reconstructed several times, and each time, relocated people were made to move back and forth at great expense to the state.

The Gezhouba dam was a rehearsal for the Three Gorges project. Since some people found it difficult to think of immediately starting the Three Gorges project in the early 1970s, the Gezhouba dam was hurriedly launched: the dam's location at the lower reaches of the Yangtze River shows disregard for the priorities of the development process. Since the Gezhouba dam was started before the plans and design had been completed, the construction period lasted 18 years. Even today, there still remain many worrisome problems. I am very concerned that if the Three Gorges project is started, it would be impossible to stop. After its completion, if some unpredictable disasters occur, people of my age will not be there to see and so can escape being held responsible; but what will our children do?

Once the project severs the golden waterway, the river will be irretrievably gone. Even if the dam were later blown up, I really doubt that the Chinese people could dig another Yangtze River.

# CHAPTER SEVENTEEN

## RESETTLEMENT AND LAND LOSS WILL SERIOUSLY DISRUPT PRODUCTION
### An Interview with Wang Xingrang[1]
by
Chen Ying[2]

*Chen Ying:* Discussions have been going on for decades as to the feasibility of carrying out the Three Gorges project. But little has been reported to the public. The assessment meetings are given only simple and biased news coverage. The departments concerned, and some leaders, are said to be unwilling to have the issue debated openly. Do you think the project should be discussed by people throughout the country?

*Wang Xingrang:* My position is very clear. It is not only important but also essential to discuss openly whether this project should be launched immediately, even if a decision has been reached by the Central Committee. The reasons are the following:

1. Since articles in favor of the Three Gorges project have appeared in the Party's official newspapers, the atmosphere is one of anticipating an early start of the project.

2. Discussions on the project have lasted for years, have gone beyond the issue of engineering technology, and have become a test of the Chinese Communist Party's decision-making procedures. Will it listen to and consider different opinions and suggestions concerning the project so as to reach a decision in a scientific and democratic manner? The question of whether the

---

[1] Wang Xingrang, a member of the Chinese People's Consultative Conference, was once the vice-minister of commerce. This interview was included in the original Chinese edition of *Yangtze! Yangtze!*
[2] Chen Ying is the editor of *Workers' Daily.*

project should be started can only be broached once the issue of proper decision-making procedures has been settled.

3. The project is closely related to many other important issues facing the Chinese Communist Party, all of which raise the question of whether or not the Central Committee of the Party is truly determined to improve the economy into order, and deepen its reforms. People will have reasons to doubt the probability of economic reform if the Party agrees to carry out a project that requires so many human and financial resources.

4. Many specialists have studied the project. Public and open discussion of the project would contribute to further studies.

*Chen Ying:* Some say that it is pointless to debate the project openly, since the state now lacks the financial ability to carry it out in the near future.

*Wang Xingrang:* Of course, it is impossible to launch the project when there is no money. But does that mean the project should be started as soon as there is money? The essential point in the discussion is whether it is wise and appropriate to fund this project at all.

*Chen Ying:* What do you think of the leading group's assessment?

*Wang Xingrang:* The reassessment of the project is absolutely necessary. Otherwise, a hasty launching of the project would result in unpredictable disasters. But the leading group's assessment, presided over by the Ministry of Water Resources and Electric Power, did not deal with the feasibility of the project. Rather, it limited its assessment to the question of how to start the project as soon as possible and assumed that there was no alternative to it. The assessment focused on technical subjects such as the location of the future reservoir and the height of the dam. In a nutshell, it only discussed the project as it stands. I believe it was a one-sided and arbitrary discussion, rather than a scientific assessment based on facts and realities. The assessment cannot provide a comprehensive and reliable point of reference for decisions to be taken by the State Council.

*Chen Ying:* The Three Gorges project will involve the relocation of 1.1 to 1.3 million people, the most ever for the construction of a hydro-electric dam. This is not only an issue of technology and financial resources but also a social issue. With reference to the assessment of the resettlement issue, those who support the project believe the relocation of 1.1 million people would require Y11 billion, and would improve their living standard. The earlier the resettlement, the lower the cost. How do you view this issue?

*Wang Xingrang:* The problem of population relocation is closely connected with the issue of submerging vast amounts of land and both may be viewed together from certain perspectives.

1.   The project would submerge 430,000 *mu* of land and a dozen towns, whose industrial and agricultural productivity would be destroyed. Even if we don't count the loss in productivity over generations, the physical damage alone will be tremendous. The budget for compensating the relocated population is estimated to be at least Y11 billion. If there were no Three Gorges dam, there would be, at most, just one or two floods in 100 years, each of which would cause losses of only several billion *yuan*. Furthermore, if we take only a very small amount from the project budget to develop flood-control facilities in the middle and lower reaches of the Yangtze River, we can easily prevent floods in the future.

2.   By constructing a number of medium- and small-scale reservoirs along the tributaries at the upper reaches of the Yangtze River, using monies allocated for population relocation, a capacity for storage and power generation beyond that of the Three Gorges project can be created. These projects would involve a shorter construction period and require less land and productivity loss in the areas concerned.

This type of research is absent in the assessment report. This indicates a problem in the assessor's way of thinking and in the principles of decision making.

3.   As for the development in the Three Gorges area, some have said that if there is no project, there will be no hope for the economic development of the area. In fact, while waiting for the construction of the Three Gorges reservoir to begin, officials have done little to develop the local economy in order to reduce the compensation budget. Local economic development has been delayed for 30 years and will lag further as time goes by. Irrevocable losses have been suffered even before the project starts. As some have commented: "The Three Gorges project can be a historical monument," but it can just as well become a disaster.

*Chen Ying:* Population relocation for reservoir construction has in the past proved to be a complicated job with serious economic consequences. Do you think the Three Gorges project might have such consequences?

*Wang Xingrang:* All the reservoir constructions in China have caused serious economic effects. "Those who have suffered are not the beneficiaries while those who have benefited are not the sufferers." In practice, this has meant sacrificing agricultural interests in order to benefit industry.[3] This principle applies equally to the Three Gorges project, which would result in an even more unprecedented disaster.

---

[3] Reflecting the heavy industrial and urban biases of China's developmental model, loss of cultivated areas to industrial and other uses averaged about 520,000 hectares per year between 1957 and 1988. See Smil, *China's Environmental Crisis*, p. 56.

# CHAPTER EIGHTEEN

## THE LIMITED BENEFITS OF FLOOD CONTROL
### An Interview with Lu Qinkan[1]
by
Chen Kexiong[2]

*Chen Kexiong:* I understand that as early as the Nationalist period you were sent to America to study and work out the first draft plan of the Three Gorges project.

*Lu Qinkan:* Yes. In 1944, J. L. Savage, an American expert in high-dam design, came to do an investigation in China and put forward a plan for Yangtze River development. Then, Savage wrote a report to the Nationalist Government that piqued their interest. So the National Resources Committee co-chaired by Qian Changzhao sent 50 engineers (myself among them) to Denver, Colorado to do research under Savage's direction on a final design for the Three Gorges project. At the same time, field investigations were started at home. In the original plan for the project scheme, I remember the high water level of the storage reservoir was around 200 meters, and the reservoir was supposed to generate more than 10 million kW of electricity. But after one year of study in the United States, the work had to be stopped.

*Chen Kexiong:* Why?

*Lu Qinkan:* At that time, the Nationalist government was on the verge of defeat in the civil war, and the domestic political situation was so unstable that the United States withdrew its proposed investment in the project. Among the 50 of us sent to America only 30 returned home and the rest stayed abroad.

---

[1] This interview was included in the original Chinese edition of *Yangtze! Yangtze!*

[2] Chen Kexiong is a journalist with the *Literary Gazette*.

*Chen Kexiong:* Since 1949, the question of whether to start the Three Gorges project has recurred on numerous occasions. What has been your stand on this matter?

*Lu Qinkan:* Between 1955 and 1957, as a representative from the Ministry of Water Resources and Electric Power, I worked in the Yangtze Valley Planning Office (YVPO), in charge of hydrology and water utilization studies. There, I did some research on flood control and power generation on the Yangtze. At that time, I believed the Three Gorges project would require too large an investment and would take too long to build. Based on these, and other, more technical problems, I thought it better to delay the project. That was the time when Chairman Mao Zedong had already swum across the Yangtze River, and written the poem "A Smooth Lake Over the High Gorges."

At that time, Lin Yishan, the director of the YVPO, and Li Rui, the director of the Hydro-electricity Bureau, were writing journal articles publicly arguing whether the project should be started. Soon after, in 1959, Li Rui was politically persecuted at the Lushan Conference where he was accused of opposing Chairman Mao's desire to build the Three Gorges project. Those Party members who worked under him and shared his views were all labeled "Li Rui's Anti-Party Clique." Since I was not a Party member, I was spared persecution.

After the Chengdu Conference in 1958, when the "Great Leap Forward" was launched, the project was again pushed forward. About 10,000 scientists and researchers were gathered at Wuhan to study the technical problems of the project. I was so nervous that I dared not oppose the project any longer and had to swim with the tide. However, the project was suspended as a result of the country's difficult economic situation in 1960-1962. During the 10 years of "the Cultural Revolution" (1965-1975) it was not possible to put the project on the national agenda for economic construction.

After the downfall of the leftist "Gang of Four" in 1976, the YVPO once again presented the project to the State Council. The premier, Hua Guofeng, and several other vice-premiers had agreed to it. But Zhao Ziyang, who was then the first Party secretary-general of Sichuan province, expressed some reservations, saying that too much land had to be submerged, too many people

183

had to be moved and Sichuan was far from ready for such large-scale reservoir resettlement.

*Chen Kexiong:* Why didn't you sign the leading group's assessment? After all, 400 experts did.

*Lu Qinkan:* There were 14 specialized experts' groups. The experts could sign only their own specialized group report. I was on the experts' group dealing with flood control. Since I had done research in this field, I believed the role of the Three Gorges reservoir in flood control would be very limited, and was overestimated in the assessment report.

*Chen Kexiong:* Really? But it is the general understanding that flood control is precisely the major function of the project.

*Lu Qinkan:* Yes. In the 1950s and 1960s, flood control was stated as the primary function of the project. Yet, recently, the main function has changed to a more comprehensive role including flood control, power generation, and navigation.

*Chen Kexiong:* But the assessment states that the Three Gorges reservoir is irreplaceable as a means of flood control and that "the reservoir can effectively control the major source of floods in the lower and middle reaches."

*Lu Qinkan:* Let's analyze the floods that have happened since 1949 along the Yangtze River. They are of three types:

1. Big floods throughout the whole river, such as in 1954;
2. Floods that are serious only at the upper reaches, such as that in 1981; and,
3. Floods that have occurred due to local storms only at the lower and middle reaches, such as that in 1991.

The flood of 1954 was the biggest of the past century. The total volume of flow in July and August, 1954, was 458.7 billion m³, of which 103.2 billion m³ exceeded the flood-control capacity of the dikes. Serious damage was inflicted on 18.88 million people and 47.55 million *mu* of cultivated land. Over the past 30 years, the dikes along the Yangtze River have been reinforced several times. Also, after the completion of the flood-control scheme planned in 1980 for the lower and middle reaches, the discharge capacity of the Yangtze River has been enlarged. If a flood as severe as that of 1954 recurs, the volume of the flood waters overflowing the dikes could well be reduced by half, and the remaining 50 billion m³ could be disposed of in the assigned flood diversion areas. Conversely, the Three Gorges project can only control floods from the Chuanjiang River at the upper reaches, and cannot control the floods from many of the large tributaries at the lower and middle reaches such as the Xiangjiang, Zishui, Yuanshui, Lishui, Hanjiang and Ganjiang rivers. According to the leading group's flood-control report, the Three Gorges project could only substitute for a part of the flood diversion areas. If a flood like that in 1954 recurred, requiring the diversion of 50 billion m³ of flood water, the Three Gorges project could only divert water above Chenglingji, leaving 30 to 40 billion m³ of flood water to be diverted. The Three Gorges project could only save 1.77 to 3.27 million *mu* of arable land from submersion, leaving 6.7 to 8.2 million *mu* submerged at the lower and middle reaches. And, for the city of Wuhan, the project would neither lower the flood level nor reduce the water volume in nearby flood diversion areas. The project would be even more useless for Jiangxi and Anhui provinces on the lower reaches.

The second type of flood, represented by the 1981 flood, was very serious at the upper reaches. The peak discharge at Chongqing of 85,700 m³ per second, was already reduced to 70,800 m³ per second at Yichang further down river as a result of channel storage. The lower and middle reaches were not affected at all Therefore, the Three Gorges project is hardly necessary for this type of flood. But the Three Gorges project would increase an already high flood level at Chongqing, because of the storage of flood water and sedimentation in the reservoir. As a result, flood damage in Sichuan province would become even more serious.

As for the third type of flood, it need not be said the project would be totally useless. Hence I maintain that the role of the project in flood control is limited.

*Chen Kexiong:* In both the report submitted by the YVPO and that of the leading group, flood control was cited to demonstrate the necessity of the project, with the added warning that "if the 1870 flood recurs, the dikes on both sides of the Jingjiang River would burst; if a break occurred at the middle reach on the northern dike near Yanka, the death toll could reach 500,000." What do you think of such claims?

*Lu Qinkan:* According to flood-level marks, the 1870 flood at the upper reaches was indeed more serious than the one in

1981. Yet, in Wuhan, the highest flood level was between 27.36 and 27.55 meters, which was more than two meters lower than that of the flood in 1954 and ranks as the sixth-highest in the past 120 years. The 1870 flood was not serious at the lower and middle reaches. The flood discharge of the Jingjiang River first ran southward and broke the southern dike at Songzikou, rushing into Dongting Lake. And the northern Jingjiang River dike, weak as it seemed at that time, withstood the flood above Jianli.

Today, river networks have been established at Songzikou and the northern Jingjiang River dike has been strengthened and heightened too. As the northern dike had not been broken by the floods 100 years ago, how could one say, after the conditions have been much improved, that today it would burst in the high-risk areas near Shashi city and take hundreds of thousands of lives? Furthermore, according to frequency calculations, floods like the one in 1870 happen only once every 2,500 years. I therefore find it hard to justify an immediate start-up of the project.

*Chen Kexiong:* Do you totally object to the Three Gorges project?

*Lu Qinkan:* No. I only meant to show its limited role in flood control, which is not as effective as some people have predicted. I think a realistic evaluation should be conducted, and I think we should choose the proper time to launch the project.

*Chen Kexiong:* When would that be?

*Lu Qinkan:* To be more optimistic, I would say, in five to 10 years. That gives sufficient time for the national economy to improve and for technological problems to be solved. Along the Yangtze River, floods occur every five to 10 years. At present, the best way to control floods is to improve dikes, securing the facilities for flood diversion areas; build more reservoirs on tributaries, and continue work on soil conservation at the upper reaches.

*Chen Kexiong:* What is your biggest concern if the project is started immediately?

*Lu Qinkan:* First, funds for other important hydro projects would have to be diverted to the Three Gorges project. Since 1984, because of the financial needs of the project, plans for the Ertan project in Sichuan province (3 million kW), for the Wuqiangxi project in Hunan province (1.2 million kW), and for the Geheyan project in Hubei province(1.2 million kW) have already been suspended. There are still many other projects in danger of being delayed as well, such as the Pubugou on the Dadu River (3.3 million kW), the Goupitan on the Wujiang River (2 million kW), the Longtan on the Hongshui River (4.2 million kW), and the Pengshui on the Wujiang River (1.2 million kW). Although Chairman Mao talked of "A Smooth Lake Over the High Gorges," he also said in 1969: "It is very bad for the city of Wuhan to carry a basin of water on her head" and that "investigation is needed to develop the tributaries of the Yangtze River in Sichuan province." However, some people only quote the first comment. Why do they keep forgetting the latter?

*Chen Kexiong:* If the state set aside more funds for the project, would it be possible to start it soon?

*Lu Qinkan:* No. Until the end of this century, economic development in all areas requires extensive funding, such as in energy resources and raw materials, as well as transportation, education and scientific research. How can the state spare extra funds to finance a project that requires the investment of Y100 billion, 20 years to build, and the relocation of 1.13 million people? If the project ever got started, it would be impossible to stop it. Therefore, we should be careful in making this decision.

*Chen Kexiong:* Have you ever made your points known before?

*Lu Qinkan:* Yes. I have voiced my views at the Chinese People's Political Consultative Conference (CPPCC) and to the leading group. The night before the 1988 assessment meeting, I prepared a speech that I hoped could illustrate my points in more detail. But, the following day, I might not have been able to finish the speech, had it not been for Madam Qian Zhengying, who stood up to say that I was speaking not just for myself but also on behalf of Sun Yueqi, a specially invited advisor. Only then was I able to carry on. Certainly I was very grateful to the minister, and the first sentence of my speech went something like, "I am grateful that the old minister has given me the privilege of speaking again."

*Chen Kexiong:* But these different views are actually unknown to the public.

*Lu Qinkan:* The press has not given fair coverage to the debate on the project. They have provided publicity only to the views favoring an immediate launch and have rejected articles submitted by us against it. People have been misled by such one-sidedness. At the CPPCC in 1988, I and five other members submitted a proposal calling for fair media coverage for both sides of the issue. But the Party Propaganda Department replied that "it is inappropriate to debate such issues openly in the newspapers." I really don't understand such a position, since the 1987 Thirteenth Party Congress stated that with regard to the reform of political structures, "important issues should be made known to the public to enhance transparency." We don't understand why we can't argue openly about projects that will have such an extensive impact on the life of the people. The people ought to know about it and contribute their thoughts and comments on the issue.

*Chen Kexiong:* I understand that the leading group's 10th session will be held on February 20, 1989, in Beijing and then it will present a report to the State Council for approval. What do you have to say about this?

*Lu Qinkan:* I am already over 70, and will not live much longer. My sons and daughters and even my grandchildren have tried to persuade me to give up. But I can't. I agree with what Professor Huang Wenxi of Beida University who said: "We should not leave our children a monument of stupidity."

*Chen Kexiong:* Some vowed that they will not rest until they see the project constructed. Since you are among the first generation of planners for the Three Gorges project, would you also regret not seeing the project in your lifetime?

*Lu Qinkan:* No, not at all. Because everything should be judged in terms of our national interests now that we are on the threshold of the 21st century.

# CHAPTER NINETEEN

## THE THREE GORGES PROJECT: AN ENORMOUS ENVIRONMENTAL DISASTER
### An Interview with Hou Xueyu[1]
by
Zhu Jianhong[2]

*Zhu Jianhong:* Is it true that you didn't sign the assessment report concerned with the environmental aspects of the Three Gorges project?

*Hou Xueyu:* That is true. I think the Three Gorges project will do more harm than good to the environment and the natural resources of the Yangtze River valley.

*Zhu Jianhong:* But the assessment does admit this in its conclusion.

*Hou Xueyu:* The report has put forward many solutions to the environmental problems. But I doubt that they could be effective.

*Zhu Jianhong:* Perhaps, being an ecologist, you tend to overestimate the nature of this problem?

*Hou Xueyu:* In fact, I think the assessment report underestimates damage to the local environment. For several decades now, those engaged in hydro-electric power construction have given little consideration to environmental concerns, including the impact on the lives of local residents [3]

---

[1] Hou Xueyu, now deceased, was a botanist, a member of the Standing Committee of the Chinese People's Political Conference, and an advisor to the Experts' Group on Ecology and Environment. This interview was included in the original Chinese edition of *Yangtze! Yangtze!*

[2] Zhu Jianhong is a journalist with the *People's Daily.*

[3] Problems frequently encountered include the disruption of livelihoods and local social and economic structures, increases in deadly diseases such as malaria and schistosomiasis, and pollution from the reservoir.
    (continued...)

*Zhu Jianhong:* Is this only a prediction or has it happened in reality?

*Hou Xueyu:* Of course it has happened. Due to the lack of knowledge about ecology and sediment deposition, 40 percent of the Sanmenxia reservoir was blocked within 20 years of its completion and had to be reconstructed several times. The dam also seriously endangered the industrial and agricultural production of the western plain area and the city of Xi'an. Recently, *The Social and Environmental Effects of Large Dams*[4] was published, which analyzed 31 dams in 23 countries and concluded that most of them have damaged the lives of local residents. The book examined cases such as the Aswan dam in Egypt, and dams built under the Tennessee Valley Authority in the United States. This book is now being translated into Chinese. I hope it will help in further assessments of the Three Gorges project.

*Zhu Jianhong:* Once the Three Gorges dam is built, it will be the largest hydro-electric project in the world. I presume its effect on the environment would be tremendous. Could you tell us something more about its impact?

*Hou Xueyu:* The project would submerge 19 counties and more than 400,000 *mu* of cultivated land, including some of the richest soil along the river basin. Along with the well-known mustard tuber, medicinal herbs and grain, 73,900 *mu* of orange groves, which produce a net profit of Y1,500 per *mu*, will be lost. The losses would be at least Y100 million per year, Y1 billion in a decade.

*Zhu Jianhong:* It has been suggested that, in order to make up for the losses caused by the project, new land for orange groves be opened up on terraced fields.

*Hou Xueyu:* This is an irresponsible suggestion. After the rich plains are gone, only rocky hills with thin layers of poor topsoil

---

[3](...continued)
According to the Ministry of Water Resources, 30 to 40 percent of the 10 million people who have been relocated to make way for hydro-electric dams since the late 1950s are still impoverished and lacking adequate food and clothing. See "China Plans New Resettlement Rules," *Water Power and Dam Construction*, March 1990, p. 2.
[4] See Goldsmith and Hildyard, eds., *Social and Environmental*.

would be left. Those terraced fields could easily be washed away by heavy rainfall in the area.

*Zhu Jianhong:* Some researchers have published reports arguing that the changes in climate will hardly be noticeable after the project is completed. In winter, the predicted temperature would be a bit higher and in summer a bit lower, accompanied by an increase in moisture, which, it is argued, would favor agriculture. What do you think of this?

*Hou Xueyu:* This is a one-sided statement. The water surface can regulate temperature, which is also affected by the altitude above sea level. Granted, the temperature after the completion of the reservoir would be 0.4 degree centigrade higher than before, but the temperature decreases as the altitude increases. If the dam was 180 meters high, the temperature increase would be offset by the increased elevation.

The major orange groves are currently located to the east of the future reservoir site in Zigui county. In the northern section of this area, at Xing mountain (275 meters above sea level), the lowest temperature ever recorded was -9.3 degrees centigrade, which is low enough to freeze oranges. If the orange groves were moved to 600 meters above sea level, the danger of freezing would be even greater. Therefore, the suggestion of developing orange groves just below 600 meters above sea level is dubious. From an environmental point of view, this hilly area does not provide favorable soil or climate conditions for growing oranges.

*Zhu Jianhong:* However, after the completion of the reservoir, the newly developed water resources could be used as fish ponds, even if the soil were destroyed. So the losses can still be made up. What you think of this?

*Hou Xueyu:* I don't think it could be made up in this way. Water and soil are not interchangeable. The rich arable land destroyed by the reservoir could never be reclaimed. Of course, fish could be raised; but, as you know, reservoir construction will destroy some existing fish ponds. Besides, the present fishery production in our country is very low.

Apart from irreparable damage to the soil, the natural beauty and cultural heritage of the area would be permanently damaged as well. I think the Three Gorges is the most beautiful of all of the world's gorges. The surrounding areas have many national treasures, some more than 5,000 years old. These include the famous ruins of the ancient Daxi culture, and tombs from the Warring States period [475-221 B.C.], the Eastern Han [25 B.C.-200 A.D.], and the Ming and Qing dynasties, most of which are scattered below 180 meters. Further, the Three Gorges has unique geological features that provide very important physical data for research. All of this would be inundated if the reservoir were built, and tourism would suffer incalculable economic losses.

*Zhu Jianhong:* But some have suggested that these historical relics could always be moved to safer places.

*Hou Xueyu:* They have, and one even recommended building a museum to display these relics. Even if they could be moved, their authenticity would be destroyed, together with the unique value and cultural significance of the original context. For instance, how would it strike you to compare the on-site remains of 5,000 year-old tombs with museum reconstructions?

*Zhu Jianhong:* Do you mean to say that all of the scenic and historical relics are worth preserving?

*Hou Xueyu:* Definitely!

*Zhu Jianhong:* You mentioned that the construction of the project could destroy fish ponds. Can you elaborate on this point?

*Hou Xueyu:* The middle reaches of the Yangtze River from Chongqing to the Chenglingji section of Dongting Lake is one of the major breeding grounds for black, silver, grass and variegated carp. Some of these sections happen to be in the area of the future reservoir.

Breeding requires a water temperature of 18 degrees centigrade. However, with the discharge of reservoir water, that temperature cannot be retained, thereby reducing the breeding period by 20 days. Because of changes in the river-bed after the completion of the reservoir, the quantities of fish would be reduced, eventually resulting in decreased output. Some rare species would be affected too, including Lipotes-vexillifer, Chinese paddlefish, and sturgeon. In danger of extinction, these species have been given priority protection by the state. These species breed in the upper reaches and migrate to the lower and middle reaches. Once the dam is constructed, they will obviously suffer major population reductions. In fact, since the Gezhouba dam was built, dead Chinese paddlefish have been discovered at the base of the dam.

Furthermore, reservoir construction would bring about changes in water quality and temperature at the mouth of the

Yangtze River, and consequently reduce fish production. For instance, anchovies, white bait, hilsa herring, and prawns—all found in semi-salty water—will probably diminish in quantity. Even the breeding ground of the famous Zhoushan fish is likely to be affected.

*Zhu Jianhong:* From a geological point of view, what impact would the Three Gorges project have?

*Hou Xueyu:* The reservoir area sees frequent landslides and mud flows; altogether 214 potentially dangerous spots have been identified. The largest potential for landslides is along the river banks in Wanxian and Zigui counties. In June, 1985, 2,000,000 $m^3$ of earth slipped into the Yangtze River at the Xintan area. The landslide caused waves 36 meters high and 100 meters wide and destroyed a warehouse, and 77 boats, and took 10 lives.

Because of the effects of the reservoir water soaking into soil and sand along both sides of the reservoir after construction, the stability of the existing landslide spots will be reduced. During the storm season, there areas are more likely to experience landslides and collapses, since there is no vegetation to protect the slopes and hillsides.

Also, the geological structure of the reservoir area shows that there is a possibility of induced earthquakes. If that happens, there could be large-scale landslides and rock collapses that would endanger the reservoir and block the Yangtze River.

*Zhu Jianhong:* What other serious effects would the Three Gorges project cause?

*Hou Xueyu:* Tremendous losses would be inflicted on industry and mining. The plan to set the high-water level at 180 meters would submerge 624 factories, including six major factories in Chongqing. Some mineral resources would also be lost since the mining areas would be below water level after construction of the reservoir.

I am also worried about the effects of population relocation. Some have suggested moving the agriculture and industries of the submerged areas to the hills behind the reservoir site. Of course, this is a better solution than just distributing financial compensation to the local people. But there are negative side effects that we should also pay attention to.

First, industrial pollution: After the completion of the reservoir, poisonous particles from submerged coal and phosphorus mines would settle on the bottom of the river bed. Also, poisonous byproducts from the reconstructed factories would be ingested by the local people in the area. The slow wind velocity, heavy fog, high humidity, industrial smog, and traffic would quickly result in pollution and induce acid rain.

Second, soil erosion by farming: At present, along the river banks of the future reservoir site, the ecological system is very weak, with forests covering only 5 percent and grassy hills 30 to 40 percent.

With the completion of the reservoir, the heavy population concentration would result in deforestation as a result of local agricultural development programs. This, in turn, would make soil erosion even worse, landslides more frequent, and the disasters of drought and flood more severe. It would be the start of a vicious circle, which would only put more pressure on the environment.

*Zhu Jianhong:* Some have said that a new environmental balance can be reached if the programs for population relocation and development of new towns and cities are carefully formulated and properly carried out.

*Hou Xueyu:* I think the destruction would outweigh a new balance. The saying, "man can conquer nature" is unrealistic. The formulation of development programs must be based on current natural conditions. For example, in China, most of the population is concentrated in the east where natural resources are located. Although we can move people west, we cannot move resources. Nature will not allow it. If one doesn't consider natural conditions, it is impossible to work out a program beneficial to the people.

*Zhu Jianhong:* Do you think the Three Gorges project will have some positive effects on the environment?

*Hou Xueyu:* Of course, hydro-electric power is cleaner than thermal power and safer than nuclear power. But it is not necessary to develop a hydro-electric power plant in this area. Why not in the upper reaches?

*Zhu Jianhong:* Are the negative effects you just analyzed all irreparable?

*Hou Xueyu:* Some are definitely irreparable, for example damage to the natural and scenic beauty, and the cultural heritage. Others may be remedied, but only after considerable research; still others will be very costly. Some of the environmental effects will be felt in the short term while others would become evident only in the future; some can be calculated in financial terms while others are harder to evaluate as such. We haven't discussed, for example, the likely damage of the project to the river mouth area, or the effects of a change in the salt content of the water on industrial and agricultural production, soil resources, and the coastal ecology of the delta area. At this point in time, it is very difficult to calculate accurately the seriousness of the effects or the resulting economic losses.

*Zhu Jianhong:* Some feel it incvitable that the environment pay some price for the economic benefits the project will produce. What do you think?

*Hou Xueyu:* Environmental interests and economic benefits go hand in hand. A better environment will enhance economic benefits. Otherwise, the economic benefits, no matter how high, will have to pay for the environmental damage. In the end, it is the common people who will suffer these losses. It is one-sided and unscientific to consider only the benefits, such as the production of electric power, without counting the cost to the environment and natural resources.

*Zhu Jianhong:* Do you mean that it is impossible to achieve economic benefits at the expense of environmental interests?

*Hou Xueyu:* Yes. The Three Gorges project is supposed to serve three functions: flood control, power generation, and navigation. Yet, all three are determined by environmental factors. Since 1949, there has been serious soil erosion of the upper reaches because of deforestation. The forest coverage has shrunk from 40 or 50 percent in the 1950s to the present 10 percent in the southeast, 4 percent in the Sichuan basin, and as little as 1 percent in other areas.[5]

The annual volume of sediment flowing from Sichuan into the Three Gorges was 510 million tonnes per year in the 1970s and increased to 680 million tonnes per year in the 1980s. We can see therefore that soil erosion can increase sedimentation, which will becomes more serious due to landslides, and land cultivation on the hills near the reservoir. This will not only affect the functions of flood control, navigation and power generation, but will

---

[5] See the full discussion of deforestation problems in China, in Smil, *China's Environmental Crisis*, pp. 61-64.

also shorten the life expectancy of the reservoir itself. At the Wujiang River hydro-electric power plant completed in 1980, sedimentation, after four years of operation, had already reached the level predicted for 50 years later. What then will become of the Three Gorges reservoir? For how long can it be kept serviceable? It is really a very serious question.

The environment and human survival are dependent on each other, and the environment and economic interests are not at all contradictory.

*Zhu Jianhong:* Should the old way of assessing a hydro-electric project be modified, or changed?

*Hou Xueyu:* Yes. The environment is so important that a systematic study of the ecology and conservation of natural resources at the Three Gorges has strategic significance, and is a prerequisite in the assessment of the project. In recent years, due to the lack of attention to the environment and the conservation of natural resources, the construction of reservoirs has had to be reduced in scale or suspended in many countries. For example, in Brazil, the construction of 25 dams along the Amazon River has been canceled; in Australia, a dam project on the Franklin River was abandoned in 1983; in India, the project in the Silent Valley was suspended by the government in 1980, after eight years of construction and a $3 million investment. The Tehri dam in India, which would have required the relocation of 50,000 people, the submergence of ancient towns, the possibility of induced landslides as a result of deforestation, and serious sedimentation problems, was halted because of mass protests.

*Zhu Jianhong:* But some people may agree that we Chinese have different values from the West.

*Hou Xueyu:* These people are evading the issue of the environment.

*Zhu Jianhong:* Among the 412 experts who participated in the leading group's assessment, only 10 refused to sign the assessment report, and you are one of the 10.

*Hou Xueyu:* I was invited only to show the public that people of different opinions were included. There were many others who possess valuable knowledge and insight with regard to this project who were not invited. However, having conducted environmental research for many years, I must bear in mind my responsibilities to the country and our future generations, and must make my point of view clear to all. One is bound to say something that may prove incorrect in the end, but never should one make a false statement. I have been saying what is on my mind. Right or wrong, it should be judged by the public and tested by history. As far as I know, some experts who were not in agreement with the report, signed it, for various reasons.[6]

*Zhu Jianhong:* What are the "various reasons"?

*Hou Xueyu:* That's very complicated. For example, some experts were persuaded by their leaders, who went to their houses to ask their approval. How could they refuse? Some were told that it was already finalized by the Party Central Committee. What was the use of opposing it? So on and so forth.

*Zhu Jianhong:* Will you still insist on your position?

*Hou Xueyu:* Certainly yes. Again, I think that in terms of the environment and the conservation of natural resources, the question concerning the Three Gorges project is not the timing of the project, nor the height of the dam, but the advisability of the dam's very construction. Our generation will have made an irrevocable mistake if navigation on the golden waterway is severed

---

[6] For more on this issue, see Appendix C.

# CHAPTER TWENTY

## THE TRIBUTARIES FIRST AND THE MAINSTREAM OF THE RIVER SECOND: A PRINCIPLE FOR THE DEVELOPMENT OF THE YANGTZE RIVER
### An Interview with Chen Mingshao[1]
by
Gang Jian[2]

*Gang Jian:* I gather that you used to work in the field of water resources. One might assume that you would be very enthusiastic about the immediate start of the Three Gorges project, and yet it turns out that you are opposed to a hasty start. What are the primary reasons for your position?

*Chen Mingshao:* It is true that I care deeply about my work on water resources. Progress in this field has been quite encouraging and it is certainly my hope that the government can give more attention to it. Our country is rich in water resources, ranking first or second in the world, but only 5 percent of the resources have so far been tapped. The Yangtze River can have the transportation equivalent of 14 railway lines if it is put into full use. But, today, its efficiency is less than that of two railway lines, which is really too little. I therefore agree with all of the suggestions in favor of the development of water resources. This is my basic point. But the issue of flood control in the context of the exploitation of the

---

[1] Chen Mingshao was born in Dapu, Guangdong province, and graduated from Qinghua University in 1936 with a degree in civil engineering. He is now vice-president of Beijing Engineering University, vice-director of the Standing Committee of the Beijing People's Congress, and vice-president of the Central Committee of the Jiu San Society. This interview was included in the original Chinese edition of *Yangtze! Yangtze!*

[2] Gang Jian is a journalist with the *Enlightenment Daily*.

Yangtze River demands thorough and careful research. Any passion or zeal in this regard is inadvisable.

*Gang Jian:* Let's leave the details aside for the moment. Do you think it's necessary to establish principles for the discussions on the project in order to facilitate reaching an agreement?

*Chen Mingshao:* Principles are certainly necessary, but they should not be formulated only on the basis of subjective goals. They must follow some general rules, most probably drawn from the philosophy of Chinese culture. I say this not because of my personal love of the philosophy of our culture, but because it provides solid guidelines. Here, then, are four principles that should be used to guide the water conservation project:

1. The simple problems first and the difficult ones later. During wartime, Mao Zedong emphasized the importance of dealing with smaller and scattered enemies first, and fighting against the stronger ones later. He had, in fact, led many battles according to the traditional principles, which I believe apply to any kind of job. So it would work with water conservation problems, too.

2. The upper reaches first, the lower reaches later. In traditional Chinese philosophy, there is a saying *heng ben qing yuan,* which means that the "root cause must be treated first." Applied to a river, it means the source is the most important section. Therefore, priority should be given to the upper reaches, making things easier for the lower reaches.

3. The tributaries first, and the mainstream of the river later. The problems of the Yangtze River, such as floods, sediment deposition, and navigation difficulties in the low water season, are all related to its tributaries.

4. River basins first, and the river channel second. Water and soil conservation in the river valley will greatly facilitate that of the river.

*Gang Jian:* Apart from these principles, your speech at the Chinese People's Political Consultative Conference (CPPCC) has put the issue of the Three Gorges project onto a political level. What is the basic theory that you apply in this sense?

*Chen Mingshao:* I believe all important large-scale projects should be regarded from a political point of view, especially the

199

Three Gorges project. Until now, all the technical problems including sediment deposition, possible earthquakes, national defense, financial implications, population relocation and the social impact of ecological damage, remain unsolved and are still under debate. Yet all these problems may become political if not dealt with properly.

The impact of the Yangtze River on production as well as on the daily life of the Chinese people is also a political issue. Sichuan province, the well-known "Land of Plenty," is at the upper reaches; two rich lakes known for "providing all the needs under heaven" are at the middle reaches; the provinces of Zhejiang, Anhui and Jiangxi, known as "the Lands of Fish and Rice," are at the lower reaches; and then comes the city of Shanghai, the window for our international economic contacts and communication with the outside world, at the river's mouth.

The river basin has a population of 390 million, accounts for 38.8 percent of the total population, takes up 19 percent of the land area of the country, generates 40 percent of gross national product, and enjoys the highest production per capita in all of China. The Yangtze River, regarded as the heart and artery of our country, is considered the central arena for our national development strategy. Since so many poor national minorities live in the area of the upper reaches, implementing a project of such a large scale is by no means a trivial matter, but involves significant political implications which require caution.[3]

*Gang Jian:* Could you tell me something more about the present physical conditions of the Yangtze River?

*Chen Mingshao:* First, floods are very serious and frequent, affecting large tracts of land for long periods of time. There are reservoirs on the upper reaches and little modern technology for

---

[3] This is particularly true since political tensions between the Han majority and minorities have been on the rise in recent years. Indeed, the government blundered in 1993 when the *China Daily* announced that 470,000 evacuees from the Three Gorges dam would be resettled in Xinjiang province, populated by the Uygurs who are Muslims. The announcement caused an international outcry. The Chinese government soon retracted its statement although it is still not clear where all 1.3 million to be displaced will be resettled.

flood control and water conservation. In this sense, the Yangtze is the worst river in all the world.

There are now seven large rivers in both the south and north of our country that can withstand the big 20- and 100-year floods. But the Yangtze can only stand the smaller floods, those which happen once every 10 years or so. Therefore, some think that if the Three Gorges project were built, all the problems would be automatically solved. But this is not a rational and comprehensive approach to managing the river as a whole. If it is followed, the administration of flood control and the overall development planning for the Yangtze River will not be ensured, which can only be seen as a tactical failure.

Secondly, the environment at the upper reaches is becoming more degraded. Increasing soil erosion and deforestation have caused more sedimentation and induced climatic changes as well. So, I regret to say, the physical condition of this precious river is worsening. Effective measures need to be taken immediately.

*Gang Jian:* But those supporting the immediate start of the project use the same arguments that you do when they claim that there is no alternative to constructing the project.

*Chen Mingshao:* I don't agree with them. The fact that the river needs treatment doesn't mean that the only way is to build the Three Gorges reservoir. In fact, I agree with the proposal to establish protected areas and resource development areas in the upper reaches of the Yangtze put forth by many of the affected provinces, and the suggestion that water-power stations be built at Xiangjia and Xiluodu on the upper reaches. Compared with the Three Gorges project, these stations could generate as much electric power with a similar storage capacity, but involve much less population relocation, require smaller budgets, have fewer environmental effects, and require less time to recapture the investment. On the five major tributaries (the Jinsha, Dadu, Yalong, Jialing and Wujiang rivers), at the upper reaches, 27 small- or medium-scale power stations (some are cascade water-power stations) have undergone feasibility studies, and so far, have proved better than the Three Gorges project.

*Gang Jian:* In 1985, when you were director of the Committee on Engineering Technology in the Jiu San Society, you organized discussions on the Three Gorges project and proposed to the authorities: In treating the Yangtze River, the tributaries should be dealt with first and the mainstream second. In your recent speech at the CPPCC, you emphasized the same idea. As a responsible person of a democratic party, this outspoken spirit is very admirable.

*Chen Mingshao:* Although I am an engineer, I am not a bookworm cut off from the outside world. As a student, I was quite active in the Students' Union. When I started teaching, my concern with politics remained, and brought me lots of trouble; I was labeled as an "Anti-Party and Anti-Socialist Element" in 1957 (the Anti-Rightist campaign) and was sent to the countryside. But I still refused to give up my concern for political issues. As for the Three Gorges project, I must express my differing opinion. The suggestions about the project which the Jiu San Society put forth to the Central Committee have attracted the attention of the departments in question and have also won the support of the CPPCC. There is still a long way to go towards democracy, and I would like to make my contribution to this process.

# CHAPTER TWENTY-ONE

## THE THREE GORGES PROJECT: AN UNREASONABLE OPTION FOR ELECTRICITY GENERATION
### An Account of an Interview with Luo Xibei[1]
by
Wu Jingcai[2]

Having worked almost all his life in the field of hydro-electricity, this subject should be Luo Xibei's favorite and most familiar topic of conversation. But, when referring to the grandiose Three Gorges project, he moved away from the topic of electricity generation, and urged me to consider instead the purpose of generating this electricity. So far as the project assessment is concerned, electricity production has been of primary importance. Of course, flood control and navigation are important as well, but they will generate little in the way of profits. Power production is the single most profitable function of the project. The leading group's assessment has predicted an annual output of 84 billion kWh for the project. But Luo asks an important question—where is the electricity generated by the Three Gorges project supposed to go, and whom will it serve?

---

[1] Luo Xibei is a member of the Chinese People's Political Consultative Conference, is vice-president of the Board of the China International Engineering Projects Consulting Corporation and head engineer and president of the Planning and Design Institute for Hydro-electric Resources in Beijing. Luo has held positions including chief engineer at the Survey and Design Institutes of Beijing and Chengdu, chief engineer at the Liujiaxia Gorge hydro power station, and head of design and construction of the Longyangxia Gorge hydro power station. This account was included in the original Chinese edition of *Yangtze! Yangtze!*

[2] Wu Jincai is a journalist with the Xinhua News Agency.

The present scheme is to transmit electricity to eastern and central China in order to reduce the amount of coal now required to meet regional economic demands. But according to Luo, this may not be the most reasonable option.

Luo suggested combining electrical power with coal production, in an effort to narrow the economic gap between the west and the east of China.[3] According to present calculations, the eastern areas will require between 900 and 1000 billion kWh by 2015. By then, the Three Gorges project may produce 84 billion kWh, which would fall short of the total needs. But why should the eastern part of China consume so much electricity? This, as Luo pointed out, is because a large number of enterprises which consume a disproportionate amount of energy resources are concentrated along the eastern coastal areas where energy resources are scarce. This is irrational. Why not try to reduce the pressing need for the Three Gorges project by redistributing the industries in the eastern and western parts of China?

The present pressure for an immediate start to the Three Gorges project immediately stems from an old and traditional form of economic management that transmits energy wherever it is needed, with little consideration given to the consequences, such as the losses resulting from the submersion of land, navigation problems, population relocation, and sedimentation.[4] In Luo's opinion, the government should give due consideration to economic development in the western part of China while assessing the project. It does not seem appropriate for the state to spend so much money on a project that cannot satisfy the tremendous energy needs in the eastern part of the country.

The present emphasis on eastern and central China will increase the existing economic gap between the east and west, and will eventually affect national economic growth as a whole. Luo suggested moving some of the high-energy-consumption enterprises to the west as soon as possible in order to make full use of the rich mineral and energy resources in these areas. This will be

---

[3] An increasingly serious problem in China's development and a source of considerable political conflict. See He, *China on the Edge*.
[4] This perennial problem in China's centrally planned economy generally ignored any calculation of real costs in developing such huge projects.

much more profitable and efficient than transmitting power from the west to the east of the country. This new approach would require a new hydro-electric project, of moderate scale, on the Yangtze River, thus making the Three Gorges project much less urgent and, perhaps, even unnecessary.

At the end of our interview, Luo emphasized again his preference for delaying the project. He said some calculations in the assessment might not be accurate. He called for attention to the lessons to be learned from the Gezhouba dam, which is, in Luo's opinion, a very unsuccessful project. Despite the enormous budget of Y4.8 billion, which resulted in the suspension or cancellation of some other hydro power stations in the 1970s, the Gezhouba dam has had the most severe problems with the regulation of water flow and the quality of electric power.[5]

The Gezhouba dam should have been built only after the Three Gorges project. But, in the 1970s, it was considered a preparation for the Three Gorges project. Since the scientific evaluations and criticisms of the Gezhouba project have never been made known to the public, there has been much praise for the project. In any assessment of the Three Gorges project, attention must be paid to the lessons learned from Gezhouba.

---

[5] The supply of electricity from the Gezhouba dam is erratic.

# CHAPTER TWENTY-TWO

## INTERNATIONAL OPPOSITION TO THE THREE GORGES PROJECT
### An Account of an Interview with
### Tian Fang and Lin Fatang[1]
by
Zhang Shengyou[2]

Tian Fang and Lin Fatang have worked together as the editors-in-chief of: *A Sound Distribution of Productive Forces in China*, *Population Relocation in China*, *An Outline of the History of Population Relocation in China*, and *Population Relocation in the World*, among others. Needless to say, they have shown great concern about the Three Gorges project. After careful investigation and scientific research, both objected to the launching of the project. They subsequently edited and compiled the following two books: *On a Long-Range Strategy For the Three Gorges Project* and *A Second Look at a Long-Range Strategy For the Three Gorges Project*. Both books contain a preface by Zhou Peiyuan and have been reviewed by Wang Xizhang. On several occasions, both have also been denied publication by various department heads. The following is a summary of an interview with them.

The Three Gorges dam will be the largest hydro-electric project the world has ever seen. As soon as the project was announced publicly, there was an enormous response from overseas.

On January 28, 1986, Xiong Jie (James Hsiung), a Chinese-American professor from New York University, pointed out that the project would turn the area near the Three Gorges into a

---

[1] This interview was included in the original Chinese edition of *Yangtze! Yangtze!*

[2] Zhang Shengyou is a former journalist for the *Guangming Daily* who now works for the Guangming Publishing Co.

huge water pool necessitating the resettlement of nearly one million people. Xiong argued that the construction would disrupt the environment and hygienic conditions, thereby destabilizing society and causing incalculable and long-lasting damage to the Chinese nation. In addition, local cultural treasures and scenic spots would be almost entirely lost.

Between May 26 and June 10, 1986, a group of experts took a World Bank-sponsored trip to the Three Gorges area. The experts included: D. Campbell from Canada; J. Cotrin, Brazil's representative to the Two County Committee of the Itaipu power station; L. Duscha, from the U.S. Army Corps of Engineers; D. Graybill, from Management Resources International Inc.; A. Hochstein, Louisiana State University; L. Mueller, from Austria; F. Lyra, the Brazilian director of the Export Group for the Itaipu project; J. F. Kennedy, an American sedimentation expert; B. M. Moyes, from the U.S. Bureau of Reclamation; along with hydrology and electricity experts from China.[3] Upon its return, the group submitted a report expressing many doubts and concerns centered on the following issues: geology, sedimentation, flood control, navigation, hydraulic engineering and construction, electric systems, economic analysis, and environmental issues.

Opposition to the project from Canadian scholars and experts was very strong. In August, 1987, Professor Vaclav Smil, an internationally known geographer from the University of Manitoba, contributed an essay entitled "Why the Three Gorges Dam Should Not be Constructed" to *The World Energy Resources Herald*, a Chinese domestic newspaper. He argued that such a huge dam and power station would require an enormous financial investment and a great number of well-qualified technicians.

He considered it inadvisable to work on a project that would result in so much destruction. Citing the great landslide of 1963 at Vaiont in Italy as an example, he predicted possible large-scale landslides around the proposed site of the reservoir. He suggested that building more small-scale power stations would be much more efficient economically and cost less initially.

---

[3] Campbell, Duscha, Graybill, Kennedy, and Lyra were members of the World Bank panel of experts who reviewed the Canadian feasibility study.

In May, 1986, the Canadian edition of *World Daily* carried an essay titled, "Deteriorating Natural Ecology Will Worsen With the Construction of the Three Gorges Dam," which stated that construction would induce serious natural disasters that would endanger millions of lives in the area. The paper also noted:

> Zigui county, where the home town of [the poet] Qu Yuan is located, will be completely submerged by the reservoir. Famous historical sites such as the Zhang Fei Temple, the Kong Ming tomb, and the Fenbi Temple will all disappear. As for the Baidi Tower, although it may survive, the surrounding scenery will be lost.

In another article, the newspaper quoted from a letter by four American environmental organizations arguing that, "from an environmental and social perspective, the Three Gorges project will be the most disastrous dam in the history of mankind."

In March, 1980, a 24-member U.S. delegation undertook a three-week fact-finding tour of the Three Gorges. The group was headed by Mr. Freeman, chairman of the Tennessee Valley Authority (TVA), and Mr. Higgenson, from the Bureau of Water and Energy Resources. Upon returning to the United States, Freeman stated, "In my opinion our delegation has killed the idea of a 700-foot dam that some Chinese engineers have been in love with for so long." One member of the delegation, Mr. Morris, the Commander of the U.S. Army Corps of Engineers, commented that the Three Gorges dam would be disastrous for navigation: "The results would be as if someone wanting to go up one floor were sent up to the top of a skyscraper."[4] In his summary to high-level Chinese leaders, Morris also stated:

> From the perspective of navigation, the idea of building a dam with [numerous] shiplocks and a vertical incline of 200 meters is a dubious proposition. As for the plan

---

[4] Two additional trips of scientists under contract to the U.S. Bureau of Reclamation were also made in April-June, 1981, and June-July, 1984. Unfortunately, the reports from these trips remain classified at the request of the Chinese government.

for flood control, it is also inappropriate. It's like putting all of your eggs in one basket.

Finally, Mr. Morris also questioned the merit, in terms of national security, of putting 25 million kW of electrical capacity in one place.

An American physics professor, Feng Pingguan, made the following calculation about the project: the estimated construction cost of the Three Gorges dam would be US$20 billion (approximately Y110 billion) and would require 20 years to complete. Enormous funds would be tied up in interest costs on this investment, coming to as much as $40 billion (Y220 billion). Twenty years could well make a nation prosperous; for instance, the economic take-off in Taiwan needed only 20 years, as well as that of Meiji Reform in Japan.

What will we gain by investing 20 years and $20 billion in such a huge dam? The ambition to build the dam is a grand overall plan that would involve almost every aspect of the country's economic development. Such a plan is a day-dreamer's delight and a pragmatist's nightmare, like those that dominated the "Great Leap Forward."

Every small investment must be expected to achieve future profits, which can in turn be reinvested for still greater economic returns. However, the Three Gorges project is not in line with this economic principle.

On December 6, 1988, an editorial that appeared in the *International Daily*[5] commented that there are many ways to manage the Yangtze River, and the Three Gorges project is only one of the alternatives. Plans have not been adopted to deal with the problem of soil and water conservation at the upper reaches, of the dredging of the tributary waterways, and of protecting the environment around the Three Lakes area. Similarly, work is needed on the plans for population relocation, for regional economic development and for overall economic feasibility. All of this must be dealt with before construction begins.

Since the Leading Group for the Assessment of the Three Gorges Project announced, on November 30, 1988, that "an early

---

[5] A Chinese-American newspaper.

start-up for the project is better than a delay," more than 10 Chinese newspapers in Hong Kong including *The Express, The Economic Daily, The Literary Gazette, The New Daily News, Xingdao Daily*, and *The Daily Trust*, along with Taiwan's *New Life Daily*, responded with opposition to the immediate start-up of the project. Some newspapers suggested that the total budget indicated in the assessment was an underestimation, while others suggested that funds for the Three Gorges project be put into the development of national education.

In the August 8, 1988, overseas edition of the *People's Daily*, Tian Fang noted that the final report of a feasibility study conducted by a Canadian consultancy group was expected to be submitted by the end of September.[6] The article went on to state that, according to the Canadian group, the proposed water level of the project is appropriate,[7] the benefits are feasible and the project would not have any major environmental impacts. In response Tian Fang noted:

> I was fairly shocked by the report. Over the past 30 years, hundreds of experts and scholars have been involved in the assessment, and many opinions about the project have been expressed. How could a group reach a final conclusion in favor of the project in only two years?

Finally, at a meeting of the International Rivers Network held in San Francisco in June, 1988, more than 30 experts from Indo-

---

[6] Using Canada's Access to Information law, Probe International obtained this feasibility study. Conducted by CIPM Yangtze Joint Venture, a consortium of private engineering firms (SNC-Lavalin and Acres International) and two state utilities (Hydro-Québec International and B.C. Hydro International), the study was paid for by the Canadian International Development Agency, Canada's bilateral aid agency. *Damming the Three Gorges* is a critique of the Canadian study.

[7] The Canadian study recommended a normal pool level of 160 meters and included a cautionary note from the World Bank that "The feasibility report contains evidence to indicate that increasing the normal pool level from 160 meters to 170 meters and higher would not be an economically viable proposition." See CIPM, *Three Gorges*, p. 4-1.

nesia, Malaysia, Holland, India, Canada, the United States, Australia, the Federal Republic of Germany and Brazil signed a letter asking the Chinese government to publish the feasibility study by the Canadian consultative group for an open discussion.[8]

---

[8] The letter is available from Probe International in Toronto, Canada.

# Part Four

## The Essays

# CHAPTER TWENTY-THREE

## TEN CONTROVERSIAL ISSUES ON THE THREE GORGES PROJECT[1]
by
Lu Qinkan

Opinions differ both at home and abroad over whether to construct the Three Gorges project. The main points of view in support of and in opposition to the project will now be summarized.

## I. Construction

*Pro:* The location and environment of the dam site are very favorable. The project will help solve, in an efficient manner, the problems of flood control, electricity generation, and navigation. Therefore, this grand project should be carried out as soon as possible so that the dream of "A Smooth Lake Over the High Gorges" can be realized in our generation. Some have even vowed that they will not rest until they see the completion of the project.

*Con:* The immediate start-up of the project is not advisable, considering the scale of certain problems, mainly: excessive investment requirements, a long construction period, extensive population relocation, sedimentation that will hinder navigation, increased chances of flooding in the upper reaches and destruction of the natural environment. The priority at present should be given to work on the tributaries in order to meet the energy requirements for the second phase of the national economic plan, which is to double the gross national product by the end of this century. In other words, plans that can bring immediate results should be

---

[1] This essay was included in the original Chinese edition of *Yangtze! Yangtze!*

carried out first, such as flood-control projects in the plains, establishment of hydro-electric power stations on the tributaries, and dredging of the main waterways. Some in the Expert's Group on Flood Control are totally opposed to the Three Gorges project, arguing that a disaster of unprecedented scale would result if the dam became a military target.

## II. Flood Control

*Pro:* The Three Gorges project will play a key role in flood control at the lower and middle reaches of the Yangtze, and no alternatives exist that could have the same or nearly the same result. The dam will have a capacity for storage and flood diversion of 9.5 to 22 billion m³ for the areas around the middle reaches. If a flood as serious as the one in 1870 occurred, the Jingjiang River dikes might burst, and hundreds of thousands, even millions, of lives might be lost.

*Con:* All along the Yangtze River, there are sources of floods from both the upper reaches and the lower and middle reaches. The Three Gorges project can only control flooding from the Chuanjiang River[2] in the upper reaches, but is helpless against floods coming from the Xiangjiang, Zishui, Yuanshui, Lishui, Hanjiang, and Ganjiang rivers and many other tributaries in the lower and middle reaches.

If a flood as serious as that which occurred in 1954 is to be avoided, 50 billion m³ of water will need to be diverted at the middle and lower reaches. Yet the dam will only work for the area above Chenglingji, which means there will still be 30 to 40 billion m³ of water left to be controlled.[3] Wuhan is a key city to protect from floods. Yet the Three Gorges dam will neither lower Wuhan's water level, nor divert water from the nearby areas, leaving it helpless in the face of flooding from Jiangxi and Anhui provinces in the lower reaches. Therefore, the flood-control ability of the project is very limited.

---

[2] This section of the Yangtze, stretching from Yibin to Yichang, is 1,030 kilometers in length.
[3] Because the maximum storage and flood diversion capacity of the Three Gorges dam is only 22 billion m³.

The weak Jingjiang River dikes did stand up to the big flood in 1870, which had flowed southward towards Songzikou and then into Dongting Lake.[4] This was quite a rare case. Today, Songzikou has its own diversion channels and the Jingjiang River dikes have been strengthened, greatly reducing the possibility of an incident resulting in the death of millions. So, using the flood protection argument to hasten the project is a bit far-fetched. Moreover, the flood level in Chongqing in 1870 was 4.7 meters higher than that of the serious flood in Sichuan in 1981.[5] If the Three Gorges reservoir is used to store flood waters along with increased sedimentation, this will raise the water level at Chongqing and consequently increase the chances of a flood in Sichuan province. Since there is a chance of a big flood along the Yangtze River occurring every five or 10 years, there is now an urgent need to strengthen and heighten the river bank, to set up more safety facilities in the risky areas, to continue with the construction of reservoirs on the tributaries, and do more work on water and soil conservation, so that the flood-control capacity of the Yangtze River can be gradually increased.

## III. Electrical Power

*Pro.* Most of the waterpower resources along the Yangtze are concentrated in the southwest. But they are quite scarce in the east where there are also limited coal resources. The location of the dam will make it an important source of electrical power to the areas of central and eastern China. Based on a normal pool level of 175 meters, the dam would generate 17,680 MW with the annual production of 84 Twh of electric power. Thus, the dam can

---

[4] "The peak flood level recorded in 1870 was 27.36 meters.... It was 2.37 meters lower than the peak flood level of 1954. The total volume of flood flow for a four-month period was far less than in 1954." See Luk and Whitney, *Megaproject*, pp. 223-224.

[5] Although the water levels in the 1981 flood were higher than those in the 1870 flood, the 1870 event flooded Chongqing whereas the 1981 event did not. This is because the 1981 event was caused by flooding in the tributaries downstream of the proposed dam site whereas the 1870 event was caused by upstream flooding of the Yangtze River mainstream.

share some of the work of the thermal power plants, because hydro-electric power will replace 40 million tonnes of coal burned annually, reducing the pressure for the production and transportation of coal.[6]

*Con:* It will be 12 years before the Three Gorges project generates power and 20 years before it goes into full operation. Such a long delay can hardly help solve the immediate problems of serious energy shortage in nearby areas.[7] At this time, priority should be given to building more water-power stations and thermal plants in the tributary areas, which have the advantages of being small in scale, requiring less construction time, and achieving faster economic results. But, if these small projects were canceled in favor of the Three Gorges project, the rate of development of the power industry in the near term would certainly be slowed, delaying the whole process of national economic development.

## IV. Navigation

*Pro:* When the backwater of the reservoir reaches Chongqing, a series of rapids will be covered, thus making it possible to control the slope of the descent and speed of the water. This will

---

[6] In all likelihood, the vast majority of China's coal-fired power is uneconomic due to the inefficiency of coal mining and of coal-fired generation. In liberalized electricity markets, the generation form of choice is high efficiency gas technologies, or cogeneration based on fossil fuels. Cogeneration has an efficiency two to three times that of a conventional coal-fired station.

[7] It is estimated that "at the 1982 per capita electricity consumption level of 325 kWh, population growth would absorb the entire output of Three Gorges in 16 years—only one year longer than the projected 15-year-construction period for the dam. This assumes [the continuation of] the current low living standards; the time needed for the power consumption rate from new additions to China's population to absorb the $57.2 \times 10^9$ kWh annual output expected from the 13,000 MW installed capacity generating plant would be even less if living standards were to improve." See Philip M. Fearnside, "China's Three Gorges Dam: 'Fatal' Project or Step Toward Modernization?," *World Development*, Vol. 16, No. 5 (1988), p. 626.

make it possible to sail 10,000-tonne ships rather than the current 3,000-tonne vessels. As a result, the carrying capacity and transportation efficiency will be increased and shipping costs reduced. In this way, the demand for 50 million tonnes of freight per year in the upper reaches can be met. At the same time, the water level during the low-water season will be increased by reservoir regulation, thus improving navigability from Yichang downstream.

*Con:* The Three Gorges reservoir will be located below Wanxian County, making it a perpetual backwater area where navigation will certainly be improved. But, in the area near the end of the reservoir, things could be very difficult. When the backwater level is lowered, the natural river channels will be exposed with their huge sediment deposits that could block navigation. When the clean water from the reservoir washes down the river bed, the water level at Yichang may be lowered, in which case the water level in the locks of the Gezhouba dam will also be lowered, thereby hindering navigation. Improving navigation in the Chuanjiang River area can be better achieved by dredging the waterways in stages, which would increase the annual transport capacity from the present five million tonnes to 18 million tonnes by the year 2000 and 30 million tonnes by 2015. All this needs much less investment than installing shiplocks at the Three Gorges. Only when the waterways of both the tributaries and the mainstream are dredged can an overall network of water transportation be established.

## V. The Control of Sedimentation

*Pro:* There is less sediment in the Yangtze than in the Yellow River. In spite of serious soil erosion due first to deforestation and then to wasteland reclamation on the slopes in the upper reaches, there has been little change in the deposition of sediment in the river.[8] During the high-water season, the water level at the dam will be lowered to the level required for flood control. When this season is passed, muddy water will be replaced with clean water.

---

[8] In contrast to this optimistic conclusion, data cited by He Bochuan suggests that sedimentation has increased dramatically in the Yangtze over the last several decades. See He, *China on the Edge*, p. 31.

This method can clear away most of the sediment. After 100 years, the sediment will be washed away and a balance restored in such a way that the capacity of the reservoir can be kept at between 86 and 92 percent.

Of course, according to models of the backwater area at the end of the reservoir, sedimentation may indeed become serious in the main trough at Chongqing. Sand may pile up, blocking the mouth of the Jialing River, and the flood level in Chongqing will greatly increase. But the sedimentation problem can be solved by improving the regulation system in the reservoir, modifying port facilities, and dredging the river.

*Con:* The Yangtze River ranks fourth behind the Yellow, Brahmaputra, and Ganges rivers in terms of sedimentation. In recent years, especially in 1981 and 1984, the annual water volume was about average, but sediment deposition was 70 percent and 30 percent higher respectively, and the amount of sediment deposited by the river continues to increase. This problem will become more serious unless water and soil conservation measures are strengthened and soil erosion controlled. Since flood control is the major purpose of the dam, its reservoir water level must be raised when necessary and at the same time, the sand flow must be held back. Sedimentation at the end of the reservoir will inevitably increase and ultimately endanger navigation.

So far, there is no satisfactory solution to the sedimentation problem. Moreover, the relatively clean water from the reservoir will cause erosion of the embankments at the area below Yichang, which might endanger the Jingjiang River dikes. After the wash-down sediment is deposited in the river section between Chenglingji and Wuhan, it will harm flood control in the areas around Dongting Lake and Wuhan.[9]

## VI. Population Relocation

According to the plan, the normal pool level in the reservoir would be 175 meters, below which, according to the 1985 census,

---

[9] For an analysis of sedimentation problems in the Three Gorges project, see Qian Ning et al., "Some Aspects of the Sedimentation at the Three Gorges Project," in *Megaproject*, eds. Luk and Whitney, pp. 121-160.

there is a population of 725,500. When national population growth and the resettlement of entire cities, towns, and factories, are taken into account, the number of people involved could reach 1.13 million by 2008. The rising water level caused by sedimentation might bring the figure to 1.3 million.

*Pro:* If a spirit of self-reliance and hard work is encouraged, plus compensation of Y11.1 billion, the population relocation can be completed in 20 years. After the reservoir starts generating power, revenue retained at the rate of Y0.003 per kWh produced should be used to pay for population relocation and for construction around the reservoir area. The counties and towns in the area concerned have shown their willingness to be relocated. And they are anxious for an early decision, so they can start developing a new economy in a relocated area and achieve prosperity in the near future.

*Con:* Massive population relocation like this is rare both at home and abroad. Outside China, the biggest resettlement of this kind involved only 100,000 people, and some projects have had to be abandoned because the population involved was too large.

China's largest resettlement project took place during construction of the reservoirs at the Sanmenxia Gorge, the Xin'anjiang River and the mouth of the Danjiang River. Each case involves more than 300,000 people.

The land around the future Three Gorges reservoir is already overworked and its food production is insufficient. To bring more than one million additional people into the area exceeds the environmental capacity of the land. At present, those who have been promised compensation for migration will be happy, and there are even others outside the reservoir area who are eager to be included, just to get "extra" compensation. But things might become quite different when relocation actually takes place. If the compensation falls short of expectations, social and even political problems could arise.

## VII. Environmental Protection

*Pro:* According to the 175-meter normal pool level, the storage capacity of the reservoir is 3.93 billion $m^3$, with a flood-control storage capacity of 22.15 billion $m^3$. Compared with the volume of water flowing in the Yangtze River (453 billion $m^3$

annually at Yichang), the storage capacity of the reservoir is relatively small. Shaped like the gorges, the reservoir will not seriously endanger the local climate, water quality, and temperature. The power produced by the reservoir is a clean energy resource, and will reduce the pollution now caused by the burning of coal. The Three Gorges will become a more attractive scenic spot after the reservoir is completed. Historical relics in danger of being submerged can always be moved to other places. In order to maintain the environmental balance and reduce the damage caused by the submergence of land resulting from the reservoir construction, a more satisfactory plan can be worked out to better facilitate the relocation and reestablishment of cities.

*Con:* The project will seriously endanger the environment and natural resources of the gorges; for example, the land submerged by the dam and reservoir construction cannot be recovered. Following the 175-meter proposal, the project will submerge up to 357,000 *mu* of arable land and 74,000 *mu* of orange groves, which make up the richest land in the area. In the 19 counties involved, hilly areas constitute 96 percent of the land while plains account for only 4 percent. After these relatively flat arable areas are submerged, resettlement will have to be in the hills, where the vegetation will inevitably be destroyed and the soil stripped. Furthermore, a large number of relics below the 180-meter mark will be damaged and the natural beauty of the area ruined.

Along the banks of the reservoir area are 214 hidden landslides, which will become active after being soaked by the reservoir. Being more than 100 meters deep, the reservoir could also cause earthquakes. If landslides and earthquakes induce one another, the entire project will be threatened. If the dam is subject to attack, the biggest flood in the history of the Yangtze River would likely occur. Such a disaster could be catastrophic for the lower reaches.

## VIII. Technology

Some important technological problems are beyond present domestic and international standards. Consider the following figures:

| PROGRAM | THREE GORGES PROJECT | DOMESTIC STANDARDS | INTER-NATIONAL STANDARDS |
|---|---|---|---|
| Capacity of hydro-electric generating set / Diameter of rotor wheel in water turbine | 680 MW/ 9.5 m | 320 MW/ 6.0 m | 700 MW/ 9.223 m |
| Multi-level shiplocks / Width x length | 5 levels / 34x280 m | 2 levels / 8x56 m | 4 levels / 18x100 m |
| Total lifting height | 113 m | 43 m | 67 m |
| Level one largest water head | 49.5 m | 27 m | 34.5 m |
| Total weight of vertical ship lifting | 11,500 tonnes | 450 tonnes | 8,800 tonnes |
| Lifting height | 113 m | 50 m | 73 m |
| Length of cofferdam at the upper reaches / Height/water depth | 1,070 / 84 / 60 m | 895 / 50 / 18 m | 580 / 90 / 40 m |
| Fill/largest volume per month | 6.33 million / 1.5 million m$^3$ | 2.74 million / 1.03 million m$^3$ | 5.75 million / 1.5 million m$^3$ |
| Annual concrete depositing strength | 4.1 million m$^3$ | 2.03 million m$^3$ | 3.03 million m$^3$ |

*Pro:* These technical difficulties can be overcome with Chinese experience and imported technology.

*Con:* It might be difficult to overcome some of these unprecedented technical difficulties.

## IX. Scale of Construction[10]

The height of the dam and the water level (above sea level) are the major factors to be considered in determining the construction load of the project, the storage capacity of the reservoir, and the installed capacity. This has always been a controversial issue. Needless to say, the higher the level for normal storage conditions, the more efficient the reservoir will be for flood control, power generation, and navigation; at the same time, losses caused by submerging land, relocating so many people and damaging the environment will increase proportionally. As a result, investment will be larger and the construction period longer.

In the early days, Dr. Sun Yat-sen and Yun Zhen put forward proposals to build locks and small-scale cascade projects at the Three Gorges. In the 1940s, J. L. Savage, an American, suggested a hydro-electric station with a normal pool level of more than 200 meters. In the 1950s, the Yangtze Valley Planning Office proposed a project with a 235-meter water level. In 1958, at the Chengdu conference, the Party Central Committee decided that the future dam should not be higher than 200 meters.[11] In the 1980s, the proposed water level was lowered to 150 meters. But recently, it was raised to 175 meters by the leading group's assessment.

The arguments about water level continue. A 160 meter proposal was suggested by some senior hydro-electric experts, as well as by the Canadian feasibility study of the project.[12] Others proposed a double project, that is to build a low dam near Peiling

---

[10] The material in this section was not presented in a "pro" and "con" format.

[11] For a review of various decisions on the Three Gorges project from its inception until the late 1980s, see Hong Qingyu, "A review of the Work during the Early Stages of the Three Gorges Project," in *Megaproject*, eds. Luk and Whitney, pp. 40-63.

[12] The $14 million feasibility study was conducted by a Canadian consortium in 1988. For a complete evaluation of that study, see Barber and Ryder, eds., *Damming*.

in addition to a high one at the Three Gorges, so as to make full use of the resources, and to help navigation around the Chongqing area. Some navigation departments and the Chongqing Municipal Bureau hope that the level can be raised to 180 meters, so that a fleet of large-capacity freight vessels could have a better chance of directly reaching Chongqing. There are still others who favor a level of 200 meters, or even higher, arguing that flood waters and the water level during the low-water season could be better regulated, or that water could be diverted from the reservoir to flow northward.

## X. Investment Plans

The investment estimates vary, depending on when the calculations are made and on the scale of construction and the interest rate during the construction period. Based on a 175-meter normal pool level plan, proposed by the Ministry of Water Resources and Electric Power, and on the basis of the price index at the end of 1986, it was estimated that the key construction would cost Y18.5 billion, population relocation would cost Y11.1 billion, and long-distance power transmission would cost Y6.3 billion, totaling Y36 billion. This represents static investment only and does not include interest costs.

*Pro:* Apart from state-allocated funds, investment funds can be raised in various ways, including: 1) raising foreign capital funds by issuing state bonds abroad; 2) issuing domestic construction bonds; 3) switching from oil to coal and selling the oil to foreign countries; 4) delaying the repayment of loans and credits for the construction of the Gezhouba dam, and using profits generated by the dam; 5) using income from the partially completed Three Gorges power plant.[13]

*Con:* Considering that static investment is Y36 billion, the Three Gorges project will be an extraordinarily large program for our national capital construction. Because of the long construction period, interest on the funds should be taken into account. In the next few years, large amounts of capital funds will be needed to develop energy resources, transportation, and raw materials, as

---

[13] Electricity can be generated before the entire project is completed.

well as to conduct research in education and technology.[14] It will be extremely difficult for the state to meet these huge financial demands, and, at the same time, provide funds for the Three Gorges project. Once the project is started, many other development programs will have to be sacrificed.

The interest rates for overseas bonds are very high. How can foreign currency be duly returned? Is it really workable to expect the Gezhouba dam and the Three Gorges dam to turn their income into construction funds without repaying their loans and interest? All these problems, and many more, still remain unanswered. Under such circumstances, the implementation of the project should be carefully considered.

---

[14] Growing deficiencies in investment in education and other social infrastructure are analyzed in He, *China on the Edge*, pp. 157-74.

# CHAPTER TWENTY-FOUR

## RESETTLEMENT IN THE THREE GORGES PROJECT[1]
by
Dai Qing

In contemporary China, many decision makers ignore the possible consequences of flooding the upper stream of the Yangtze River,[2] and of blocking this vital waterway for 20 years in order to construct the Three Gorges project. China needs a solid financial environment for its economic reform, but decision makers insist instead on building a super dam at China's most beautiful scenic spot on its largest river. The project will force the resettlement of between one million and 1.6 million people.

China's official media have been eager to depict happy peasants thanking the government for their decision to move them out of their poverty-ridden villages on the Yangtze and give them new homes, jobs and farmland. But this is not the whole story. The Three Gorges valley—which has nurtured Chinese civilization, enjoys beautiful weather, and serves as the transportation hub of one of China's richest provinces—has been denied economic development for years. The "wise decisions of the Communist Party," as they are often referred to in the media, have, in practice, done great harm to the region. For example, the policy of "using grain as the key link to develop collective agriculture," has caused deforestation and soil erosion. The policy of "larger population, greater labor force, and increased working morale," led to the doubling of the Chinese population from 400 million to 800 million in 30 years. But it also led to the destruction of forests to make room for farmland to encourage "self reliance."

---

[1] This essay, written in March, 1993, was not part of the original Chinese edition of *Yangtze! Yangtze!*
[2] Including the loss of 430,000 *mu* of farmland, about half of the total paddy land of the area.

While these harmful policies were being implemented, the country's top leadership undertook a protracted debate on whether to build the dam. Local residents, however, were never consulted. They had no choice but to wait for the decision from the top, which would tell them whether they would be moved, when to move, how to move and where to move to. As the proposed dam site, or "submerged area," had been denied any opportunities for economic development before the leadership reached their final decision, the poor local residents could do little more than advise the media of their willingness to be resettled and their gratefulness to the state.

Overlooking repeated warnings from dissidents, scientists, sociologists and environmentalists that the Three Gorges resettlement program would stir up social unrest and create many unforeseen environmental effects, the determined dam builders entrusted the job of resettlement to Li Boning, an ex-official from the Ministry of Water Resources and Electric Power. Li is viewed by many as being extremely brash and reckless. He has never implemented a resettlement project before.

Li argues that the resettlement program for the Three Gorges project is different from the forced inter-provincial and inter-county resettlements used by the Chinese government since the 1950s (when people received "one-time compensation").[3] The Three Gorges strategy has been termed "population relocation for development" and posits that people will be resettled up on the hillsides of the Yangtze valley rather than in other communities. The Chinese have termed this "the local solution." But there are several problems with this strategy.

Population relocation for development is a theoretical concept useful only for propaganda purposes. Since there are no cases of successful implementation,[4] the new approaches have not been corroborated by experience. Moreover, officials have not even devised a plan or model to guide implementation. Finally, even if there were one or two successful trial applications, there is no

---

[3] Usually a simple cash settlement for those being moved.
[4] See the discussion by Chen Guojie, Research Fellow at the Institute of Mountain Area Disasters and Environment of Chengdu, Chinese Academy of Sciences, in Tian and Lin, *A Third Look*.

evidence the program could be successfully applied to a resettlement project as complicated as the Three Gorges.

The Three Gorges lacks the environmental capacity for resettling such a large number of people. The environmental balance is very fragile. The vegetative cover has been reduced from 20 percent in the 1950s to 10 percent at present. In some areas close to the river bank, the cover is as low as 5 percent. Farmland with a slope of over 25 degrees (which is not permitted legally in China) accounts for 30 to 50 percent of the total farmland in the resettlement area. Soil erosion, which affects 80 percent of farmland, also poses a serious problem for resettlement. About 40 million tonnes of sediment is flushed into the river annually. The dense forests that used to cover the Gorges area have gradually turned into bushes, then grass, and now the whole area could become barren. Such a degraded environment cannot sustain the quality of life of present or future generations unless emergency measures, such as tree planting, grass growing and the suspension of farming, are adopted immediately.

Of the Three Gorges project's Y57 billion budget, resettlement accounts for Y18 billion, or Y16,000 per person. This figure does not, however, take into account increased costs due to pollution and soil erosion resulting from the process of resettlement, the expenses of future resettlement should the dam silt up, or the compensation now being demanded by the residents whose homes and land will be shared by the new settlers.

Even without considering these additional costs, the current resettlement budget remains inadequate. In 1990, the average per capita cost for resettlement exceeded Y20,000, Y4,000 more than will be provided for the Three Gorges project. For the Ertan Hydro-electric project, on a tributary of the Yangtze River, the figure reached Y36,000 per person. If Li is confident that only Y18 billion will be sufficient for resettlement, then let the public be informed of the detailed plans. If not, the people should be told as soon as possible. Li and other dam proponents' use of the media to conceal the truth is not something new. They are simply using a small budget to get the project approved, knowing they can increase it afterwards.[5]

Qian Zhengying, ex-minister of the Ministry of Water Resources and Electric Power and the head of the leading group, stated in 1992:

> We have learned many lessons from previous resettlement programs. During the Cultural Revolution, people from places like Danjiangkou and Xin'anjiang [Zhejiang province] came to Beijing to protest their fate. I told the people in the Ministry of Water Resources and Electric power that I took these criticisms very seriously. Resettlement is an issue of economic and political significance.

Despite such statements, the judicial structure in China has never held decision makers responsible for the effects of forcible resettlement. Rather, decision makers are above the law: they are rewarded by the Party if projects are successful, but are exempt from penalty when projects fail.

Chinese people have suffered the consequences of numerous policy disasters. This time, however, when the decision concerns the beautiful Three Gorges and more than one million people, the old decision-making model should not be used.

---

[5] This appears to be happening. See Appendix E, in which a recent State Council Examination Committee estimates that the cost of the Three Gorges project has risen to Y75.1 billion (static investment) and Y224 billion (dynamic investment).

# CHAPTER TWENTY-FIVE

## HIGH DAM: THE SWORD OF DAMOCLES[1]
by
Yang Lang[2]

On December 22, 1988, then U.S. president Ronald Reagan issued a televised threat against a Libyan chemical plant in the depths of the North African desert. The attack did not take place, but the impact was far-reaching.

As a result of the threat, Libya was put on a war alert, and residents started fleeing the capital en masse. According to western news agencies, people were fleeing because of a fear of chemical leaks, since the plant was only 96 kilometers away from the capital. Although he did not bomb the plant, President Reagan did successfully "psychologically bombard Colonel Qaddafi." Then U.S. secretary of state, George Shultz, made it clear on January 5, 1989, that America was deliberately making Qaddafi uncomfortable.

The threat to the chemical plant caused havoc throughout Libya. After carefully studying this event, a new term, "designated deterrence," was coined by our military analysts to refer to this kind of military threat. While the international situation on the whole is developing toward relaxation, regional conflicts and crises are still occurring in many areas. The power and impact of this type of psychological deterrence cannot be overestimated.

---

[1] This essay was included in the original Chinese edition of *Yangtze! Yangtze!*

[2] Yang Lang is deputy director of the Department of Domestic Political Affairs, *China Youth News*. He expresses gratitude for the assistance provided by General Tan Shanhe, General Xi Guangyi, Lieutenant-Colonel Wang Xiaojiang, Captain Qi Changming, and Captain Wang Jiang. Notes 3 and 4 were written by the author.

The question of whether China needs or has the capacity to employ such methods, and at the same time whether we are vulnerable to such threats, should be a focus for discussion when assessing the Three Gorges project from a military perspective.

Experts have pointed out that the construction of the Three Gorges dam would threaten our national defense. Sichuan's Political Consultative Conference Investigation Group stated:

> If a war breaks out, the Three Gorges dam will inevitably become a primary target. Should the dam be destroyed, large cities in the lower and middle reaches would immediately be submerged, resulting in incalculable losses....[3]

Those who are for launching the project believe that:

> There have always been threats of a modern war, and the dam has large gates at its base that could let the stored water out very quickly. At most it would take seven days to reduce the water level to that of flood-control level. Even if the dam were blown up, the rushing water would be constrained by the narrow valley (200 to 300 meters in width) of the Nanjinguan pass in the lower reaches. This could protect the cofferdam and the foundation of the dam and reduce the volume of flood water, thereby limiting land areas affected and preventing the disaster from involving the entire lower and middle reaches. Therefore, the threat of a flood disaster resulting from an attack should by no means be a deciding factor in the construction of the Three Gorges dam.[4]

## I. The Threat of a "Modern War" and Possible Countermeasures

Generally, there are warnings of coming conflicts between countries, or between groups of countries. Such warnings might

---

[3] *Science News*, 14 June 1986.
[4] *People's Daily*, overseas ed., 28 November 1988.

include military friction on the borders, deteriorating relations, concentration of troops, or theater confrontations, all of which normally require 10 days to one month of preparation. In this sense, the signs of war are obvious.

But future patterns of war may be entirely different. Politicians are faced with the sometimes conflicting goals of protecting state interests and the strategic interests of the region, and taking all possible means to avoid serious damage to the national economy through an all-out war. For these reasons, "surgical strikes," or "single-target attacks" have become an increasingly popular strategy of modern warfare; examples include the long-distance surprise attack on the Libyan capital by the U.S. Air Force in 1985 and the two successful strikes by the Israeli Air Force against the Iraqi nuclear facility.[5] In many of these cases, there is no forewarning at all. On the other hand, even if war is impending, it is very difficult to predict when it will take place, whether it will be a long- or short-range strike, and what the strategic or tactical targets might be.

In the face of war, the Three Gorges dam would place the military and politicians in a dilemma: If the water is left in the reservoir, a disaster of massive proportions could occur were an enemy to successfully bomb the dam; If, however, the water is let out of the reservoir, to mobilize for a possible attack, there would be serious economic consequences and the possibility that no attack would take place. In other words, it is possible that future enemies could use the threat of an attack to inflict serious economic consequences on the Chinese people. We shall discuss this point in detail later.

## II. On the Assertion That Only Limited Disaster Would Result from a Collapse of the Dam

It is necessary to analyze the possible effects of a dam collapse to properly assess the project. In this area, there may be some differences between the analysis from a military point of view and that of the department in charge of water resource

---

[5] The hi-tech nature of the 1991 Persian Gulf War, which was closely observed in China, can only heighten such concerns.

construction. While direct losses from disasters caused by the collapse of dams may appear restricted to the local environment, the indirect effects can be much more extensive. For example, while the bursting of the Huayuankou dam[6] in 1938 did not prevent invading Japanese troops from driving southward, large areas of land all the way to Anhui province and the northern part of Jiangsu province were affected by the flooding waters. This flooding created serious political problems for the Nationalist government and gave Chiang Kai-shek the lasting stigma of "the historical criminal" who caused the loss of hundreds of thousands of lives.

In 1954, in order to control floods in the Jingjiang River, the diversion of flood water affected 19 million people, and resulted in the loss of more than 30,000 lives and the interruption of railway lines between Beijing and Guangdong for 100 days, even though every effort was made to limit the consequences of the disaster.

The Banqiao reservoir in Henan province, with only 490 million $m^3$ of water storage, collapsed in 1975, submerging a city and four counties, killing more than 10,000 people, and suspending rail travel between Beijing and Guangdong for 18 days. According to military analysts, should the Gezhouba dam which stores 2.3 billion $m^3$ of water burst, it would be catastrophic for the middle reaches along both banks of the Yangtze River within Hubei province. It would endanger the city of Wuhan and disrupt communications between Beijing and Guangdong for at least two months. So, if the Three Gorges dam with a 185-meter water level and a reservoir that stores 15.7 billion $m^3$ of water bursts, the catastrophe would not simply be a "localized disaster."

---

[6] In June, 1938, the Nationalist army blew up the flood-control walls in the Huayuankou section of the Yellow River, north of Zhengzhou, in an attempt to prevent Japanese invaders from attacking the city of Zhengzhou, therefore endangering Wuhan, the headquarters of the Nationalist government. Three thousand square kilometers of farmland in Henan, Anhui, and Jiangsu provinces were inundated by the flood, tens of thousands of people were drowned and many became homeless. Despite this, the Japanese army stepped up its attack along the Yangtze and took over Wuhan on October 25, 1938.

### 1.   Impact of the Disaster—the Loss of Effective Strength

Central China is an important strategic area in war time and a very desirable place for stationing troops in peace tim.

Within the three military regions of central China, there are 10 army groups, two armored divisions, 28 infantry divisions, and three divisions of paratroops. These forces represent 100 percent of the paratroop forces, 45 percent of the army troops, 38 percent of the infantry, and 20 percent of the armored divisions in China.

Should the dam burst, these troops would be subject to floods. Not only would the country's defensive military strength be affected, but also its strategic striking forces, including such paramilitary forces as national defense research groups, reserve forces, scientific research groups studying national defense, iron and steel ordnance industries, and communication and transportation facilities. Such losses would be unbearable in a time of war.

### 2.   Impact of the Disaster—the Cutting of Communication, Transportation and Energy Supplies

Military analysts argue that, should the Three Gorges dam burst, rail transportation between Beijing and Guangdong would be completely destroyed by flood waters, necessitating complete reconstruction.

Even if reserve forces were not seriously damaged, their mobility and flexibility would be substantially reduced by the suspension of travel between Beijing and Guangdong, the suspension of shipping on the Yangtze by the destruction of the shiplocks, the underdevelopment of the transportation system and the poorly designed system of railway lines, the lack of alternate routes on roadways, and inadequate air transportation. Under such conditions, reserve forces could not be transported to the southeast and the southwest.

If we assume, optimistically, that within seven days of a war alert the water level of the reservoir could be lowered to the warning level, a substantial reduction of the electricity supplied to central, east, and south China would result, causing the fast-turning wheels of economic preparation for war to be drastically slowed down. This, in turn, would reduce the war-sustaining capability of Chinese industrial enterprises. It must be emphasized, however, that the time between the launching and arrival of modern strategic weapons is not counted in days but in minutes and seconds, and the precision of their impact on target is between seven and 150 meters.

### 3. Impact of the Disaster—the Increase in the Tasks for Maintaining Internal Security

At first warning, there would be a reduced water level in the Three Gorges reservoir, an acute shortage of energy, and a strain on the supply of electricity for production and daily consumption; such processes would inevitably induce factors of instability both socially and psychologically. In order to maintain military production and social stability and mobilize reserve forces, strength would have to be diverted from the military forces to meet the above-mentioned internal needs.

### 4. Impact of the Disaster—the Competition for Equipment and Weapons

Should strategic reserve forces be insufficiently large or concentrated to meet the demands of war and the sustained economic shortages of wartime, we must consider the possibility of fighting a war within national boundaries. Although this is still far from having a place on today's agenda, we must consider the following: the destruction of the Three Gorges dam would create in the center of the country a body of water with a surface area of tens of thousands of square kilometers, which would give rise to a serious new situation with considerable military consequences. Any military maneuvers would have to navigate around this body of water, thereby reducing mobility and increasing exposure to attack. The key to overcoming these difficulties lies in competitive equipment and sophisticated weapons. It would be very difficult for our troops to gain the upper hand in this area, even in the next century.

So the edge of the sword would be very sharp. The disaster caused by the collapse of the dam would not just be "a restrained flood in a narrow pass of 200 to 300 meters in the river valley," but a total catastrophe.

After looking at the possible effects of disasters caused by the collapse of the dam in wartime, we shall now look at possible effects of the dam's collapse on national defense in peacetime.

## III. The Concepts of "The Degree of Safety" and "The Degree of Risk"

Since World War II, there have been tremendous changes and developments in the national defense policies of the United States and the Soviet Union and in their use of strategic deterrence to achieve their respective national interests. The formulation of a strategic starting point, in fact, reflects an assessment of national security interests in case of war. In actual practice, a state of security is sought by working out strategic objectives and carrying out strategic maneuvers, so as to contain or remove the dangers facing the nation.

In this sense, the Three Gorges project has not been adequately assessed in terms of national defense and the threat of war. And, yet, it is not only the war scenario described above that could lead to catastrophe. Many experts have noted the possibility of earthquakes being induced by such a large reservoir, and examples from both home and abroad abound.[7] In addition, landslides caused by the reservoir could result in surging waves that could, in turn, threaten the security of other reservoir dams. The landslides that occurred after completion of the Gezhouba dam, and the recent collapse of the Yanziyan cliff at the Three Gorges, clearly demonstrate the seriousness of these threats. Satellite photos have shown tangible movement of a huge body of rock on the Yushan slope on the upper reaches of the Yangtze River. Should this rock fall on the dam, severe damage would occur.

Unquestionably, there exist many potentially dangerous factors, many of which have yet to be recognized. Here "Murphy's law" may well apply: "If anything can go wrong, it will." The tragedy of the U.S. Challenger space shuttle is a case in point. In

---

[7] The Koyna dam in India initiated an earthquake that registered approximately 6.5 on the Richter scale. The earthquake occurred in an area that had not been seismically active, killing 200 people and rocking Bombay.

life, some of the probabilities of danger can be calculated, allowing us to think in terms of the degree of risk. In fact, such calculations regulate all production and all of the activities in our lives. In order to reduce the degree of risk, it is necessary to invest heavily in preventive measures or "lightning rods."

## IV. "A Lightning Rod" for National Defense

Should the Three Gorges reservoir be built, an enormous basin of water would be created, threatening people and property along the middle reaches. In 1984, when floods threatened, newspapers warned that there were two huge basins of water, the Guanting and Miyun reservoirs, above the city of Beijing. This resulted in the construction of large-scale dikes and embankments as a preventive measure against possible floods. Even if the geological structure of the Three Gorges reservoir were sound, there would still be a need for "lightning rods."

In terms of national defense, this would include the following measures:

1.  In order to limit the possible losses of troops and equipment caused by a dam collapse, military reserve forces would have to be redeployed. In case of war or a flood disaster, consideration would have to be given to dividing the reserve forces into two bodies, one in the north and the other in the south, so as to make it possible for troops to move quickly in either direction, should the need arise.

2.  It would be necessary to arrange troops in accordance with new points of military importance. After the construction of the dam, the Yangtze River would be divided into two navigation parts: the first extending from the upper reaches to the middle reaches; and the second from there to the lower reaches. Given the country's expected economic development, the shiplocks at the dam would eventually serve as a crucial link in the communication chains between the north and south and east and west, making them no less important than Wuhan at the very center of China. In order to guarantee the safety of this important link, extensive military forces and weapons would have to be stationed at the shiplocks in order to protect them.

3.   New military installations and equipment are needed for this purpose, which would have to include strategies for dealing with such a large surface of water.

4.   To deploy long-range conventional offensive weapons of high precision and enhance the capacity of such weapons to penetrate the enemy defense, a strong deterrence must be formulated.

5.   An advance-warning system must be established to shorten the time lag and increase the capacity to sustain a first strike.

In order to guarantee national survival and reduce the threat of, or remove, "the sword of Damocles," the above-mentioned military developments must be carried out simultaneously with the construction of the Three Gorges project. This would call for a short-term concentrated investment of at least Y10 billion, which has never been included in project budget estimates. Obviously, it is an enormously large investment that is beyond the capabilities of our national economy.

Some people, who do not recognize the threat, claim that "within 25 to 50 years" world wars will not be possible. We must ask two questions of them:

First, does this justify the construction of a project costing dozens of billions of *yuan* that will last only 50 years?

Second, did anyone know when the Vietnamese troops successfully took over Saigon in 1975, that only four years later a war between Chinese and Vietnamese troops would break out?

History has taught that the highest principle of a country should always be national interest, never morality.

Now, let's take a detour into an imaginary scenario to illustrate some of these points. Assume the Three Gorges project has been built and it is now the year 2040, 50 years from today. The 185-meter dam is standing proudly and gloriously in central China. The dam is providing the power needed to promote the rapid acceleration of economic development along the crescent-shaped coastal areas of our motherland. Since China is a country with 1.3 billion people with the fewest resources per capita in the world, it is extremely important to our resource development.

Then, a small-scale conflict develops with Country A over disputed islands along the coast of the continental-shelf.[8] As the conflict worsens, our navy gains the upper hand, and having successfully brought the disputed islands under control, prepares for their exploration and development. Country A, however, gains regional support and threatens to escalate the conflict. National pride, the islands' valuable resources, and population and labor problems at home all lead China to maintain her position in this conflict. Those Chinese calling for a soft approach to the conflict are quickly overwhelmed by the cry of the majority for a hard line to be maintained.

On December 22, 2040 (the anniversary of Reagan's threat against Libya), the chief of the general staff of Country C, which has been allied by Country A, informs Country A that it is seriously considering a conventional surprise attack against China's Three Gorges dam. The military situation continues to intensify, bringing about the largest "designated deterrence" in the history of modern warfare. The war alerts sound!

Within ten days, just after January 1, 2041, the water in the reservoir is lowered to the flood-control level. A large number of enterprises and factories in central, southern and eastern China are now operating below capacity as a result of the drastic reduction in the electrical supply and the shortage of resources. Shipping capacity on the upper reaches of the Yangtze has also been drastically reduced. The hectic mobilization of troops puts additional pressure on already strained transportation facilities. The supply of daily necessities to citizens is short, and an uneasy feeling is spreading among the people.

Within this very tense environment, the Chinese, first in Yichang, then in the Jingjiang, Hanjiang, and Xiangjiang river basins, begin a disorganized emigration in the hope of avoiding probable disaster. The short supply of electricity, food, and grain enhances spreading anxiety and moves the whole country into a state of semi-paralysis.

Facing increasing political and civil pressure, politicians and military leaders begin heated and tense discussions in an attempt

---

[8] Possibly a reference to China's ongoing conflict with Vietnam over the Spratley islands in the South China sea.

to work out a policy able to deal with the situation. Assuming that the war will not escalate from conventional to nuclear weapons, the best choice is reciprocal deterrence. But since the needed corresponding long-range conventional offensive weapons are not available, and since there is no target as important as the Three Gorges dam in either of Countries C or A, what can be done?

As time passes, China tries to stabilize the situation by strengthening the organization and administration of the state machinery, by making the maximum possible use of the available resources, and by using all possible international means to save the national pride and reduce tension at home.

In the fall of 2041, country B is about to mediate between the two antagonistic parties, the reservoir is starting to store its water again, and the situation at home seems to be returning to normal; but then, the president of Country C once again threatens to strike the dam.

The impact, once again, is very powerful. In the face of this turbulence, an editorial appears in the *Central China Times* describing "an enormously burdensome construction project, costing several dozens of billions of *yuan* left to us by our predecessors 50 years ago."

From the point of view of national defense, the Three Gorges dam, which will cost more than Y30 billion to construct, is a sword which is not in our hand. Just like a double-edged sword, the water resources could be of benefit but could also cause serious disasters: we might use one side of the sword to blaze new trails while at the same time, the other edge might sever the life artery of our nation, including the process of our national development. At the very least, we will have squandered several dozens of billions of *yuan* to create a strategic target that could not be bought back from our enemies with a ransom of several hundreds of billions of *yuan*!

Both Dr. Sun Yat-sen and Chairman Mao Zedong have favored this project.

The Three Gorges project might be a sword that cuts at the heart of the Chinese nation. Soldiers, whether generals or young staff officers, are all very concerned. In interviews with them, I was surprised to find that, except for some perfunctory questions, no adequate and systematic assessment has ever been undertaken concerning the impact of war on the project, its effects on national defense and other questions that have an important bearing on the security of the entire nation.

One old general, who during the Korean War commanded troops to defend dams from attack and took charge of disaster relief work, told me: "Why has no one asked us about such an important issue?"

A young officer in charge of large-scale military construction, who has contributed many valuable ideas in his field, commented: "You are the first one to come and ask me about this."

In fact, as early as 1986, some experts argued that war was the key factor that should determine whether to build the Three Gorges project. But no commanders, army generals, strategic or information analysts, general staff, chiefs of the general staff or other military personnel participated in the leading group's recently concluded assessment, although there were 412 experts. Although 14 specific subjects of scientific inquiry were assessed, none dealt with military and national defense! This must be regarded as a grave and regrettable defect!

Luckily enough, the high dam we are talking about is only on paper, and so is the envisaged sword.

According to an old Chinese saying: "When engaging troops in combat, one must consider all possible dangers." The highest principle in military action is to prevent and remove as many dangers as possible. If there is a real need to build the reservoir—"the Sword"—then please do not forget the soldiers who must protect it!

Damocles, a courtier of ancient Syracuse, sat at a banquet beneath a sword suspended only by a single hair. Danger is impending overhead. Are we going to make a sword that will hang over the heads of future generations for decades to come?

# CHAPTER TWENTY-SIX

## MUST A FINISHED PROJECT FINISH
## ITS ENVIRONMENT?[1]
by
Mao Yushi[2]

Since 1979, when I began to pay attention to the Chinese strategy of capital construction, I have noticed many serious problems in the decision-making process. For example, the pipes for natural gas were laid before the resources had been explored; coal was transported from the north to the south of China but the boilers that originally used coal for fuel had been changed to burn oil, and so had to be reconverted in response to the oil shortage.

Such changes caused great losses. Personally, I believe that under the present system, it is very difficult to make good decisions. Having taken part in the decision-making process, I have discovered that decisions reflect the political hierarchy.

Since 1949, national investment in capital construction has always been overextended despite very ineffective results. One reason is that decision makers are spending the state's funds rather than their own, and, as a result, issues of economic efficiency and profit are being neglected. To those who support the immediate start of the Three Gorges project, I will ask only one question: "Are you willing to support the 20-year project by personally investing in construction bonds?" Here, the essential issue is that of investment systems, which need changing.

In the old days, when my uncle, Mao Yishen, designed the Qiantan River bridge, the director of the construction office in

---

[1] This essay was included in the original Chinese edition of *Yangtze! Yangtze!*

[2] Mao Yushi is a researcher at the American Studies Center of the Research Institute in Social Sciences, and is the past editor-in-chief of the *Journal of the Chinese Economy*.

Zhejing province told him he would take care of the budget, and that my uncle was to be in charge of personnel. But one point was made clear: if the bridge turned out to be a failure then they both had to take responsibility and jump in the river. Today, however, after many failed and defective projects, people no longer feel personally responsible. It is ridiculous to make a final decision on the extraordinarily large Three Gorges project without an established decision-making process and a practical investment system.

Although there were several hundred experts and specialists at the assessment meeting, their responsibilities were not well defined. It is dangerous to make a final decision by relying on an assessment for which no one is responsible! Finally, I would like to draw your attention to another problem that has apparently not been mentioned by either side's assessment: the life span of the reservoir.

We all know that the Aswan dam brought many problems to Egypt.[3] What will happen to the Three Gorges reservoir after it is operational? At present, it seems that plans for nuclear power plants are not very promising, because after they are no longer in use, the land on which the plants are located is unusable. At the moment the Three Gorges' scenic beauty seems much less important than its hydro-electric potential. However, in a few decades, when several hundred million kWh of electricity will be very easy to produce, or to replace by other energy resources, won't we regret the irreplaceable loss of the scenic Gorges?

Another point I want to make relates to the problem of terrorism. Perhaps it is not a threat in today's China. But what about the future? If terrorists choose the Three Gorges reservoir as their target, what costs might it inflict? The government would deplore its predecessor, which spent such large sums to create a project that could so easily become the target of terrorists.

---

[3] Problems included increases in the water table, in salinity and water logging, in erosion of the riverbed of the Nile, and in rats and scorpions, and in decreased fish stocks.

# CHAPTER TWENTY-SEVEN

## THE THREE GORGES PROJECT IN THE CONTEXT OF PRESENT ECONOMIC AND POLITICAL CONDITIONS[1]
by
Wu Jiaxiang[2]

Before a large project is carried out, the social, economic and political environments should be considered as well as questions of technical feasibility and profit. At present, these considerations do not favor the start of the Three Gorges project.

First, we are in a transition period in which a new dynamic system is replacing an old static one. Until this new system has been fully established, it cannot provide us with an efficient means to gather the extensive capital funds needed for the project. Indeed, there are many defects in the old system, which nonetheless retains its one advantage, that of attaining at any cost certain economic objectives.[3] In this, some see a paradox—for example, a satellite is successfully launched into outer space, while toilets in apartment buildings leak every day with no means to repair them; there are too many missiles, but too few eggs.

Today, this old system is gradually being cast out, along with the so-called advantage. Since the old administrative methods for mobilizing resources are no longer as efficient as they once were,

---

[1] This essay was included in the original Chinese edition of *Yangtze! Yangtze!*

[2] Wu Jiaxuang is an economist and former researcher at the Office of Policy Research under the General Office of the Communist Party Central Committee. Wu was purged and jailed after the 1989 Tiananmen Square massacre.

[3] Namely, the capacity of the pre-1978 communist apparatus in China to mobilize the entire system of supply and transportation etc. for national goals.

and since the project is not able to produce immediate economic profits, market incentives cannot be used to justify funding for the project. Therefore, it is likely that the project will become "long-and-dragged-out." The progress of the project will be determined by whether it hits a bottleneck. Once it does, it will be halted. In order to eliminate such bottlenecks good money will have to follow bad. The glorious monument we had hoped the project would be might well become an ugly scar on the body of our motherland.

Second, the start-up of the Three Gorges project would increase the gap between supply and demand, which would narrow the bottleneck even further. The project would consume huge amounts of resources, especially those already in short supply, such as energy and raw materials, without producing profits in the near future. At the same time, enormous pressure would be brought to bear upon the already strained transportation and communication systems.[4] Because of the lack of adequate materials, the ever growing demand for funding would surely result in the need to issue new currency, thus leading to more serious inflation and price increases.

Some may argue that if the project were built, the acute shortage of electricity would be eased. But this is a very long-range view that ignores immediate problems. Everyone knows that the next few years are the key transition period in construction and the development of reform. We must be extremely cautious when making important decisions and avoid any man-made instability that would bind us. I doubt whether our present economic conditions can continue to support us until the Three Gorges dam begins to generate power. The risks to our plans for national economic reform and development are too great.

Third, this particular stage, when neither old nor new rules and regulations can work effectively in our management and administration, offers numerous loopholes that could be taken advantage of. Experience shows that whenever the country completes a major project, a small group of people benefit, becoming

---

[4] The pressure would be especially acute for the railroads, which already suffer severe bottlenecks throughout the country. See He, *China on the Edge*, pp. 65-89.

"fat cats." The bigger the project, the more fat cats. For instance, according to the newspapers, there have been some underworld gangs, the "Black Rings" for example, who frequent the Asian Game construction sites, in order to take legal or illegal advantage of these projects.[5] This is happening even in Beijing, the capital city. Should the Three Gorges project, which is much larger both in scale and budget, be launched in a place where "the sky is high and the emperor is distant," how much of the funding would disappear through such legal or illegal loopholes? Given our present management and administration systems, the Three Gorges project will become a "bottomless pit" demanding endless investment. In ancient times, the practice was to prepare provisions and supplies before setting out with horses and men. But now, the practice among some is to enjoy the benefits of funding even before beginning a project. Even at the site of the devastating *Daxing Anling* fire in Heilongjiang province in 1988, numerous cadres began fighting over promotions and privileges. What is to keep the Three Gorges project from becoming nothing but a venue for those seeking promotions and privileges while showing off?

Finally, the Three Gorges project would invite social unrest through mass resettlement and price increases, which in addition to other, already destabilizing problems, could bring about a profound social crisis. The year 1990 is a peak time for the government to repay both its domestic and foreign debts. In the face of such a difficult financial situation, the Three Gorges project would be a terrible burden for the state.

Having read the assessment report on the project, I have found that the factors and elements I have just discussed were mentioned either perfunctorily or ignored altogether. Because of such important omissions the assessment is defective. I believe there is a need to reassess the project from a more comprehensive perspective. If those who did the assessment insist on the early start of the project, they must be prepared to take personal responsibility for its success and those who are in charge of implementing it should give their personal guarantee to the people of the country.

---

[5] Rumors of corruption surrounding contracts for the Asian Games and other large projects abound in Beijing.

# CHAPTER TWENTY-EIGHT

## MADAM QIAN ZHENGYING, ANSWER MY QUESTIONS[1]
### by
### Dai Qing

Though 70 years old, Qian Zhengying distinguishes herself as the leader of the pro-dam faction for the Three Gorges project. But even this may not adequately describe her role. For the past few decades, she has been the key leader in mainland China's water-engineering programs.

Beginning with responsibility for East China's water resources, Qian quickly made her way to Beijing in order to assume the office of vice-minister and then minister of water resources and electric power. Finally, she obtained the seemingly less prominent yet crucial position of chief of the Leading Group for the Assessment of the Three Gorges Project of the Ministry of Water Resources and Electric Power. Despite strong opposition and suspicion from the National People's Congress (NPC), she pursued every possible means to have the resolution on launching the project passed. When the executive body for the implementation of this resolution, the Commission for Construction of the Three Gorges Project of the State Council, was established, again we found her there acting as its "advisor." She has been a relentless advocate for the earliest possible start, and the grandest possible dam on the Yangtze. She is the pro-dam faction's spiritual leader.

Like many Communist Party officials who have reached retirement age and have had to step down, Madam Qian is a

---

[1] This essay, written in February, 1993, was not included in the original Chinese edition of *Yangtze! Yangtze!* Notes 2 through 4 were prepared by the author, Dai Qing.

member and vice-chairman of the Chinese People's Political Consultative Conference (CPPCC). The CPPCC has changed considerably from its founding session in the summer of 1949. That first session was attended by Chairman Mao Zedong and vice-chairmen Zhou Enlai, and Li Jishen, but those days are just a memory. The present-day CPPCC has no real power and no longer makes laws. It is an organization heavily influenced by Party patronage, established to unite the democratic parties and overseas Chinese, and assist the Party. Nevertheless, an increasing number of communist cadres continue to compete for CPPCC positions. Qian did not want to miss such an opportunity. By the time she was to retire as minister of water resources and electric power at age 65, she had already made a deal with the late CPPCC chairman, Li Xiannian, to become one of its vice-chairmen.

Qian joined the CPPCC in 1988 as an expert in water engineering but, ironically, was assigned the portfolios of medicine, public health, and sports. Important as these are, she has done little in these fields. She has devoted her energy to her earlier passion, the Three Gorges project, and has determined that this project is going to be the prime focus of her entire life. To her critics, she continues to be a witty and quixotic opponent.

In 1983, Li Rui asked her: "Shall we talk, once again, about the Three Gorges?"

"On that matter," she replied, "I'm prepared to be thrown into prison even at age 70!"[2]

Her latest remarks, hollow as they are, are stern as ever. When her own children asked her:

> What is the point of all that you're doing? Look at the number of projects you've built; do you not think you

---

[2] See Li Rui, "Cancel the Three Gorges Project," January 1992. Here Qian used the Communist Party's love and protection of its cadres. Though China's criminal code does contain penalties for dereliction of duty, bureaucrats are never penalized for squandering public funds when they do so with brimming revolutionary passion. Thus her remark is not surprising. For Madam Qian's most vociferous defense of the Three Gorges project, see the speech by Qian Zhengying at the Meeting of Ministerial Level Cadres, 23 January 1979.

have done enough? Why must you leave behind one final project, which might sully your name? Once you fail at the Three Gorges, you might even be beheaded.[3]

She replied, "If I am kept from damming the Three Gorges, I will not rest even in death!"[4]

Recently, she has become even more vigorous. At a meeting in 1993, she once said, with a victorious smile on her face: "Why does the opposition still refuse to surrender?"

In response, Zhou Peiyuan said: "Because we are concerned, we can't rest assured." Li Rui said: "Facing danger, how can one fail to speak out?" Lu Qinkan continues to warn that "the most important thing for flood control on the Yangtze is strengthening the dikes and developing flood diversion zones." Huang Wanli, Tian Fang and Lin Fatang write one letter after another to the state authorities, calling on them to reconsider the launch of the project. Sun Yueqi, who is more than 100 years old, can only share his past experiences with the occasional younger visitor. Every Chinese citizen is entitled to add his or her opinion to the Three Gorges debate. It is a project to be built with their money and on their land, so why should they not voice their opinion?

Qian's role model, Mao Zedong, once said: "Crush the enemy who refuses to surrender." But it is also part of Chinese culture to "surrender to reason, not power."

Here, for Qian, are some questions for which we who do not have official titles yearn to know more about:[5]

## I. The Assessment Report

1. According to an article published in the *Literary Gazette* on March 17, 1992, entitled "How Has the Three Gorges Project

---

[3] See Chen Kexiong, "The True Story of the Three Gorges Project," *Literary Gazette*, 17 March 1992.
[4] Remark made to National People's Congress staff members at Beidaihe during the summer of 1992.
[5] Chinese leaders are generally inaccessible to journalists who challenge government policy. The format of this chapter and the following questions show dam opponents' frustration with official silence.

Been Worked Out—an Interview with Qian Zhengying" you stated in 1986, "I did not expect that I would be chosen to head this fresh round of feasibility studies (the leading group's assessment)." I am surprised. Those of us who are concerned with the Three Gorges remember how hard you lobbied Song Jian, head of the State Science and Technology Commission, for the position. You did this even though the State Council had already given control of the assessment to the State Science and Technology Commission and the State Planning Commission. When you spoke to the journalist, had you forgotten your earlier lobbying efforts—or were you trying to evade responsibility should the project fail?

2. When you became head of the leading group in 1986, you filled all of the leading positions with dam supporters. All of them were ministers or vice-ministers, chief engineers or deputy chief engineers of the Ministry of Water Resources and Electric Power, officials from the Yangtze Valley Planning Office (YVPO) or the Preparatory Office of the Three Gorges Project Development Corporation.

No access to leadership positions was provided for government officials in charge of transportation, geology and seismology, environment, electrical equipment or public finance. Most of the 412 experts involved in the assessment were under the control of officials from the ministry. Thus, the majority of experts had no chance to air their views in sessions that examined the subject reports and the conclusion of the assessment report. Those meetings were limited to only the leading group members, leaders and deputy leaders of the experts' groups, and their advisors.

Was this leadership structure not a product of the ministry's monopoly, for which you should be held responsible? How, under such circumstances, could the assessment report meet the requirements of the joint document issued by the Communist Party Central Committee and the State Council in 1986—that the report, "in the spirit of technological democracy, should enable sufficient discussion for experts with diverse views, in order to base its conclusions on scientific grounds"?

3. During the months prior to the 1992 NPC examination of the project, many experts submitted their opinions to the media. When these opinions were then submitted to the ministry, why did its officials censor those views which opposed the project and permit only those in support of the project to be released? During

the NPC session, why did the ministry issue only its own propaganda material to the delegates, and not the criticisms raised both within and outside of the assessment? Was the principle of "letting one hundred schools of thought contend" put into practice? Were the NPC delegates allowed to "derive wisdom from diverse views?"[6] Can this kind of decision making be in any way called democratic or scientific?

## II. Flood Control

1. During your interview with the *Literary Gazette*, you said "the number one task" of the Three Gorges project was "flood control on the Yangtze." May I ask what you meant by the Yangtze? Did you mean only its middle reaches or the entire Yangtze valley? I assume that you, once the minister of water resources and electric power, still remember the 1981 floods in Sichuan. After the dam's completion, the Three Gorges will raise the water level upstream. How then can the project not place Sichuan under even more serious threat of flood? Nor should you have forgotten the flood that hit Jiangsu, Anhui and Zhejiang provinces in 1991. Will the Three Gorges project in any way curb floods due to flooding of the Yangtze's downstream tributaries?

2. The project, once built, will control only 20 percent of the Yangtze's yearly flow. Will it be able to guarantee flood control in the river's middle reaches, namely at Hunan and Hubei provinces? The Yangtze's 1954 flood swept over 47.55 million *mu* of farmland, but the project, as you said, will protect only 1.77 to 3.27 million *mu* of farmland from the threat of flood. Is this all that will be protected from a 100-year flood?

3. Even an extremely large-scale flood, such as the one in 1870, did not breach the Jingjiang River dikes. Since the dikes have been reinforced many times since then, why do you allege that "once such a flood occurs, it is likely to burst out of the dikes on both banks of the Yangtze and kill 100,000 people"? The threat of a catastrophic flood has been the crucial point in your argument for damming the Three Gorges. Why have you not mentioned that, if built as designed, the dam will raise the flood level at

---

[6] A Chinese proverb.

Chongqing to more than 200 meters, which is two to four meters higher than the level reached during the 1870 flood? Must the Yangtze's upper reaches make such a sacrifice for the sake of the middle reaches?

## III. Sedimentation

1. How knowledgeable are you about the Yangtze's sediment content? Are the river beds of the upstream tributaries mainly gravel and sand or, like that of the Yellow River, mainly mud? If it is gravel and sand, does it change its formations? If so, under what conditions, and driven by what force? Is this movement in any way measurable?[7] The estimates of sediment build-up in the future Three Gorges reservoir are based on a simulation test assuming that the river bed, contrary to fact, never moves. Was this test designed by fools, or was it designed to fool others?

2. The Yangtze is recognized as having the fourth-largest sediment content of any river on earth. This fact is acknowledged in the report of the Experts' Group on Hydrology: "Due to rampant deforestation and destruction of vegetation, land reclamation, road building and development of the mining industry, soil erosion has increased over the past few decades to an extremely serious point." Yet how could this statement be followed by the conclusion that the Yangtze "shows no sign of increasing sediment content"? Can anyone be convinced by this logic? Dare you be convinced by it?

3. I assume that you are aware, Qian, that roughly 20 percent of the reservoirs built in China in the past 40 years have now become totally silted up. There has been no mention, so far, of how long the Three Gorges reservoir will last. Do you believe that a reservoir can accommodate an unlimited amount of sediment within a limited area? Do you have plans for removing the sediment build-up in the area near Chongqing? Surely, maintenance of the Chongqing harbor reach and flood control in Sichuan are important. Why then do you not treat them as such? As for the possibility that the middle reaches of the Yangtze would become choked with sediment, your only response up to now has been:

---

[7] For more on this topic see Chapter 15.

"Haven't I told you many times that the coming generations are bound to have greater intelligence than we do? Let's trust their ability to solve their problems." What a sense of responsibility!

4. On how to operate the reservoir: A method has been proposed to slow down the sedimentation of the reservoir, namely "storing the clear water and flushing out the muddy." In practice, sediment flushing is accomplished by releasing large volumes of water—thereby lowering the reservoir's pool level—during the Yangtze's flood season, from June to September. But how can flushing sediment through the dam prevent the on-going sedimentation of Dongting Lake—a problem that has drawn your particular concern? Moreover, if the reservoir's water level is being lowered during the flood season, how can it fulfill its flood-control function of storing flood waters? And how can you possibly flush out the sediment that builds up towards the end of a reservoir that will extend for hundreds of kilometers?

To "store the clear water and flush out the muddy" is not a new approach. It has been applied to the Liujiaxia, Yanguoxia, and Qinglongxia gorges and its failure has compromised all of the projects' objectives—electricity generation, navigation, irrigation, and flood control. Will the objectives of the Three Gorges project also be compromised? If so, will the project have any purpose at all? Even by sacrificing all of the project's objectives, you still cannot guarantee the success of the sediment-flushing method.

## IV. Navigation

It is claimed that the Three Gorges project will enable 50 million tonnes of goods per year to be carried to Chongqing on 10,000-tonne cargo ships. This was preached to Deng Xiaoping as one of the "four greatest advantages" of the project and, as rumor has it, was the most important reason for his support.

1. Do you know of a high-sediment river, anywhere in the world, which has remained navigable after being dammed? At the Hoover dam on the Colorado River, and the Aswan dam on the Nile, navigation has been possible only within the reservoir zone. The Mississippi is also a large, navigable river, but it is dammed only on its upstream. The Danube, the Rhine and the Volga have strong flows and light sediment content, but none has been dammed on its main course. Is this because foreigners have no

interest in exploiting their water resources, or because they refuse to believe that a river not dammed is a waste of energy?

2. The Hanjiang River, one of the tributaries of the Yangtze, was once a navigable river. However, since the Danjiangkou reservoir was built under your leadership it no longer is. Within the reservoir's backwater zone, the original navigation channel has been altered and tends to even disappear, while the new channel, frequently interrupted by rapids, is not suitable for navigation. The broad river course has been filled with solid sediment banks and build-up, causing numerous shipping accidents. Zhou Enlai said in 1971: "The Yangtze is too important a waterway to permit anything to go wrong. If navigation is interrupted, then the dam has to be blown up. That would be a great crime." I wish his words still rang in your ears.

3. In a low-flow year, the Yangtze can carry 10 million tonnes of goods. But according to the Yangtze Navigation Administration, dredging the river course would allow for the annual transportation of 18 million tonnes of goods per year between now and 2000. By 2015, the amount would increase to 30 million tonnes per year. By 2030, with the help of efforts to coordinate water storage in the upstream reservoirs, it might reach 50 million tonnes per year, which is the navigation target set for the Three Gorges project. This three-stage construction would require a total investment of Y3.34 billion. As you know, Qian, this is not even one-tenth of the budget for the Three Gorges project.

4. The Yangtze, once dammed at the Three Gorges, would still be hard pressed to accommodate the transportation of 50 million tonnes of goods per year. It would require the year-round operation of large ships (20 percent of them with 3,000-tonne capacity, and 80 percent with 10,000-tonne capacity), and no interruptions due to undesirable navigation conditions. Madam Qian, is this realistic? Besides, how well will the five-stage shiplocks function? Will their highly sophisticated design facilitate navigation after all? Dam advocates have never mentioned the limitations of the locks; for instance whether they will be able to work continuously, whether they will help avoid accidents and what maintenance they will require. Not to mention the limitations imposed by construction lasting up to 20 years. Given this, I wonder: is the lofty goal of having 10,000-tonne cargo ships arrive in Chongqing just a propaganda ploy?

# V. Electric Power Generation

1.  For the past 50 years, power generation has been a main consideration for those who support the earliest possible start-up and grandest possible design for the Three Gorges project. Not only does the Yangtze have abundant water resources, but central and south China have serious shortages of power. However, it will take at least a decade before the Three Gorges begins to supply power. China's economic development, as you know, cannot afford to wait that long. Various provinces on the coast are now negotiating joint development projects requiring less resettlement and consisting of small and medium-sized hydro power stations on the tributaries of the Yangtze, and down the Lancang River valley. Describing the Three Gorges project as "indispensable" is simply not true, is it?

2.  The estimated installed capacity for the project is 17.68 million kW, while its firm capacity is 4.99 million kW. Is this not a waste? In order to provide enough water to keep the power plant working during the dry season, the flow from the Three Gorges to the Gezhouba dam will have to be frequently adjusted, affecting navigation on the golden waterway. Does such low-efficiency power generation constitute a worthwhile project?

# VI. Resettlement

1.  Of the many large reservoirs built outside of China, none has required the resettlement of more than 120,000 people. In China, by contrast, there are three reservoirs that have each involved the resettlement of more than 300,000 people, and all have created a series of lingering problems. According to the project design for the Three Gorges dam, one million people will have to be relocated, and their resettlement alone will consume nearly one-third of the project's entire budget. Is this a rational design?

2.  How many people will be resettled by the current plan for a dam with a 175-meter normal pool level? The project's original plan, which called for it to be launched in 1989 and completed in 2008, would have relocated an estimated 1.13 million people. Now that both the launching and completion dates have been postponed, and the population continues to grow, how many additional people will need to be relocated? Because the

dam will be 185 meters high, it is estimated that another 200,000 people will have to be moved from their homes in order to achieve "overstorage."[8] A few years later, when sediment builds up in the river bed, more people will be threatened by the new flood level, and will have to be moved. Taking all of these factors into account, how could the Three Gorges resettlement plan involve only 1.13 million?

3. According to the figures you provide, the total resettlement budget will be Y18.5 billion, or Y16,000 per person. Assuming there is no embezzlement or waste during the process (a highly unlikely assumption), the budget will still be drastically affected by newly increased costs for resettlement compensation, new compensation standards, and inflation. China's average rate for resettlement compensation in reservoir construction increased 40 percent from 1984 to 1988, to at least Y20,000 per person (compensation in the building of the Ertan reservoir on the upstream of the Jinsha River was Y36,000 per person in 1990). May I ask you, Qian, how Y18.5 billion will be sufficient to allow the resettled population from the Three Gorges project, more than half of whom are urban residents, to maintain at least the same living standard? If the resettlement plan is allowed to go ahead despite its insufficient budget, how can you guarantee that it will not give rise to any major economic and political problems?

4. During the past 40 years, while your career advanced, more than 10 million Chinese citizens were relocated to make way for water-engineering projects, bearing untold suffering. How could you have the conscience to remove more than one million people for the building of a single dam? I doubt that the Chinese people will accept your orders as readily today as they have in the past.

## VII. Budget

1. The capital requirements for the Three Gorges project are calculated according to a method which ignores factors such as the interest on bank loans and inflation. This is called "static investment." No other long-term construction projects in the world

---

[8] Storage of water in excess of the normal pool level.

leave these costs unaccounted for. I am told that you have had these additional costs estimated and that they significantly increased the total cost of the project. Why, then, did you fail to inform the NPC of this estimate?

2. The state budget is the main source of investment for the Three Gorges project. In fact, it is the main source of funding for all dams in China. This, however, can no longer be the case now that, since its Fourteenth National Congress in 1992, the Chinese Communist Party has embraced the market economy. I am curious to know whether you, as a veteran communist, will prove your dedication to the Party's new cause by reevaluating your project in light of the new concepts of the market economy, or whether you will maintain your old ways of doing things. It seems that, by boasting about a "double celebration in 1997," you are trying to pressure the state financial authorities for money in the name of a political slogan. Will this not undermine the entire economy's transition?

3. Dam supporters claim that a major source of investment for the Three Gorges project will come from revenues generated by the sale of electricity from the Gezhouba dam. In other words, the Gezhouba dam is to turn its revenues over to the Three Gorges Project Development Corporation. May I ask, first of all, how the Gezhouba dam, whose construction lasted 18 years, will be able to pay back its Y4.80 billion in static investment (actually well over Y10 billion dynamic investment)? Secondly, will this policy be applied to other rivers? In other words, will existing power plants turn their profits over for the construction of new power plants on the same rivers?

It is also argued that once the Three Gorges power station begins commercial electricity generation, its revenue would be immediately reinvested into the project. But as the Ministry of Finance argued during the project's assessment, there are no provisions in the state financial administration for a project to use its own revenue—whether before or after paying back state loans. Is the Three Gorges project so important for China that it can ignore the country's financial authority?

4. It is also proposed that the charge for electricity use will be increased and the revenue generated will be set aside for the dam at the Three Gorges. This charge will be collected from areas whether they benefit from the project or are victimized by it, and

from individuals whether they support or oppose the project. The revenue generated cannot be considered a loan; it is a national levy. Will such a levy help stabilize China's economy?

5.   The Three Gorges project ranks first among large development projects in terms of its hidden costs and its potential for exacting follow-up investment. Its aggregate investment was said to be Y36 billion in 1988 and Y57 billion in 1990. But the latest figure for static investment has soared to Y75 billion.[9] Based on this latest figure, projections of the project's real cost or dynamic investment now total Y220 billion, even with inflation and interest rates at their lowest possible levels. Yet, will this be enough for your financial appetite? I seriously doubt it. At a time when nothing could be more valuable to China's economy than its sustained development, how much benefit will come from this overinvestment in the Three Gorges project?

## VIII. Environment

1.   According to the "Report on the Environmental Impact of the Three Gorges Project" by the Chinese Academy of Sciences, "after systematic evaluation comparing all the advantages and disadvantages, we find that the potential hazards of the Three Gorges project still appear to outweigh its possible benefits." What is your opinion of this conclusion, from an authoritative organization that does not stand to benefit from the project? Why try so hard to have a dam built, despite warnings from the nation's environmental scientists? Has it ever occurred to you that the days in which the construction of a megaproject could justify the destruction of nature have passed? Look at the precautions the World Bank, which you used to regard as a prospective money lender, has taken against financing projects likely to cause environmental problems.

2.   The Three Gorges has been overexploited. How can its environment accommodate the relocation of so many people to the hills on the sides of the gorges? Are you and your colleagues aware that it is against the law to reclaim land on a slope steeper

---

[9] See Appendix E.

than 25 degrees? Are you prepared to bear responsibility for devastating soil erosion in this area?

3.   I know of no measures to maintain the quality of drinking water in the proposed reservoir area. Will water quality be affected by ongoing pollution along the river, the submergence of abandoned mines, and the fishing industry in the reservoir? Why, on an issue that is so important to the livelihoods of millions of people, have no actions or plans ever been taken to address this issue?

4.   As designed, the main body of the dam will be able to resist an earthquake measuring 7.0 on the Richter scale, indicating that the reservoir may indeed cause earthquakes. What about the residents in the reservoir area? Have any earthquake-resistance standards been set for their houses and public structures? Are there any precautions to protect against landslides which will accompany the earthquakes?

Finally, I would like to ask Vice-Chairman Qian: How long do you feel the reservoir will last—100 years, 80 years, 60 years, or 30 years? If it will last no more than a dozen years, how will it be able to provide flood control during a 1,000-year or 100-year flood? How, under such circumstances, will 10,000-tonne cargo ships be able to continue to reach the Chongqing harbor? How much electricity will the power station be able to generate? And when the reservoir is silted up, as has occurred at the Sanmenxia Gorge, what is China supposed to do—reconstruct the dam or dredge the reservoir? Where will the debris and sediment be disposed of?

The Yangtze River has nurtured Chinese civilization for thousands of years. It cannot afford any disturbance from conceited, clever, and powerful individuals. Is it by sheer luck that no one has yet destroyed it? If there is such a destroyer, I suspect, it may be you, Vice-Chairman Qian. You seem to have the ambition to leave such a God-forbidden personal mark on history. Please, think again.

# CHAPTER TWENTY-NINE

## THE ASSESSMENT OF THE THREE GORGES PROJECT SHOULD HAVE INVOLVED SOCIOLOGISTS AND ANTHROPOLOGISTS[1]
by
Jin Jun[2]

I would like to analyze the problem of population relocation from a sociological perspective. Although the Liujiaxia Gorge reservoir has been completed for many years, the resettlement problems created by its construction are still with us and can be used as a point of comparison with the Three Gorges project.

When people are resettled from low-lying areas of natural irrigation to the hillsides with less arable land and poorer soil quality, their self-sufficiency is destroyed. The insufficient nature of state compensation, a situation aggravated by improper and impractical distribution, only makes things worse. In many cases, the compensation never reaches these people, who, because of their hardships, inevitably feel resentment against the government.

One constructive approach to the problem is to compensate peoples' losses and improve their situation by introducing lifestyle changes and modern methods of production. But, in China, this seems difficult or even impossible, because of poor national economic conditions, the low levels of education of many local people, and the inappropriate policies governing population relocation. As a result, the lives of the people are worsened rather than improved. For a long time, they feel resentful and even cheated. They rely on the government for everything, and try to

---

[1] This essay was included in the original Chinese edition of *Yangtze! Yangtze!*

[2] Jin Jun is a former journalist and researcher at the Institute of Sociology, Beida University. He is currently completing a PhD at Harvard University in the United States.

get as much as they can from it. This mentality, known as the "culture of poverty," makes the economic situation worse, hindering the effort to alleviate poverty and causing a vicious circle.

Chinese society is based on an established pattern of relationships among various clans, each having its own social customs and family roots in different regions. The process of resettlement inevitably breaks existing relationships and increases the chances of friction and conflict among the different groupings of newly resettled people, thus negatively affecting society as a whole.

The population to be relocated from the Three Gorges area would probably reach 1.3 million—far more than that from the Liujiaxia Gorge reservoir, or on any other previous project. These are not only farmers, but also city dwellers, who may make up as much as 40 percent of the people to be moved. The land to be submerged includes villages and numerous towns and cities, where all of the industrial establishments would be destroyed. This massive economic loss could lead to complicated and unpredictable problems. Since the beginning of our economic reform in 1978, economic relations among urban and rural areas have undergone a great deal of change. In the rural areas the economic pattern is neither that of collective (the state) nor of household ownership, but rather of community ownership. Therefore, the policy concerning resettlement should be based on contracts between the community and the government rather than on an administrative basis. But at present, all of the policies are of an administrative nature, and could easily cause failure.

Resettlement on such a large scale is not just an economic or engineering issue, but is also a social one. Therefore, sociologists and anthropologists should be invited to participate in project assessment. However, decision makers always tend to treat projects merely from an economic perspective, rather than from a sound overall perspective.

During a recent conversation concerning China's hydroelectric projects with Ma Rong, the vice-director of the Institute of Sociology at Beida University, Michael Cernea, an American sociologist employed by the World Bank, was surprised to learn that no sociologists had participated in the assessment of the Three Gorges project. He went on to say that in the contemporary world, the participation of adequate numbers of sociologists in the assessments of hydro-electric or agricultural projects of such a large scale has become a criterion for determining the appropriateness of the project. Whether to assess large-scale projects for their social impacts relates to the broader question of how to treat the interests of the common people. Cernea has written a book titled *Putting People First*;[3] and we hope, during the assessment work on the Three Gorges project, the people's interests will be put first.

---

[3] Michael M. Cernea, *Putting People First, Sociological Variables in Rural Development*. (Oxford: Oxford University Press, 1985).

# CHAPTER THIRTY

## AFTERWORD TO THE CHINESE EDITION
by
Dai Qing

It's not difficult to tell that this book was compiled in a hurry. The initiative to publish it came from news reports in late November, 1988, that the 14 subject reports had been passed in principle by the Leading Group for the Assessment of the Three Gorges Project. This insured that the Yangtze Valley Planning Office (YVPO) would conduct a feasibility study on the basis of the assessment report. The feasibility study would then be submitted to the State Council in the spring of 1989. If it were to pass, according to the proposal for an "early start to construction," this high-profile project could be started as early as 1989. Other proposals would have the project start in either 1992 or 2001.

The Yangtze River will soon be severed in two. Should it matter to us, the common folks, the journalists, the scholars and veteran cadres long retired from their important posts?

On the one hand, the answer seems to be "no." Who knows more—we, or the 412 experts from the leading group? On the other hand, over the past 40 years there have been numerous occasions when someone should have stood up and said "no" to bad policies. But in practice, except for a few whispers, dead silence prevailed. "Forget about it—the decision has already been made by the authorities." It was so 30 years ago. It was so 20 years ago, and it is the so today. Everyone wonders, yet no one asks, "Is policy made on the basis of science or political power?"

The Three Gorges project, however, is a rare exception to this trend. Just as history is formed by the specific acts of individuals, if not for the efforts of Li Rui the Yangtze River would certainly look different from what we see before us today. The debate has lasted for 30 years. Those who favor the project argue that the duration of its assessments show that it is well considered and feasible, while those who oppose it argue that so long an assessment without implementation indicates unfeasibility. From within the central leadership group, Li Rui alone opposed the project for 30 years. Today, we know that almost all of the engineers in the YVPO who opposed the Three Gorges project in 1959 were accused of being rightists. Directors of hydro-electric planning and design institutes in the eight southern provinces were also accused of being members of the "Li Rui anti-Party gang."

In 1985, following the end of the Cultural Revolution and the 1978 Third Plenum (which initiated China's current economic reform), the old scholars stood up. Sun Yueqi shouted out the first "no." In 1988, Zhou Peiyuan—contrary to the present tradition of not uttering opposition until after retirement—led an inspection team to the Three Gorges and submitted a letter in his own name directly to the general secretary of the Communist Party. Given the profession and rank of the inspection team, and the urgency of the issue, major newspapers should have reported on the event. But they did not and only a few articles appeared in small professional journals.

To redress this situation journalists came forward to help air the views of the inspection group by helping to compile this book. They came from the *New China News Agency*, the *People's Daily*, the *Liberation Army Daily*, the *China Youth News*, the *Literary Gazette*, and the *Enlightenment Daily*. They were not sent by their newspapers; they represented only themselves and acted according to their own judgments. They were a group of journalists in mid-career whose names and reputations were well known to their readers. They did not hesitate for an instant, and said what they had to say.

All of the participants—journalists, editors, and scholars, young and old—came together on January 23, 1989, and decided to promulgate their opposition just prior to the decision of the State Council. But in what form? Time was short and they felt the best option was to convey their views through newspapers. But this proved impossible. Perhaps through a journal? Seven or eight journals expressed initial interest, but eventually all turned us down. The last option was to publish a book. There was, however, only one month left before the National People's Congress and Chinese People's Political Consultative Conference (CPPCC) meetings, and the Chinese New Year would occur in the interim.

Considering that it generally takes between six months and two years to have a book published, the journalists felt this option to be impossible. In addition to time limitations, no publisher would touch the material.

Finally, one publisher, the People's Publishing House of Guizhou, did agree to publish the book and appointed Xu Yinong as editor.

The cover design of the [original Chinese] book was completed in two days. Senior art editor, Ma Shaozhan of the Sanlian Publishing House, gave it her all without compensation, despite having just been released from hospital.

Many thought a book could not be published in so short a period of time. Of course, it could. China is full of talented people. All in all, it took only fifteen days for *Yangtze! Yangtze!* to see the light of day.

The last difficulty we confronted was that of financing the project. Twenty thousand *yuan* was needed. It was a very large sum, but was no more than large companies pay for one-page advertisements in many newspapers. However, at a time when, despite the introduction of market reforms, business was in many ways still dependent on non-market factors, we could not secure their help.[1]

The only option left to us was to have the book published with borrowed money which would be repaid from royalties. In approaching various writers, scholars, and other interested parties for loans, I was never once turned down. A woman manager at a private hotel promised to make up any shortfall. She was not that wealthy herself, and had had a very difficult life, but she was now willing to help those in need with benevolence and generosity.

There is only one Yangtze River and we have already subjected it to many stupid deeds. Such stupidity must not be repeated. The Yangtze River belongs to all Chinese people and to the entire world.

The poet Bei Dao once wrote: *I-do-not-believe!*

Today, I too declare: I do not believe...

---

[1] Dai Qing is intimating here that any business that sponsored the book would suffer at the hands of the state.

*I do not believe that the Chinese will forever*
*refuse to think for themselves;*
*I do not believe that the Chinese will never*
*speak out through their writings;*
*I do not believe that morality and justice will*
*vanish in the face of repression;*
*I do not believe that in an age in which*
*we are in communication with the world,*
*'freedom of speech' will remain an empty phrase.*[2]

---

[2] Poem translated by Geremie Barmé, Research Fellow at the Australian National University.

# APPENDIX A

## Historical Chronology of the Three Gorges Project

**1919:** First mention of the Three Gorges dam project in Sun Yat-sen's "Plan to Develop Industry."

**1932:** Construction Committee of the Nationalist government proposes the building of a low dam at the Three Gorges.

**1944:** American design engineer J. L. Savage of the U.S. Bureau of Reclamation presents a plan for the construction of a dam at the Three Gorges site.

**1947:** Nationalist government terminates all design work on the Three Gorges dam.

**1949:** Communist takeover of China.

**1951:** A flood-diversion project for the Yangtze River is approved and implemented.

**1953:** Mao Zedong proposes building a dam at the Three Gorges site to control floods.

**1954:** The largest flood along the middle and lower reaches of the Yangtze in over 100 years causes destruction in the cities of Wuhan and Nanjing, and kills 30,000 people.

**1955:** Planning for the comprehensive utilization of the Yangtze River begins.

**June, 1955:** Soviet experts arrive in China and assist Chinese engineers in the systematic survey, design, and study of the Three Gorges site.

**1956:** Lin Yishan, a supporter of the Three Gorges project, and Li Rui, an opponent, engage in published debate over the feasibility of the Three Gorges project. The Yangtze Valley Planning Office (YVPO) is established.

**May-June, 1957:** During the Hundred Flowers Movement, critics of the Three Gorges project take the opportunities created by short-term press freedom to castigate proponents for ignoring difficult technical issues and for seeking to build the dam solely for reasons of national prestige.

**June, 1957:** Anti-Rightist Campaign involves the persecution of critics of the Communist Party including engineers who had spoken out against the Three Gorges project. Dam opponents within the YVPO are labeled as "rightists."

**October, 1957:** "Report on Major Points of the Outline Plan for Comprehensive Utilization of the Yangtze Valley" is issued.

**January, 1958:** Mao Zedong convenes a Central Committee meeting in Nanning and hears the contrasting views of Li Rui and Lin Yishan. The Central Committee agrees that construction of the project should begin only after "enthusiastic preparation and complete reliability." Mao appoints Zhou Enlai to take personal charge of planning along the Yangtze River valley.

**February, 1958:** The Ministry of Water Resources and the Ministry of Electric Power are merged into the Ministry of Water Resources and Electric Power (MWREP).

**March, 1958:** Central Committee meeting in Chengdu at which Sichuan province receives the "Report on the Main Design Features of the Three Gorges Project." The meeting concludes that preliminary work for the project be completed by the early 1960s, but sets no deadline for construction.

**June, 1958:** Three Gorges Scientific Conference is convened in Wuhan.

**May, 1959:** YVPO completes a draft of "Report on the Main Points of Preliminary Design" and decides to locate the dam at the Sandouping site.

**1960s:** Disastrous policies of the Great Leap Forward delay for several years further preparation work on the dam. The dam at Danjiangkou is halted after discovering the use of substandard concrete in the construction.

**1966:** YVPO issues "Report on Design Issues on the Yangtze Three Gorges," but all work is halted by the outbreak of the Cultural Revolution (1965–1975).

**1969:** Mao Zedong voices opposition to the construction of the Three Gorges dam "when the country is preparing for war"; evidently a reference to ongoing tensions with the Soviet Union.

**December, 1970:** The Central Committee decides to build the Gezhouba dam as a "preparation for the actual battle of the Three Gorges."

**1972:** A fundamental redesign of the Gezhouba dam is ordered, delaying its completion until 1989.

**1973:** The Danjiangkou dam construction is completed, 15 years after it started.

**March, 1976:** YVPO submits "Report on Supplementary Studies on the Three Gorges Dam Sites."

**November, 1977:** MWREP asks the State Council to convene a meeting on the Three Gorges dam.

**February, 1978:** MWREP convenes a "Preparatory Meeting for Site Selection."

**February, 1979:** MWREP is broken up into two separate ministries, the Ministry of Water Resources and the Ministry of Electric Power.

**April, 1979:** Lin Yishan is appointed by the State Council to preside over site selection meetings with the active participation of Madame Qian Zhengying. Li Rui is rehabilitated after years in political disgrace.

**May, 1979:** Site selection meeting is convened in Wuhan where opposition views on the construction of the Three Gorges are expressed and submitted in a report to the State Council.

**July, 1979:** Li Rui writes a proposal to Party leaders endorsing the construction of a series of smaller dams on the tributaries of the Yangtze.

**March, 1980:** American specialists visit the Three Gorges dam site and express serious reservations about the entire proposal to Ministry of Water Resources minister Qian Zhengying.

**August, 1980:** The Standing Committee of the State Council calls for evaluation meetings on the Three Gorges project to include diverse views of experts from the State Construction Commission and the State Science and Technology Commission.

**January, 1981:** YVPO endorses phased development of the Three Gorges dam.

**April-June, 1981:** A U.S. Bureau of Reclamation team revisits Three Gorges dam site and proposes a full-scale feasibility study for the project.

**March, 1982:** MWREP is reestablished out of the Ministry of Water Resources and the Ministry of Electric Power. The Ministry of Finance is ordered to undertake the first financial analysis of the Three Gorges dam after several large-scale projects, such as the Baoshan Steel Plant in Shanghai, sustain huge cost overruns.

**March, 1983:** "Report on the Feasibility Study of the Three Gorges Water Resources Project" endorses a 150-meter-high dam while also acknowledging that solving various technical problems would require "long years of study."

**May, 1983:** The State Planning Commission convenes an evaluation meeting of 350 representatives from concerned ministries and commissions under the State Council, and the provinces of Sichuan, Hubei, and Hunan. The majority endorses the dam project, but also recognizes the severity of sedimentation and shipping problems.

**February, 1984:** MWREP endorses "recommending immediate commencement of the construction of the Three Gorges project."

**April, 1984:** State Council formally accepts the view of the State Planning Commission, approving the construction of a 175-meter-high dam with a 150-meter water level to begin in 1986.

**March, 1985:** Preliminary design work on the dam is completed by the YVPO. The State Council stipulates that the project be made part of the Seventh Five Year Economic Plan (1986–1990).

**Spring, 1985:** National People's Congress (NPC) puts off discussion of the Three Gorges project until 1987 because of growing economic difficulties.

**July, 1985:** An American consortium, including the U.S. Bureau of Reclamation, the Army Corps of Engineers, the American Consulting Engineers Council, Bechtel Civil and Mineral, Inc., Coopers and Lybrand, Merrill Lynch Capital Markets, and Morgan Bank, submits a proposal to the Ministry of Water Resources and Electric Power recommending a cost-benefit analysis acceptable to potential financiers be conducted and that the dam be built by a joint venture between the Chinese government and the American consortium with funding from the World Bank, the Asian Development Bank, Sweden, Japan, and Canada.

**Mid-1985:** Leading Group for the Assessment of the Three Gorges Project is formed.

**1986-1990:** Seventh Five Year Economic Plan.

**Early 1986:** State Planning Commission and the State Science and Technology Commission are entrusted to study the cost/benefit analysis of each proposed dam height from 150 to 180 meters. The Economic Construction Group of the Chinese People's Political Consultative Conference (CPPCC), led by Sun Yueqi, conducts a 38-day field trip to the dam site. Upon their return they submit a report titled "The Three Gorges Project Should Not Go Ahead in the Short Term."

**July, 1986:** Canada announces that its aid agency, the Canadian International Development Agency, will grant $8.74 million for a feasibility study of the proposed Three Gorges hydro-electric project to be carried out by a Canadian consortium of engineering companies and electric utilities, and supervised by the World Bank. The purpose of the study is to "firmly establish, on bases acceptable to international financial institutions, the technical and economic feasibility of the Three Gorges project."

**March, 1988:** YVPO produces "Supplementary Report on the Comprehensive Development of the Yangtze River Basin."

**April, 1988:** MWREP is once again divided into the Ministry of Water Resources and the Ministry of Power, with Electric Power as part of the latter.

**August, 1988:** Canadian-World Bank *Three Gorges Water Control Project Feasibility Study* is finished. It recommends the Three Gorges dam be "carried out at an early date" with a dam crest level of 185 meters and a normal pool level of 160 meters. However, the World Bank also states in the document that evidence indicates "increasing the normal pool level from 160 meters to 170 meters and higher would not be an economically viable proposition."

**Autumn, 1988:** Dai Qing reads in the Hong Kong press that the project will be started in 1989. She begins compiling *Yangtze! Yangtze!*

**February 28, 1989:** Dai Qing and colleagues hold a press conference to release *Yangtze! Yangtze!*

**March, 1989:** NPC and CPPCC meetings begin. At the NPC meeting, 272 delegates release a report titled "[We Suggest That] the Three Gorges Project be Postponed Until the 21st Century and the Upper Reaches and Tributaries be Developed First."

**April 3, 1989:** Yao Yilin, director of one of the Examination Committee's on the Three Gorges project and a member of the State Council, states that "No large-scale projects related to the Three Gorges will be submitted in neither the present period of planned administrative reform nor in the upcoming Eighth Five Year Plan."

**April-June, 1989:** Democracy movement engulfs Beijing and over 100 other major cities in China.

**October, 1989:** *Yangtze! Yangtze!* is officially banned.

**July, 1990:** Meeting of the State Council. Qian Zhengying reports on the leading group and YVPO assessments. Many consider this the official revival of the project after Yao Yilin's comments of 1989.

**1991-1995:** Eighth Five Year Economic Plan.

**1991:** "Spring Festival Forum Promoting the Early and Rapid Launching of the Three Gorges Project" is convened by Wang Zhen and Wang Renzhong. The forum is a boost for dam proponents.

**August, 1991:** A State Council Examination Committee, headed by Zou Jiahua, approves the dam, stating that preparation work should begin in 1993.

**January, 1992:** Vice-premiers' meeting agrees to construct the project.

**February, 1992:** Amsterdam-based International Water Tribunal rules against Chinese and Canadian governments stating that "due to expediency, the very high ecological and socioeconomic risks of the [Three Gorges] megadam have not been adequately assessed by the defendant's feasibility studies." Until the populations at risk "have rights to information and consultation before the project is decided upon and implemented," and "the right to effectively participate in processes affecting their habitats and livelihoods," implementation of the project should be halted.

**February, 1992:** The Politburo Standing Committee agrees to the construction of the project. Yao Yilin fully discards his view of 1989 and also supports a go-ahead for the project.

**March, 1992:** Seventh NPC and CPPCC meetings are convened.

**March 5, 1992:** The U.S. Bureau of Reclamation signs an agreement with the Ministry of Water Resources to "provide to the [ministry] technical consulting services on technical and economic issues during the design, construction and operation of the Three Gorges project."

**April 3, 1992:** The "Resolution on the Construction of the Three Gorges Project on the Yangtze River" is passed. 1,767 delegates vote in favor, 177 oppose the project, 644 abstain and 25 do not cast votes.

**April 27, 1992:** The Canadian government announces in the House of Commons that due to "conflicting priorities...we can no longer use our limited development assistance funds for [the Three Gorges] project."

**August 29, 1992:** *Nikkei Weekly* reports that the Chinese government gave special approval to a foreign financial consortium (including a Taiwanese investment firm, the Lippo Group of Indonesia, and U.S. securities firm Merrill Lynch and Company) for financial and investment business in China, on condition the consortium provides financial support for the construction of the Three Gorges dam.

**January, 1993:** The Three Gorges Project Development Corporation, headed by Lu Youmei and Li Peng, is set up to manage the construction.

**July 27, 1993:** Three Gorges project officially enters the preparatory stage after the Three Gorges Project Construction Committee of the State Council examines and approves the project's preliminary design report, which was completed in March 1993.

**August 9, 1993:** *China Daily* reports that the People's Construction Bank of China, the Industrial and Commercial Bank of China, and the Three Gorges Security Company (approved by China's central bank) are preparing to raise funds to build the Three Gorges dam from government investment, domestic bank loans, issuing shares and bonds, and taking out foreign loans. Also, electricity rate hikes will help raise Y3 billion per year for the Three Gorges project.

**September 14, 1993:** To enhance the China Yangtze Three Gorges Project Development Company's ability to raise more cash for the Three Gorges project, the central government puts the Gezhouba hydro-electric power station under the company's management, and allows money earned from Gezhouba's electricity sales to be used for the Three Gorges dam.

**November, 1993:** *The Economist* reports that the Chinese government is so short of cash that infrastructure projects, among them the Three Gorges dam, are on hold until they can be paid for.

**December 14, 1993:** The U.S. Bureau of Reclamation informs the Ministry of Water Resources that it is terminating its agreements to provide technical consulting services for the Three Gorges dam, "effective this date." A Bureau spokesperson explains that "it is now generally known that large-scale water retention dam projects are not environmentally or economically feasible....We wouldn't support such a project in the U.S. now, so it would be incongruous for us to support a project like this in another country."

**December 28, 1993:** *China Daily* reports that Vice-Premier Zou Jiahua announces that the government's pilot resettlement project will end and the full-scale evacuation will begin in 1994.

**January, 1994:** Bidding for contracts for work related to the Three Gorges project is underway.

# APPENDIX B

**A Directory of the Sessions (Enlarged) of the Leading Group for the Assessment of the Three Gorges Project**

Persons present at the sessions included:

- leading group members (minister, vice-ministers, general engineer, and vice-general engineers of the Ministry of Water Resources and Electric Power): 10-12 persons;

- special advisors (from the relevant state authorities): 12-20 persons;

- advisors, chiefs and deputy chiefs of the 14 experts' groups: 91 persons;

- members of the Chinese People's Political Consultative Conference (CPPCC): 4-10 persons; and various others.

**The First Session** (June, 1986):
Set up the leading group and the 14 experts' groups according to the Communist Party regulations and State Council Document (No. 15) "On Issues Relevant to the Assessment Report of the Three Gorges Project on the Yangtze River."

**The Second Session** (August, 1986):
Examined guidelines for the 14 experts' groups and decided on the method for comparative study of programs proposed for the project. Attended by about 50 persons.

**The Third Session** (December, 1986):
Heard the 14 experts' groups report on their
preliminary work. Attended by about 130 persons.

**The Fourth Session** (April, 1987):
Decided on the preliminary aspects of the project program.
Attended by about 130 persons.

**The Fifth Session** (December, 1987):
Examined and approved the three subject reports
relating to geology and seismology, hydrology, and
electrical equipment. Attended by about 130 persons.

**The Sixth Session** (January, 1988):
Examined and approved the three subject reports on
the dam and related structures, construction, and
investment estimation. Attended by about 120 persons.

**The Seventh Session** (February, 1988):
Examined and approved the three subject reports
relating to resettlement, ecology and environment,
and sedimentation. Attended by about 140 persons.

**The Eighth Session** (April, 1988):
Examined and approved the three subject reports
relating to flood control, electrical system, and
navigation. Attended by about 140 persons.

**The Ninth Session** (November, 1988):
Examined and approved the two subject reports
relating to the general program and water level,
and comprehensive evaluation of economic results.
Attended by 206 persons.

**The 10th Session** (February-March, 1989):
Examined and approved the "Feasibility Report on the
Three Gorges Project" compiled by the Yangtze Valley
Planning Office (YVPO). Attended by 203 persons.

# APPENDIX C

**A Directory of the Advisors and Experts in Each Experts'
Group for the Assessment of the Three Gorges Project Who
Did Not Sign Their Respective Subject Reports, and Who
Expressed Dissenting Opinions at the Enlarged
Sessions of the Leading Group for the Assessment of the
Three Gorges Project**

(The number following the minus symbol represents the number of members who held concurrent positions on that particular group and on another.)

**Experts' Group on Geology and Seismology** (24 members)

**Experts' Group on Dam and Appurtenant Structures** (30-1)
Those who did not sign:
Chen Zongji, at the seventh session of the leading group's study, out of a concern for inadequate air raid defense.

Those who held dissenting opinions but did sign:
Zhang Changling, at the eighth and ninth sessions,
proposed a two-phase development program;
Huang Wenzhao, at the ninth session, opposed the lock design and construction process.

**Experts' Group on Hydrology** (17)

**Experts' Group on Flood Control** (26)
Those who did not sign:
Lu Qinkan; his disagreement was prepared as a paper and was attached to the report of the experts group.
Fang Zongdai also submitted a supplementary document in disagreement with the report.

Those who held dissenting opinions but did sign:

Liu Shanjian submitted a supplementary document in disagreement with the report.

### Experts' Group on Sedimentation (31)
Those who held dissenting opinions but did sign:
Zhang Qishun, at the ninth session, proposed that the pool level should not exceed 160 meters.

### Experts' Group on Navigation (28-4)

### Experts' Group on Electrical Power Systems (32)
Those who did not sign:
Qin Xiudian, Cheng Xuemin, and Wu Yingzhong; all three submitted supplementary documents in disagreement with the report.

### Experts' Group on Electrical Equipment (57-2)

### Experts' Group on Resettlement (28)
Those who did not sign but did sign:
Li Yuguang (General Engineer of the State Bureau
of Land Administration).

Those who held dissenting opinions but did sign:
Hu Zhiyi, at the eighth session, expressed concern with regard to flood control and sedimentation in Sichuan.

### Experts' Group on Ecology and Environment (52-7)
Those who did not sign:
Hou Xueyu submitted a supplement in disagreement with the report.
Chen Changdu (Professor at Beida University
Department of Geography).

Those who held dissenting opinions but did sign:
Ma Shijun, at the eighth session, argued that the
project would do more harm than good to the environment;
Xi Chengfan, at the third session, argued that

278

the project should not be considered before there is a solution to the problem of soil erosion.

Liu Yinong, at the fourth session, out of a concern with the environmental impact of resettlement.

**Experts' Group on Multipurpose Planning and Reservoir Operating Levels** (38-21)

Those who did not sign:

Qin Xiudian submitted a supplement in disagreement with the report.

Those who held dissenting opinions but did sign:

Shi Jiayang, at the eighth and ninth sessions, proposed that the pool level should not exceed 160 meters;

Luo Xibei, at the 10th session, proposed that the pool level should not exceed 160 meters.

**Experts' Group on Construction** (23-1)

Those who held dissenting opinions but did sign:

Li Heding, at the 10th session, proposed that the pool level should not exceed 160 meters.

**Experts' Group on Comprehensive Economic Evaluation** (56-10)

Those who did not sign:

He Gegao, Huang Yuanzhen, and Guo Laixi, who all submitted supplements in disagreement with the report.

Those who held dissenting opinions but did sign:

Zhang Wenzhu, at the ninth session, was concerned that investments would be diverted for other uses;

Wu Boshan, at the ninth session, proposed that the project was inappropriate due to the state's financial constraints.

# APPENDIX D

**The Resolution on the Construction of the Three Gorges
Project on the Yangtze River**
Passed at the Fifth Session of the Seventh National People's
Congress on April 3, 1992

As reported in the *People's Daily* (April 4, 1992):

The fifth session of the seventh National People's Congress, having examined the proposal by the State Council on the construction of the Three Gorges Water Control Project, based on the report of examination by the National People's Congress Committee of Financial and Economic Affairs, herein resolves to approve inclusion of the construction of the Three Gorges project into the Ten Year National Economic and Social Development Program (1991-2000). The State Council shall, by taking into consideration the realistic conditions of the national economic development and the financial and material capabilities of the state, seek to organize its implementation at an appropriate time; research shall continue towards the proper solution of the potential problems that have been identified.

# APPENDIX E

**Some Issues Regarding the Preliminary Design
of the Three Gorges Project**
Approved by the State Council Examination Committee of
Experts on May 26, 1993

## I. Construction Period

Based on the proposal for launching construction in 1993.

In the second year (1994), excavation of the dam base will begin.

In the third year (1995), pouring of reinforced concrete will begin. (This is considered the beginning of the main project).

In the fifth year (1997), the project to block the river channel will begin. The method of transportation through diversion channels will be adopted and the temporary shiplocks will be in operation in the next year.

In the 13th year (2006), the water in the diversion channels will be blocked and a cofferdam will be constructed to maintain a water level at 135 meters. Generation of electricity will begin and the shiplock lifters will start operation.

In the 15th year (2007), the initial stage of raising the water to a level of 156 meters will be completed and will temporarily remain that way for six years and the buildup of sediment will be observed and measured.

In the 17th year (2009), all 26 turbine power generators will be installed.

In the 21st year (2013), the water will be increased to the 175-meter level and the dam will assume normal operation.

## II. Estimated Investment

1.   A comparison of the current static investment to the past:

a. According to the assessment report, in 1986 prices, total cost will be Y36.1 billion (the central project will cost Y18.8 billion, population relocation Y11.1 billion, and electricity transfer Y6.3 billion).

b. According to the YVPO feasibility report, the cost in 1990 prices is Y57 billion (in the same order as above: 29.8 + 18.5 + 8.7).

c. According to the preliminary design, the cost in 1992 prices is Y75.1 billion (38.3 + 23.7 + 13.1)

2. Taking interest on capital and price increases into consideration:

a. The static investment in 1992 prices, without consideration of interest costs and price increases, is Y75.1 billion (Y38.2 billion prior to the generation of power).

b. If 70 percent of the investment is based on an 8.82 percent annual interest rate, total cost will be Y117.0 billion after adding on the interest incurred during the construction period (Y53 billion prior to the generation of power).

c. Assuming a 6 percent annual inflation rate, the total capital needed during the 20-year construction period will be Y224 billion (Y81.6 billion prior to the generation of power).

## III. Sources of capital

1. Revenue from power generation by the Gezhouba dam is now Y0.39 per kWh. Starting in 1993, it will be raised one *fen*[1] a year, so that by 1996, it will be 8 *fen* higher, and the total amount of funds generated during the construction period will come to Y14.2 billion (Y7.1 billion prior to power generation by the Three Gorges dam).

2. Regarding the construction fund for the Three Gorges project, the premier's office under the State Council has decided that the State Price Bureau would issue a document in 1992 that Y0.003 would be drawn from each kWh on the national power

---

[1] 100 *fen* = 1 *yuan*

network to be put into a construction fund for the Three Gorges project, with a total amount of Y40 billion to be raised during the construction period (Y22.3 billion prior to power generation by the Three Gorges dam).

3. Revenue from power generation by the Three Gorges dam will produce 507.9 billion kWh, and based on the state-regulated price in 1992 of 19.4 *fen* per kWh, the total profit will be Y54.8 billion. Adding on a depreciation fee of Y8.6 billion and the return on tax-exempt loans of Y3.2 billion, the total will come to Y66.6 billion. Assuming a 6 percent annual increase in the price of electricity, the total will reach Y169.6 billion.

4. Foreign loans will be used to import equipment, including four turbine power generators, and direct power switch equipment along with major equipment for shiplifts, which will total $1.59 billion, equivalent to Y8.6 billion (Y0.7 billion prior to power generation).

5. Domestic bank loans will come to Y15.3 billion prior to power generation. Assuming a 6 percent annual increase in prices, the total will come to Y45.5 billion.

6. Issuing of Three Gorges Project construction bonds (two years before power generation) will raise Y2 billion. Assuming 6 percent annual increase, the total will come to Y4 billion.

In summary, the total amount of funds raised in the 20 years will be Y147.6 billion (Y52.9 billion prior to power generation). Assuming a 6 percent price increase, the total will come to Y281.9 billion (Y81.5 billion prior to power generation).

## IV. Submerging of Land and Population Relocation

1. Land submerged: Based on an investigation conducted from 1991 to 1992, the area of dry land below the 175-meter line has dropped in comparison to the amount found during the 1985 investigation. However, paddy fields have increased from 110,700 *mu* to 128,600 *mu*, while the area composed of orange groves has increased from 74,400 *mu* to 100,400 *mu*.

2.   Factories: According to a recent investigation, there are 1,602 factories with fixed capital assets of Y2.277 billion, while according to a prior investigation, there were 657 factories with fixed assets of Y819 million.

3.   Population relocation: The 1991 investigation showed that 844,600 people lived below the proposed water line, a 16.4 percent increase from the 1985 investigation of 725,500 people.

4.   An additional preliminary design has yet to be proposed to deal with management of land submersion and population relocation. The investment estimate is based only on an economic evaluation of the project. The number of residents to be relocated in addition to the estimated total of 1.13 million people has yet to be made. And the exact amount of the relocation compensation cost can only be calculated after the completion of the preliminary design report regarding population relocation.

# APPENDIX F

**A List of Specialists Whose Views on the Three Gorges Project Differ from Those of the Leading Group for the Assessment of the Three Gorges Project**

1. The 28 dissident specialists who were not included in the leading group study (some of them had participated in previous studies, others voiced their opposition opinions on various occasions):

Xu Qiashi: Ex-head of the Water Resources Department of the Zhejiang provincial government. Delegate of the National People's Congress (NPC).

Huang Wanli: Professor at the Department of Water Resources, Qinghua University.

Wang Yifu: Senior specialist of hydro-electricity. Honorary Member of the National Society of Water Resources and Electric Power.

Zhu Tiezheng: Director of the planning division of the Planning and Design Institute of Water Resources and Electric Power.

Zhu Pengcheng and Jin Yongtang: Senior engineers of the Chengdu Survey and Design Institute of the Ministry of Water Resources and Electric Power.

Lin Yuanti: Chief engineer of the Kunming Survey and Design Institute. Delegate to the NPC.

Hu Shensi and An Shenyi: Senior engineers at the Central China Survey Design Institute.

Zou Siyuan: Chief engineer at the East China Survey and Design Institute.

Lei Kai: Chief engineer of the Electric Power Bureau of the Guangxi provincial government. Delegate to the NPC.

Li Rongmeng: Chief engineer of the Water Resources and Electric Power Department of the Yunnan provincial government. Delegate to the NPC.

Guan Shicong: Academic committee member of the Chinese Academy of Sciences (CAS). Advisor to the Ministry of Geology and Mineral Resources. Member of the Chinese People's Political Consultative Conference (CPPCC).

Guo Fang: Deputy director of the Environmental Science Committee of the CAS.

Chen Guojie: Research Fellow at the Research Institute of Forestry and Soil Conservation of the CAS.

Liu Dongsheng: Environmental specialist at the CAS.

She Zhixiang: Director of the Nanjing Institute of the CAS.

Deng Mingcong: Professor, Chengdu Geology Institute.

Wang Shize and Wang Zongyuan: Professors at the East China Water Resources Institute.

Li Dazhi: Professor of economics at the Southwestern University of Finance and Economy.

Xue Baoding: Research fellow at the Investment Research Institute of the State Planning Commission.

Tian Fang, Lin Fatang, Sun Xufei, and Ling Chunxi: Researchers with the Economic Research Institute of the State Planning Commission.

2. The 19 vice-chairmen, members of the standing committee and members of the CPPCC who held opposition opinions: Zhou Peiyuan, Qian Weichang, Sun Yueqi, Lin Hua, Xu Chi, Peng De, Qiao Peixin, Wang Xingrang, Lei Tianjue, Chen Mingshao, Xu Guangyi, Yan Xinghua, Zhao Weigang, Yu Enying, Yang Hanxi, Wu Jing, Kang Daisha, Guo Weicheng, Guobu Luorunqi, Wu Baoshan.

3. The nine specialists who did not sign on to their subject study reports for the last assessment report of the Three Gorges project: Tan Xiudian, Lu Xinkan, He Gegao, Huang Yuanzhen, Guo Laixi, Cheng Xuemin, Wu Hongzhong, Hou Xueyu, Fang Zondai. (The last two have died.)

Two others, Weng Changfu, the convener of the construction group of the State Council Examination Committee, and Zhang Jinsheng, a member of the same group, refused to sign the report.

4. Another 11 scientists and specialists have voiced opposing views in recent years:

Li Jiasan: Research fellow on the Comprehensive Study Committee of the CAS. (He put forward a proposal in the 1950s to construct some flood-diversion structures in the Jingjiang River region.)

Jin Yongtang: Senior engineer in the Water Resource and Electric Power Research Institute.

Zhang Pan: Vice-general secretary of the Development Research Center of the State Council.

Wei Zhaolin: Ex-deputy director of the State Science and Technology Commission.

Yang Jike: Leader of the Public Interest Party.

Tao Dayong: Leader of the Democratic Federation. Member of the Standing Committee of the NPC.

Qian Sichao: Ex-director of the Fuel and Power Department of the State Planning Commission.

Song Jiliang: Engineer of the Power Society of Shanghai.

Guo Kaiyu: Chengdu Survey and Design Institute.

Liu Peitong: Beijing Normal University.

Shi Deming: Soil Research Institute of Nanjing.

5.  At the seventh session of the 1992 NPC, dozens of delegates from Chongqing, and Sichuan, Shangdong and Zhejiang provinces raised opposition opinions on the project. Most of them were scientists and local government officials. Huo Guoben, for example, is a professor specializing in Yellow River planning.

# BIBLIOGRAPHY

Avtorkhanov, Abdurkhman. *Stalin and the Soviet Communist Party: A Study in the Technology of Power.* New York: Praeger, 1959.

*Beijing Review*, 10-16 October 1988.

Burleigh, Michael, and Wolfgang Wippermann. *The Racial State: Germany 1933-1945.* Cambridge: Cambridge University Press, 1992.

Cernea, Michael M. *Putting People First, Sociological Variables in Rural Development.* Oxford: Oxford University Press, 1985.

Chen Kexiong. "The True Story of the Three Gorges Project." *Literary Gazette*, 17 March 1992.

"China Plans New Resettlement Rules." *Water Power and Dam Construction*, March 1990, p. 2.

CIPM Yangtze Joint Venture (CYJV). *Three Gorges Water Control Project Feasibility Study.* Vol. 1 (1988), Appendix A.

Dai Qing. *Wang Shiwei and "Wild Lilies": Rectification and Purges in the CCP, 1942-1944.* Armonk, N.Y.: M. E. Sharpe Inc., 1994.

Deng Xiaoping. "On the Reform of the System of Party and State Leadership." *Selected Works of Deng Xiaoping: 1975-1982.* Beijing: Foreign Language Press, 1984.

Fairweather, Virginia. "Hydro on Hold." *Civil Engineering*, Vol. 59, No. 8 (August 1988), p. 54.

Fearnside, Philip M. "China's Three Gorges Dam: 'Fatal' Project or Step Toward Modernization?" *World Development*, Vol. 16, No. 5 (1988), p. 626.

Goldsmith, E., and N. Hildyard, eds. *The Social and Environmental Effects of Large Dams.* 3 vols. Cornwall, U.K.: Wadebridge Ecological Centre, 1984-92.

He Bochuan. *China on the Edge: The Crisis of Ecology and Development.* Ed. Xu Yinong. Translated by China Books and Periodicals. San Francisco: China Books and Periodicals Inc., 1991.

Jin Jun. "Dam Project Ignites China's Intellectuals." *Asian Wall Street Journal Weekly*, 20 March 1989.

Lampton, David, and Kenneth Lieberthal, eds. *Bureaucracy, Politics, and Decision Making in Post-Mao China.* Berkeley: University of California Press, 1992.

———, ed. *Policy Implementation in Post-Mao China.* Berkeley: University of California Press, 1987.

Li Rui. *Lun sanxia gongcheng* (On the Three Gorges Project). Hunan: Hunan Scientific and Technological Publishing House, 1985.

Lieberthal, Kenneth, and Michel Oksenberg. *Policy Making in China: Leaders, Structures, and Processes.* Princeton: Princeton University Press, 1988.

Luk, Shiu-hung, and Joseph Whitney, eds. *Megaproject: A Case Study of the Three Gorges.* Armonk, N.Y.: M. E. Sharpe Inc., 1993.

*People's Daily,* overseas ed., 28 November 1988.

Probe International. *Damming the Three Gorges: What Dam Builders Don't Want You to Know.* 2nd ed. Eds. Margaret Barber and Gráinne Ryder. Toronto: Earthscan Canada, 1993.

Reisner, Marc. *Cadillac Desert: The American West and Its Disappearing Water.* Rev. ed. New York: Penguin Books, 1993.

Rossweiler, Anne D. *The Generation of Power: The History of Dneprostroi.* Oxford: Oxford University Press, 1988.

Schneider, Lawrence, ed. *Chinese Law and Government.* Armonk, N.Y.: M. E. Sharpe Inc., Summer 1986.

*Science News,* 14 June 1986.

Smil, Vaclav. *China's Environmental Crisis: An Inquiry into the Limits of National Development.* Armonk, N.Y.: M. E. Sharpe Inc., 1993.

"The beautiful and the dammed." *The Economist,* 28 March 1992.

*Three Gorges Project: Key to Development of the Yangtze River.* Comp. *Beijing Review.* Beijing: New Star Publishers, 1992.

Tian Fang, and Lin Fatang. *A Third Look at a Long-Range Strategy for the Three Gorges Project.* Hunan: People's Publishing House of Hunan, 1992.

Wu Xiutao. "Environmental impacts of the Sanmen Gorge project." *Water Power & Dam Construction,* November 1986.

# INDEX

sedimentation (*see also* resettlement, Leading Group for the Assessment of the Three Gorges Project, Yangtze Valley Planning Office, Yangtze River flooding) 22
    analysis 77-87, 129, 140, 163, 170
    operating system 32, 68, 77, 173, 217, 252
    pattern 128, 152, 153, 163-165, 172, 195, 196
"self-criticisms" 20, 31
Shanghai 9, 36, 48, 99, 110, 141, 146, 200, 269, 287
Smil, Vaclav 207
*A Small Series on the Three Gorges Project* 33
*The Social and Environmental Effects of Large Dams* 190
"Some Issues Regarding the Preliminary Design of the Three Gorges Project" 41, 281-284
Songzikou 120, 186, 215
"Spring Festival Forum Promoting the Early and Rapid Launching of the Three Gorges Project" 27, 272
State Council 3, 6, 17, 22-24, 26, 28-30, 34, 40, 41, 44, 55, 65, 66, 73, 76, 80, 86-88, 93, 94, 97, 101, 123, 176, 179, 183, 188, 228, 246, 249, 262, 263, 268-270, 272, 274, 280-282, 286, 287
    Examination Committee 23, 26, 28, 34, 88, 101, 272
State Planning Commission 18, 26, 40, 65, 70, 72, 93, 97, 135, 137, 145, 149, 154, 249, 270, 286
State Science and Technology Commission 270
Sun Yat-sen 2, 148, 175, 222, 239, 266
Sun Yueqi 3, 5, 24, 27, 32, 122, 134, 148-155, 187, 248, 263, 271, 286

Ten-Year National Economic and Social Development Program (1991-2000) 32, 76, 122
Tehri dam 196
*A Third Look at a Long-Range Strategy for the Three Gorges Project* 75
Three Gorges area (*see also* financing, Leading Group for the Assessment of the Three Gorges Project, resettlement) 200
    agriculture 89, 90, 100, 101, 103, 129, 131, 140, 181, 190, 191, 220, 283
    climate 191
    deforestation 152, 172, 193, 195, 217
    economic development xxiv-xxv, 180, 225-226
    historical relics 191, 192, 208, 220
    land submerged 57, 151, 153, 190, 193, 219, 220, 250, 260, 283
    pollution 193
    soil erosion 152, 194, 209, 217, 225, 227
    vegetation 227
    wildlife 191, 193, 194
Three Gorges Project Construction Committee 40, 41, 73, 273
Three Gorges Project Development Corporation 30, 40, 66, 273
"The Three Gorges Project Should Not Go Ahead in the Short Term" (*see also* Economic Construction Group) 3, 6, 22, 271
Tian Fang 3, 18
Tiananmen Square xiv, xv, xxiv, 13, 15, 17, 20, 25, 29, 272
transportation 41, 49, 72, 84, 96, 125, 152, 171, 187, 198, 223, 225, 233, 238, 243, 244, 249, 253, 281
tributaries (*see also* hydro-electric power, Yangtze Valley Planning Office, Yangtze River

294